KEYS TO READING

Theodore L. Harris
Mildred Creekmore
Margaret H. Greenman
Louise Matteoni
Harold B. Allen, *Linguistic Consultant*

THE ECONOMY COMPANY   Oklahoma City   Atlanta   Indianapolis

Acknowledgments

For permission to adapt and reprint copyrighted materials, grateful acknowledgment is made to the following publishers, authors, and other copyright holders:

Abelard-Schuman, Ltd., for "A Yellow Paper Fish" reprinted from *Myeko's Gift* by Kay Haugaard. All rights reserved. Copyright 1966.

Atheneum Publishers, and Curtis Brown, Ltd., for "Tree Climbing" by Kathleen Fraser, copyright © 1968 by Kathleen Fraser, reprinted from *Stilts, Somersaults and Headstands*.

The Bobbs-Merrill Company, Inc., for "The Knights of the Silver Shield" adapted from *Why the Chimes Rang and Other Stories* by Raymond Macdonald Alden, copyright 1906, 1908, 1924, 1945 by The Bobbs-Merrill Co., and for "Strange Black Smoke" and excerpts in "Volcanic Wonders" adapted from *Our Country's National Parks*, Volumes I and II, by Irving R. Melbo, copyright 1941, 1950, 1960, 1961 by The Bobbs-Merrill Co.

Brandt & Brandt, for stanzas from "Western Wagons" by Stephen Vincent Benét, reprinted from *A Book of Americans* by Rosemary and Stephen Vincent Benét; Holt, Rinehart and Winston, Inc. Copyright renewed © 1961 by Rosemary Carr Benét.

Childrens Press, for "The Drake Players Go West" from *Pioneer Show Folk* by Edith McCall, copyright 1963; published by Childrens Press, Chicago.

Thomas Y. Crowell Company, Inc., for "Coyote in Central Park" adapted from *Coyote in Manhattan* by Jean Craighead George, copyright © 1968 by Jean Craighead George; for "A Tulip for Tony" by Marietta Moskin, reprinted from *Round About the City, Stories You Can Read to Yourself* selected by the Child Study Association of America, copyright © 1966 by Thomas Y. Crowell Co.; and for "Miss Charity Comes to Stay" reprinted from *Miss Charity Comes to Stay* by Alberta Wilson Constant, copyright © 1959 by Alberta Wilson Constant.

The Curtis Publishing Company, for "Chuka's Hawk" by Elizabeth B. Whitmore and "The Raiders" by Dorothy Harriman Leiser, adapted by permission of *Jack and Jill Magazine*, © 1964 The Curtis Publishing Co.

Dodd, Mead & Company, Inc., for "Marco and the Tiger" reprinted from *Marco and the Tiger* by John Foster, copyright © 1967 by John Foster; Dodd, Mead & Co., and Harold Ober Associates, Inc., for "Frontiersman" adapted from *Famous Negro Heroes of America* by Langston Hughes, copyright © 1958 by Langston Hughes.

Doubleday & Company, Inc., for "A Cave Is Born" and "How Nature Decorates Her Caves" adapted from *The Story of Caves* by Dorothy Sterling, illustrated by Winifred Lubell, copyright © 1956 by Dorothy Sterling; Doubleday & Co., and Curtis Brown, Ltd., for "Poison Water" reprinted from *Tree Wagon* by Evelyn Sibley Lampman, copyright 1953 by Evelyn Sibley Lampman; Doubleday & Co., and World's Work, Ltd., for "The Florist Shop" by Rachel Field, reprinted from *Taxis and Toadstools* by Rachel Field, copyright 1926 by Doubleday & Co.

E. P. Dutton & Company, Inc., and The Bodley Head, for "The Mountain" from the book *My Side of the Mountain* by Jean George, copyright © 1959 by Jean George; published by E. P. Dutton & Co.

Harcourt Brace Jovanovich, Inc., for "The Dream" by Harry Behn, reprinted from *Windy Morning*, copyright 1953 by Harry Behn.

Harper & Row, Publishers, for "Things Begin to Happen," chapters one and two reprinted from *The Wheel on the School* by Meindert DeJong, copyright 1954 by Meindert DeJong; Harper & Row, Publishers, and Lutterworth Press, for "The West Begins" reprinted from "The West Begins" in *By the Shores of Silver Lake* by Laura Ingalls Wilder, copyright 1939 by Harper & Brothers, renewed 1967 by Roger L. MacBride.

Lance Henson, author, for "Along the Battle Ridge," lines reprinted from "Scalp Dance Poem" in *Keeper of Arrows* by Lance Henson, copyright 1971 by Lance Henson.

Holiday House, Inc., for "Animal Behavior" adapted from *How Animals Learn* by Russell Freedman and James E. Morriss, © 1969 by Russell Freedman and James E. Morriss.

Holt, Rinehart and Winston, Inc., for "My Brother Stevie" reprinted from *My Brother Stevie* by Eleanor Clymer, copyright © 1967 by Eleanor Clymer.

Horn Book, Inc., for "Night Writers" by Edna Margaret Long, reprinted from *The Horn Book Magazine*, February 1971.

Houghton Mifflin Company, for "Johnny Appleseed," a chapter, pages 119-128, reprinted from *Yankee Doodle's Cousins* by Anne Malcolmson, copyright © renewed 1969 by Anne Malcolmson Von Storch; published by Houghton Mifflin Co.

Hubbard Press, for "The Great Spirit's Tower," an adaptation of a selection from *Indian Legends of American Scenes* by Marion E. Gridley, an M. A. Donohue and Company book published by Hubbard Press, Northbrook, Illinois.

Alfred A. Knopf, Inc., for "The Falcon" by Elinor Wylie, copyright 1921 by Alfred A. Knopf, renewed 1949 by William Rose Benét, reprinted from *Collected Poems of Elinor Wylie* by Elinor Wylie.

J. B. Lippincott Company, for "How Much Is True?" by John Ciardi, reprinted from the book *The Man Who Sang the Sillies* by John Ciardi, copyright © 1961 by John Ciardi.

Little, Brown and Company, and Curtis Brown, Ltd., for "Every Time I Climb a Tree" by David McCord, copyright © 1952 by David McCord, reprinted from *Every Time I Climb a Tree* by David McCord.

The Macmillan Company, and Blackie & Son, Ltd., for "Swift Things Are Beautiful" and "The Wilderness Is Tamed" by Elizabeth Coatsworth, reprinted from *Away Goes Sally* by Elizabeth Coatsworth, copyright 1934 by The Macmillan Co., renewed 1962 by Elizabeth Coatsworth Beston.

Meredith Corporation, for "The Flower-fed Buffaloes" by Vachel Lindsay, from *A St. Nicholas Anthology, The Early Years* edited by Burton Frye, copyright © 1969 by Meredith Corporation, reprinted by courtesy of Appleton-Century-Crofts, Educational Division, Meredith Corporation.

Contents

The Woven Chain

Branches for Climbing

Swift and Beautiful

Ancient Song

Written in Stone

To Tame a Land

A Selection for Independent Reading

The Woven

Chain

The Falcon

Why should my sleepy heart be taught
To whistle mocking-bird replies?
This is another bird you've caught,
Soft-feathered, with a falcon's eyes.

The bird Imagination,
That flies so far, that dies so soon;
Her wings are coloured like the sun,
Her breast is coloured like the moon.

Weave her a chain of silver twist,
And a little hood of scarlet wool,
And let her perch upon your wrist,
And tell her she is beautiful.

Elinor Wylie

The Broomstraw House

Frances Smith

One reason a reader enjoys a good story is that it appeals to his imagination. In his mind he can see what happens. He gets to know the characters in the story and to feel strongly about what happens to them.

Part of the fun of reading is deciding whether you think a story is believable. What happens in the story, its plot, will help you decide. Each happening is a part of the plot, and each part leads you on to the climax, the high point of the story. After you have read the story, you can decide whether the plot turned out as you think it should have.

The children in the following story are curious about someone in their neighborhood. Find out whether their curiosity has anything to do with the plot. Does the climax surprise you?

We were only playing. We weren't trying to find out anything so special. It was a friendly spring day, and all Saturday morning we spent making a broomstraw house in the field next door.

We pulled two clumps of tall broomstraw together and tied them in a knot. We tied two more beside the first, and two more until we had a lovely square room closed in by small round arches. Then we added more rooms.

Oh, but we were careful to leave openings for doors. We forgot to make doors once, and Andy, my little brother, came flying into our house, stumbled over the walls, and turned three flips before he could stop. He messed up everything, and he cried, too. But we built good walls and doors and then trampled down the weeds inside and felt very proud of our fine house.

Well, that's what we were doing all morning—Mary Ann, Wally, and I—and Andy, of course, but he didn't really understand about the house. You see, it was no ordinary house we built that day. It was Mrs. DuBois' house on the big square green block near the park. We shaped it with funny corners and porches and twelve rooms. Of course, with broomstraw we couldn't make the carvings and fancy trimmings that made the old house look so curious. Mama said it was a "two-door house," or something of that sort, but I counted five doors myself.

We quarreled a little about who was going to be Mrs. DuBois because, you see, I hated her and so did Mary Ann. Wally did, too, but he was a boy, anyway. It just had to be Mary Ann or me, so I finally agreed to do it. My legs were longer than Mary Ann's, and I could ball up my long, black ponytail on top of my head. Besides, I was ten and Mary Ann was only nine. But my face was too round. Mama said my face was as round and rosy as a June apple. This old lady's face was—well, more like an English walnut, I guess—long and full and wrinkled and pale. But I put my shiny dime-store brooch at the neck of my dress and decided I would do very well in the part.

Mary Ann was the maid. She was as plump and frisky as the busy maid we often saw running in and out of the big gray house. Wally made a good grocery man. He was tall and skinny, and he had a very large wagon for the delivery truck.

It was all working out fine until Andy started bellowing about being left out. We decided he could be the collie dog, and this made Andy very happy. He went galloping all over the field barking at the top of his lungs and making entirely too much noise.

Anyway, we wanted to get on with things. Next, we needed a lot of grocery bags. We saw Mrs. DuBois almost every day when we were walking home from school, but she was always doing the same thing: bringing in groceries. Every day about the same time Mr. Everett drove his big truck up the curving back drive and began unloading sack after sack of groceries. The strange old lady and her maid always came running out to carry them in.

"I know I've counted ten sacks in one day," I told Wally and Mary Ann.

"Ten?" said Wally. "I've counted thirteen!" and he licked his thumb and rubbed it on his palm and stamped it with his fist. That meant it was the truth, for sure.

I told them Mama kept a big stack of paper bags on the

back porch, so I hurried off to get some while Wally and Mary Ann collected a pile of rocks and weeds to fill them.

I heard Mama's sewing machine going when I went in, so I didn't bother her. I knew she wouldn't mind about a few old sacks. But when I went streaking back across the backyard with both arms loaded down, she saw me through the bedroom window.

"Laura-a-a-a-a!" she called. I hated stopping, but I sighed a sigh and backed up a little. "What on earth do you want with all those paper bags?"

"We're just playing, Mama," I told her, not wanting to take time to tell the whole story.

"Playing what?" she asked. "You don't have matches out there do you?"

"Oh, Mama, you know we don't," I said. "They're for Mrs. DuBois' groceries. We've built her house and we're playing 'Mrs. DuBois.' You know what? She gets ten or thirteen bags of groceries almost every day!"

"Oh, Laura, that's ridiculous. Nobody lives in that big old house except the old lady and her maid. They couldn't possibly eat that much," and she laughed and started to go on back to her machine.

But I didn't like Mama laughing at me, so I called her back to the window.

"It's so, Mama," I said. "I've counted ten bags many days,

and Wally has counted thirteen. That's the only time we ever see her, Mama, when she's bringing in groceries—except when she chases us."

"Chases you?" Mama sounded upset. Mamas are that way, I guess.

"Well, a few times Wally and Mary Ann and I have walked down her back drive to see her flowers. We wouldn't pick 'em, but golleee, she has white jonquils and red azaleas in early spring, and now she has roses as big as cabbages blooming around her goldfish pond.

"But every time we go in, old lady DuBois comes flying out of the back door, waving her arms and shouting in French. We take off like three scared squirrels."

"That peculiar old lady," said Mama. "She just hides in that big house and counts her money. Peculiar! Yes, peculiar!" Mama went grumbling back to her machine, and I walked on back to the broomstraw field, not quite so eager to play our little game.

But when I got back, Wally and Mary Ann showed me a most acceptable stack of "groceries," so we began bagging them the way Mr. Everett did at the store. Wally insisted on thirteen bags, so it took four trips with his wagon to deliver them all to the broomstraw house. When we carried them inside, the bags filled our whole kitchen and part of the dining room.

"There isn't room to walk," said Mary Ann. "Mrs. DuBois must have a very large refrigerator."

"Refrigerators don't come that big—not for houses, anyway," I told her. I pushed over one of the sacks and sat down on it to think.

"Maybe she has two or three refrigerators," said Wally, not really caring what an old lady did with her groceries.

I still couldn't forget what Mama said about only two people living in that house, and I tried to imagine how they could eat all that food.

"There's something funny about this," I whispered to Mary Ann and Wally.

"Oh, Laura, why?" asked Mary Ann in her fussiest way.

"Well, now, Mary Ann," I began. "However do you think that you and I could possibly eat thirteen sacks of food in one day—even if we were grown? Tell me that!"

"Well, there's a dog—"

"Shoot," said Wally. "A collie eats one big can of dog food a day. It sounds wacky to me." Old Wally was curious now, so we all sat down and chewed on sour grass for a while and tried to figure it out.

"I've got it!" crowed Wally, and he began cracking his knuckles the way he always did when he got excited.

"Tell us, Wally," said Mary Ann.

"Well!" he began, his eyes snapping from one of us to the other. "You know how old lady DuBois chases us every time we stop to look at her old flowers?"

"Uh-huh," Mary Ann and I agreed.

"I'll bet you this!" said Wally. "I'll bet you that old buzzard catches children and keeps 'em hidden in that big old house!"

"Golle-e-e!" said Mary Ann. "I'm never going to walk by there again!" Nobody said anything else for a few minutes, and I got an icky feeling in my stomach.

"Well, if it's true, we've got to tell somebody," I told them.

"Let's go tell my mama." That seemed to me to be the very best thing.

"Now, you wait," said Wally. "If we tell your mama, or my mama, or Mary Ann's, the police will be up there dragging old lady DuBois to jail before we can turn around and sneeze backwards. I think we had better look into this thing ourselves first."

"I'm not going over there!" said Mary Ann.

"I don't think, . . ." I started.

"Girls!" said Wally. And he spit on the ground and kicked a hole in one of the bags.

"Now, Wally Davis, you hush!" I yelled. "I guess you've forgotten who went into old man Pender's deserted barn first! I guess you've forgotten *that!*" I wasn't going to let old Wally forget my one brave adventure—not ever.

"Yeah, yeah, yeah!" Wally said. "You'll be telling that till the cows come home, but you won't slip out one night after dark to spy on old Mrs. DuBois, sissy!"

"I'm getting mad, now, Wally. You let me think this thing through," I told him.

The idea of slipping out just wouldn't work with me. Mama and Daddy never let me go anywhere at night without a grownup—except when a gang of us walked to the drugstore . . . *"the drugstore!* That's it!" I said aloud. "Wouldn't our mamas let the three of us walk to the drugstore right after supper?"

Wally jumped at the idea. We wouldn't have to tell anyone we stopped by Mrs. DuBois' house on the way home. It wasn't far. Although we lived on the edge of town, our town was small enough that we could walk to school and to the store and such places without crossing many streets.

Well, it took some fussing to get Mary Ann to agree to it, but we finally got it settled and all scooted home to work out our clever little scheme.

It was not until the next Friday night that we got together. But about seven o'clock that night, just when the air was turning into soft lavender smoke, the three of us set out for Johnson's Drug Store. We nearly ran there and couldn't think of anything we really wanted when we got there. I didn't eat half of my orange sherbet, to tell you the truth, and Wally was so excited he drank his milk shake in three gulps. We had to wait for Mary Ann. I never saw vanilla ice cream last so long.

By the time we reached the fence around Mrs. DuBois' backyard, it was dark, and that old house looked bigger and spookier than ever. We crouched down behind some bushes and waited for something to happen. Lights were on in the house, and I kept watching for that mean old lady to race past the windows chasing some poor, helpless children with a big stick or a leather belt.

Once Wally nudged me and pointed out a small figure bending over doing some work in the kitchen.

"She makes those kids scrub for her!" whispered Wally. But when the figure straightened up it was only the short, plump maid, and she wasn't scrubbing. She was carrying two large paper bags in her arms. Soon the old lady joined the maid in the kitchen, and they both began scurrying around like busy little mice.

Suddenly, we were flooded with light! Mary Ann squealed,

and I ducked. In a second the light turned. We saw that it was an old rickety car rumbling down the back drive. There was a man and a woman in the car and several children in the back seat. It stopped and a man got out and knocked on the back door.

"What in thunderation!" said Wally.

"Sh-h-h." I elbowed him.

Then we saw Mrs. DuBois and her maid open the door and place two of the big bags in the man's arms. He carried these to the car and came back for one more.

"What's in those bags?" asked Mary Ann.

Well, I knew it all by then. "It's groceries, silly," I told her. "Be still and watch."

Before the first car had pulled away, a noisy pickup pulled in behind it. The man driving it got one bag. Then a Negro woman came with five children climbing on top of one another in the back of her car. She got four bags. We watched until six cars had driven up to the back door to get free groceries! It was easy to tell that the cars belonged to the poor. In the light from the kitchen we could see that the people were dressed in overalls and old work clothes. All of them had children.

When the last car pulled out of the driveway, Wally sat flat down on the sidewalk. He propped his elbow on his knee and his fist under his chin.

"If that doesn't beat all," he said. "Old lady DuBois is giving away all those groceries!" He wrinkled up his nose and grinned.

I felt so happy about the whole thing I started giggling. Then Mary Ann began giggling, too. Old Wally got plumb disgusted with us. He got up, stuck his hands in his pockets,

started whistling a gay song, and set out for home. Mary Ann and I tagged along.

Well, Wally went back to watch Mrs. DuBois several more evenings and reported that the same thing happened every night. We figured that she must be giving food to about thirty families every week!

We didn't tell her secret to anyone. We thought that if such a kind old lady wanted to keep it a secret that she was giving food to the poor, we weren't going to be the ones to tell it.

But one afternoon soon after that, we all walked up that long back drive to look at her flowers. Sure enough, Mrs. DuBois came running out, waving her arms and shouting in French.

But we didn't move. We stood stock-still until she got close to us. "Oh, *mes petits enfants*," she said. "So glad you no run. I have no *jeune fille*, no *garçon*. Come in, *voulez-vous?* We have —you say—tea party?"

Although we knew we should never go into a stranger's house, this time not one of us hesitated. We understood Mrs. DuBois better than anyone in town. She was no stranger to us, now.

We went that day and many other days. And many times we played "Mrs. DuBois" in the broomstraw field.

But one thing we never did. We never told her secret. Not even once.

My Brother Stevie

Eleanor Clymer

*Think about the plot of "The Broomstraw House" for a
moment. Could there have been a plot without the characters?*

*Believable characters act as you expect them to act. You
find yourself saying, "Yes, that's what that boy would do."
Or you may find yourself thinking, "I know just how she feels."*

*Often a character changes in a story. His ideas may
change, or his feelings. The change is usually important to
the plot and is likely to be part of the climax.*

*Try to understand the characters in the next story. Why
does Stevie act as he does? Are his sister and grandmother
believable?*

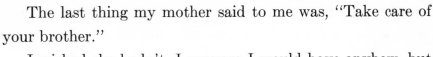

The last thing my mother said to me was, "Take care of your brother."

I wished she hadn't. I suppose I would have anyhow, but it made me mad to think of her saying it. Because why should I have to take care of him, just because I'm his sister? Why shouldn't somebody take care of me? Of course I'm older, but I didn't want to be older. It seemed like it wasn't fair to be punished for something you had no say about.

Well, that's what my mother said. Then she went away. She was always going away, even before Pa died, and leaving us with Grandma. And this time she just went away for good. I didn't know where, and when I used to ask Grandma she would get mad and say, "Don't talk to me about her. Just you and Stevie behave yourselves and grow up decent. I brought up my son and now he's dead and I have to bring up you."

The trouble was, Grandma didn't ever like Mama. Mama used to sing and dance a lot. She sure could dance. When she was home, she'd be singing and fooling and joking all the time. She'd grab us and kiss us any time she felt like it. But Grandma didn't like that kind of thing.

And sometimes it seems as if she doesn't like Stevie. I guess it's because he's like Mama. He always liked to fool and joke, even when he was real little. He was always full of the devil. Grandma said, "Act nice, sit still, keep clean." But Stevie would act silly, jump around, make everybody laugh. I'd like to be like that too, only I can't. I always had to behave, or else he'd get even sillier and Grandma would smack him.

Like the time Grandma got a new hat for Sunday, and Stevie put it on and put a towel around him for a skirt and paraded around. I laughed and put on my hat and we both paraded like grown-up ladies. Then Grandma came in and grabbed Stevie and whipped him, and then she smacked me too and said, "You're supposed to set a good example."

It wasn't so much fun after Mama went away. Just helping Grandma and minding Stevie and going to school. I don't mean I mind going to school. I like it. It gives you something to do every day—I mean something you have to do. I like getting up and getting ready and going out. Lots of other people are going out too, men and ladies going to work, kids going to school, people opening the stores and sweeping the sidewalk. You feel like you're part of it.

I like to go early so I can see my friends, have time to talk. Then we go in and start to work, see if we know our homework and that. I like when I get to do an example on the board, and the teacher says, "That's very good, Annie."

After school we'd play, then we'd come in and Grandma would give us supper. Whoever came in first could eat first, and then I'd do my homework.

Stevie would watch me do my homework—that was before he went to school himself. He used to be a terrible copycat when he was little. He wanted to do everything I did. He'd take a pencil and try to do homework too. In fact, he could almost read before he went to school, just from copying me.

That was all right, but some things weren't because he didn't understand. Like one time when I was selling raffle tickets for the church, and he took a book and went around scribbling in it, and people gave him pennies because he was so cute. Then Grandma smacked him for begging. But he wasn't really begging. He just wanted to do what I did.

Then when he got bigger, he stopped copying me and started copying other kids. He started to run around with some kids in the building, and they would fool with the washing machines, or sneak into the storeroom if the Super forgot to lock it, or jam something into the phones so the dimes would come out.

Grandma would ask me where he was, and I'd say he was playing in the street. I thought I had to cover up for him, or he would be getting lickings all the time.

One day, one of the neighbors told Grandma she saw Stevie in the subway with some other kids, fooling with the candy machines. Grandma asked him what he was doing there and he said he never went there. It must have been somebody else.

Grandma believed him, but when she wasn't looking he gave me a grin. I went in the bedroom later and said, "Stevie, were you in the subway?" He said no. I halfway believed him. Seemed like I couldn't stand the idea of him lying to me. I asked him who he was playing with, and he said Mike.

Mike is a kid about twelve; he's in my grade in school only not the same class. I told Stevie he'd better stay away from Mike, but he didn't. I couldn't watch him all the time, could I? Once in a while, I like to go out with my own friends.

Anyhow, Stevie started going with this bunch of boys. He was younger than the rest, only eight, but he was smart and could run fast, and besides he could always make people laugh.

For instance, one time I was going to the store and I saw a crowd of people. I went over to see, and there was Stevie in the middle dancing, and the people were laughing and giving him money. He was pretty funny. I had to laugh myself.

Then all of a sudden I saw a lady push through the crowd and grab him. It was Grandma. Was she mad! She pulled him out of there and smacked him so hard I thought she'd half kill him.

I think it was right about then that I started worrying that he would really get in trouble.

One day, it was Saturday, I was going downtown with my friends. I have these friends, Betty and Mary and Doris. I like them all, but Betty is really my best friend. We used to go downtown and look in the store windows and shop in the five-and-ten. We have a five-and-ten uptown, but the downtown ones are better. They have different stuff, not so much junk.

We were sitting in the subway train waiting for it to go, and all of a sudden Betty said, "Hey Annie, there's your brother!"

I asked where and looked out the window, and there was a bunch of kids trying to break a candy machine, and there was Stevie in the middle. I saw Mike too. I jumped up and was going to run out, but the doors closed and I couldn't. I banged on the glass, but just then a guard came, and the kids all ran away.

So I went on downtown with the girls, but I couldn't really enjoy it. I kept seeing Stevie there in the subway.

When I got home I said to him, "Where were you today?" And he said, "In the park." I said, "You mean the subway?" And he said, "No, why do you think I was in the subway?"

So then I knew he was lying, but I didn't say any more. It was like, if I acted as if I believed what he said, maybe it would be better. But it wasn't.

The next thing, they started throwing things at trains. See, the railroad goes past the project. And some of these kids go up on the roofs and throw things at the trains, and nobody can catch them. So they think they're real smart. This kid Mike had an air gun, and he hit a window in a train once and thought it was funny the way the people jumped up and got excited. I heard him telling about it in recess. You could hurt somebody that way, but they never thought of that.

Well, I was worried. I didn't know what to do. Take care of your brother. That's all right to say, only I didn't know how. I'd yell at him, but it wasn't any use; he got so he didn't even hear what you said to him. And it was no use telling Grandma; she didn't know what to do with him any more than I did.

I got so worried, I got my schoolwork all wrong. I just couldn't pay attention to it.

Stevie was getting so he didn't care what anybody said. They'd send home notes from school about how he disturbed the class, getting up from his seat and running all around and talking and making the kids laugh. That's really what he liked, making everybody laugh, because that meant they liked him.

I could remember when he was a little baby, and I was about four or five, and Mama would let me hold him, and he was so soft and warm and nice to hold, and fun to play with. And I thought, why do babies have to grow up and get mean and do bad things and get in trouble, just because they still want somebody to like them and play with them.

So I could understand how he felt, but still when he'd do something bad I couldn't help yelling at him, and that just made him mean. I thought he ought to have a little brother to look out for. All he had was a teddy bear, and Grandma finally threw it out because it was so dirty. I didn't know what to do. I just stayed home, I hardly had any time for my friends at all.

Well, then something lucky happened. Stevie was in the third grade and they had this new teacher. Miss Stover, her name was. I saw her in the hall, and she was real pretty. Stevie came home and told Grandma and me, "I have a new teacher." Grandma said, "Well, you behave now, and don't get fresh to her."

I wanted to tell her that that was the wrong thing to say; it would just make him do some fresh thing like make faces or tell jokes to get the kids laughing.

So I was waiting for a note to come to tell Grandma the teacher wanted to see her. But nothing came. So I figured, well, the new teacher isn't on to him yet, but just wait.

But still nothing happened. Stevie went to school, and he'd come home and do homework, and play, or watch TV, and I was starting to think maybe I could go downtown on Saturday, because Betty and the rest were going to the show. I was thinking about what I would wear, when Bingo! It happened.

It was a Thursday afternoon, and starting to get dark. It was only March, so it wasn't spring yet, and Grandma was out, and I was home by myself wondering where Stevie was, and the bell rang. And there was a strange man with Stevie. He had hold of him so he couldn't get away, and I said, "What happened?"

Stevie didn't say a word. He didn't grin at me the way he does, but just looked at the floor. And the man said, "Is this your brother?"

I said yes, and he said, "Is your mother home?"

I said, "No, we live with our grandmother."

And the man said, "Well, where's she?"

I said, "She's out. What did he do?"

And he said, "These kids were up on my roof. I'm the Super from next door. They were throwing rocks at trains. This is the only one I could catch. When's your grandmother coming home?"

I said, "I don't know."

He said, "Well, I can't wait, but I have your address, and let me tell you if I catch him again, it will be too bad."

I said, "Please, mister, don't do anything. I'll take care of Stevie."

"You give him a good licking," he said, and went away.

I was so scared I was shivering. This was the first time anybody caught him, but I thought next time it could be a cop. I think the man only wanted to scare Stevie and find out if he really lived where he said he did. He could see our apartment was clean and we lived in the project, and that's why he went away so soon. But what was I going to do?

Stevie said, "Are you going to tell Grandma?"

I said, "No, it would just make her mad. But how can I stop you from going with those kids?"

He said, "I dunno. They want me to come, so I do. Anyhow, I like to watch the trains."

I said, "But can't you watch the trains without throwing rocks at them?" And he said, "I dunno. Those people sitting there look so silly." And then he wouldn't say another word.

I thought, "What can I do? Who can I talk to?" And all of a sudden I had an idea. Miss Stover. Only how could I do it without Stevie knowing?

The next day I said to Grandma, "I have to go to school early and help my teacher." And I got out of the house before Stevie was even up. I ran to school and stood by the teachers' gate till Miss Stover came about a quarter past eight. I thought she might be mad, but I ran up to her and said, "Miss Stover, could I talk to you?"

And she turned around and wasn't mad at all. She smiled at me. I remember she had on a red dress and coat, and no hat, and the wind was blowing her hair.

"What's your name?" she said.

I said, "I'm Annie Jenner, I'm Steven's sister, and I have to talk to you, please, Miss Stover. It's about Stevie."

She said, "Come in," and took my arm, and right away I knew why Stevie liked her. She made you feel as if she liked you.

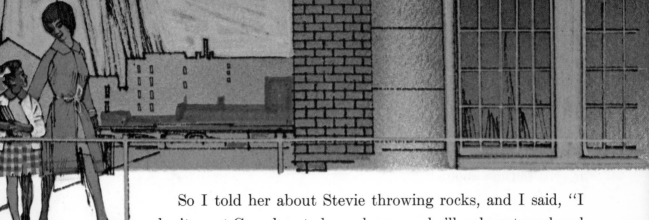

So I told her about Stevie throwing rocks, and I said, "I don't want Grandma to know because she'll only get mad and hit him, and that makes him worse. But could you think of something?" I said, "He told me he likes the trains, but still he throws rocks at them. He could kill somebody!"

She nodded her head yes, and said, "You're right, Annie. I'm glad you told me. You know your little brother is a very bright boy, and it doesn't do any good to hit him."

I said I wished I knew what *would* do some good, and she said, "I know how you feel, Annie; I had to take care of my little brother when my mother died." Then she sort of sighed and said, "Now don't worry, but come and see me again and maybe we can help Stevie." And she smiled again and I felt like hugging her, only I didn't dare. But when I walked out of the room, I felt like I had been carrying a big weight and it was gone.

So that afternoon when Stevie came home, I went in the kitchen and gave him a peanut butter sandwich and a glass of milk. I waited awhile, but didn't say anything, and at last he said, "My teacher is gonna take us on a train."

I said, "She is? How come?"

He said, "She knows all about trains. She rides on them a whole lot. And we're gonna do trains for social studies, and see a movie about them, and go to the station, and maybe have a ride."

I said, "Gee, that's great; I wish I could go too."

He said, "It's only for our class, but I could ask her—"

I said, "No, you better not, because then all my friends would want to go, and that would be too much. You could maybe tell me about it."

And he said okay.

From then on he was drawing pictures of trains, and cutting out pictures and pasting them up, and playing train in the house with chairs. I didn't hear about throwing rocks any more; all I heard was choo choo choo, and why trains are important and how they work.

The only thing was, they didn't really get to ride on the train because it cost too much. But they went to the station and walked through a train after it had stopped, and sat in the seats so they knew how it looked inside. They brought back posters, and Stevie had one in his room.

Stevie said when they saved up enough money they would go for a ride. And I said, if I got any money from babysitting I would give him some. And he was so good, I started thinking maybe I could go out with Betty and the rest and wondered how I would fix my hair and if I could get some new shoes.

But then something else happened. It wasn't a bad thing; it only meant I had to stick around.

It was Saturday, and I had to help Grandma, take the wash to the launderette, and go to the store, and I made Stevie help me. Grandma won't use the washing machines in the building. She thinks they aren't clean enough. Stevie was pushing the shopping cart with all the dirty clothes, when all of a sudden he let out a yell, "Hey! There's my teacher!"

And there she was, walking along with a dog on a leash. It

was a cute little dog, brown with white feet, and Stevie looked as if he wanted to pat it, but first he looked up at Miss Stover to see if he should.

She said, "Hello Annie, hello Steven, this is Skipper. Sit, Skipper." The dog sat down. Then she said, "Ask him to shake hands." And Stevie did, and the dog held out his paw.

Well, I thought that was pretty cute. But Stevie! He just sat down on the sidewalk and hugged the dog, and the dog washed his face with its tongue. You could see they just loved each other right away.

Miss Stover laughed. She said, "Poor Skipper! At home he has lots of children to play with, but here he's alone most of the time. Maybe I shouldn't have brought him, but I like to have him for company."

I wondered what she meant by "at home." Wasn't she at home here? Then she said, "Stevie, do you want to take Skipper for a little walk while I go into the store?"

"Yes, ma'am," said Stevie. "I'll take care of him."

Miss Stover said, "Oh, but I forgot, you're helping your sister."

"Oh, that's all right," I said. "I'll just put the wash in the machine and be right back. Then Stevie can help me with the groceries."

Well, that was the beginning. After that Miss Stover let Stevie take Skipper for walks after school. I was surprised that she lived so near us. See, we lived in the project, and she lived in the Co-op a few blocks away, and that's how come we saw her going to the store, because we all went to the same supermarket.

Stevie sure did love that dog. Miss Stover would have let

him take Skipper home, only Grandma wouldn't have animals in the house getting the floor dirty.

My friend Betty's mother didn't mind, so if the weather was bad we would take Skipper up in her house, and he was a really cute dog. He knew lots of tricks. You could hide a cookie and he would find it. And he'd roll over and play dead dog, and walk on his hind legs. And when he was tired he'd jump in Stevie's lap and snuggle down, and they'd both be happy.

One weekend Miss Stover had to go away, and she said to me, "Annie, I'd like to have Steven take care of Skipper for the weekend. Do you think your grandmother would possibly let him take Skipper home for a little while?"

I said I would ask. Grandma didn't want to, but she didn't like to refuse the teacher. I promised her I wouldn't let the dog make a mess, and we would keep him in Stevie's room the whole time. Miss Stover said if there was any trouble we should take Skipper to her house and her Super would put him in the apartment and feed him. She could have done that anyhow but Skipper would have been lonesome, and he would be happier with children.

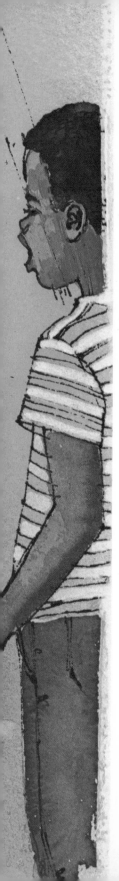

The first day Skipper was good, and Stevie spent the whole day in the room with him, except when he took him out. He talked to him. He said, "Hiya, Skipper. How do you like it here? You hungry? Wait there, I'll get you something."

They wrestled on the floor and I heard growls and giggles. Then it was quiet, and I peeked in and there they were, both sound asleep on the bed.

But after a while, Skipper got to wondering what was in the other part of the house. He got out, and found the garbage pail, and got the stuff all over the floor. I heard Stevie yelling for me, and I ran and cleaned it up before Grandma could see it.

But then he got in Grandma's room and found her slippers and chewed one. We couldn't hide that. I took a dollar of my money and bought some new slippers. She scolded me and said by rights Stevie should pay for it, but I was glad he was having a good time and anyhow he didn't have any money.

But you see why I couldn't go downtown. I had to stick around and keep an eye on things.

But I was feeling better about everything, and Grandma wasn't mad at Stevie, and when I did my homework I could even pay attention to the lesson, and my teacher said to me, "Annie, you see what you can do when you try."

I thought to myself, "She doesn't understand much, but Miss Stover does."

And at night when I was in bed I would think about Miss Stover and pretend I was going to do something wonderful for her like save her from an accident or find her long-lost mother for her. And she would say, "Annie, how can I ever thank you?" And I would say, "Don't try, Miss Stover, after all you did for us."

Texas Norther

Lloyd Besant

Every writer wants his readers to enjoy an exciting plot with interesting characters. But he may also want to share an idea with the readers.

The theme of a story, or the writer's message, is usually not stated. You have to figure it out as if it were a puzzle. You can use the plot and characters as clues to the theme.

You may or may not agree with the theme of a story. You may think, "Yes, that's true." Again you may think, "Well, bravery was rewarded in the story, but I don't think bravery is always rewarded."

Try to figure out the theme of the next story. Then decide whether you agree with it.

The Chester family had moved to a ranch in Texas. Molly and Frank liked to ride their horses over the grassy range. Each day they rode over the hill and down the far side. Then they watered their horses at a small stream.

They liked to sit by the stream while the horses drank. They sat in the shade of a scrub oak. One branch of the scrub oak had been stripped of its bark by a flash of lightning in a big storm. But that was some time ago. There hadn't been any storms at the ranch since the Chesters had moved there.

One morning Mr. Chester, Molly, and Frank sat down to breakfast. Mrs. Chester brought in sausage and pancakes.

"This is good sausage," said Mr. Chester.

"And these are good pancakes, too," Frank said.

While the Chesters were enjoying their breakfast, they listened to the radio. They heard music and the news about what was happening all over the country.

Suddenly they heard a bell sound on the radio. "We have special news about the weather," a voice said. "A cold front is moving in from the north. The wind will be very strong, and it may bring dust and rain."

Mr. Chester said to Molly and Frank, "You must be careful not to ride too far this morning. That cold front could be bad. A norther with dust and rain sometimes means a big storm."

Molly and Frank thought of this as they got on their horses.

"Be sure to get back before the storm breaks," their father said again.

"We will, Dad," they called as they started out.

They rode south across the range. Now and then they looked back at the sky. No storm was in sight.

"I'll race you to the top of the hill!" Frank said.

"All right," said Molly. They pulled their horses up side by side.

"Get set! Go!" cried Frank.

The horses leaped forward and ran as fast as they could. Frank raced on ahead. His horse, Ranger, was as swift as the wind.

Molly followed on her horse, Bill. She caught up with Frank when he stopped at the top of the hill.

They both turned to look back at the sky. Not a cloud was in sight. The air was warm and still.

They sat looking down across the grassy field. Off to the right they could just see the scrub oak by the stream. It looked like a tiny spot.

Just as they were going to turn back, they heard a sound far away. The sound was like the bawl of a young calf.

"That must be a baby calf lost from his mother!" Frank called out. "We can't leave him way out here. There may be a storm coming!"

"Maa! Maa!" sounded again and again.

"Maybe we can find the calf and drive him home so he'll be safe," Molly said.

Molly and Frank looked back at the sky. It was still clear.

There were only little whispers of wind. Now and then the wind picked up dust. It blew the dust in little swirls, then dropped it.

"We'll have time," Frank said. "We can't leave a baby calf alone in the storm!"

They touched their horses lightly with their heels and moved down the hill. They tried to follow the sound of the bawling.

They looked here and there.

"Here's the calf!" cried Molly at last. And there he was, hiding by the stream in some mesquite bushes.

"Maa! Maa!" bawled the calf.

Molly rode toward him, and he ran out of the bushes. Frank raced to head him off so that he would not go farther away.

He turned and ran away from Frank. Molly rode after the calf. She managed to get in front of him and head him back toward home. Frank rode his horse to the side to keep the calf from breaking away.

Little by little they drove the calf toward the top of the hill. By this time the wind was cooler and was coming in strong puffs. It was blowing sand and dust in their faces.

"Watch the calf, Frank!" Molly called.

The calf began to dodge here and there, trying to go with the wind back to the mesquite bushes. But Molly or Frank rode out each time to guide him into the wind toward home.

At the top of the hill a strong wind swept over them with a great "whoo—oosh!" The calf stopped a minute and lowered his head. Then he tried again to turn around and run back to the mesquite bushes by the stream.

"Don't let him get past you!" warned Frank. And Molly

rode around the calf and headed him back toward the ranch.

Far off to the right they could see the ranch house. All along the edge of the sky there was a great black cloud. The two children looked at one another. Each knew what the other was thinking. They wanted to run for home, but they couldn't leave the calf.

"Hoo-ee! Hoo-ee!" Frank shouted as he rode swiftly toward the calf. The calf started to run again. "We must guide him to the right!" Frank called.

Now blast after blast of wind swept over them, then died away. It was hard to face these blasts. The little calf kept trying to turn to get the wind behind him. But Molly and Frank drove him on and on.

A strong puff of wind picked up more sand and swirled it into their faces.

"We have to get home!" cried Molly. The wind caught her breath and filled her eyes with dust.

Then a tumbleweed came rolling toward them, and Frank pulled his horse quickly to the side to let it go past. Tumbleweed after tumbleweed went rolling by.

Over and over again the wind whipped them with sand that stung their legs and faces. For a minute they could not see the ranch house.

"The storm is coming closer!" cried Molly. Frank nodded. He could tell that she was afraid. Well, he was afraid, too.

The wind died down a bit, and the little calf stopped trying to go back to the bushes. His little legs were getting tired. He put his head down and stumbled toward the gate, bawling as he went.

Frank's horse snorted as the wind struck again. Molly's

horse gave a neigh in answer. He lifted his front legs and pawed the air.

"Hold on, Molly!" called Frank. "It's just a little way now."

Molly soon quieted the horse, and they went on. When the dust settled, they could see the ranch house again. They pushed ahead. The black storm cloud kept moving toward them.

In spite of their fear, Molly and Frank held their horses back and made them stay behind the calf.

"There's the gate!" Molly cried at last. As she spoke, a sudden cold blast of air struck them. The storm was coming fast now.

When the cold wind died down, Molly and Frank drew their horses together to guide the calf through the gate. They could see the great black cloud rolling toward the ranch house. Then there was a big flash of lightning.

"Hi!" called a voice. Molly and Frank looked into the swirling dust ahead and saw their father riding toward them. "I was coming out to look for you!" he called. "Your mother and I were worried!"

Molly and Frank smiled. They weren't afraid now.

Mr. Chester helped Frank and Molly get the calf across the barnyard and into the barn. The little calf lay down on some soft hay, breathing hard.

"Go on up to the house," said Mr. Chester to the children. "I'll take care of your horses. And I'll give this little fellow some warm milk. He's cold."

Molly and Frank started up the walk. Just as they reached the door, the storm broke. Great drops of rain began to fall. Some of them mixed with dust and threw splatters of mud around the children. They dashed into the warm house, where their mother was waiting for them.

In just a little while Mrs. Chester and the children were sitting beside a roaring fire, listening to the storm.

Afterthought

1. What made Frank and Molly seem like real people?
2. In what ways did the calf act like a real calf?
3. Can you think of any events in the story that could not really happen?
4. How do you think Mr. and Mrs. Chester felt about Frank and Molly after they brought the calf home? What would they have thought if the children had come home without the calf?
5. Do you think it is always a good idea to stick with an undertaking in spite of hardship and discouragement?

Lonesome Spooky

Sally Burke

Stories are usually imaginary. But the characters in some of them seem real, and the events could really happen. Readers may understand themselves and other people better after they read such realistic stories. Would you call the first three stories in this book realistic?

One of the characters in the next story is not realistic; he is make-believe. Some of the events in the story could not really happen. Is the writer trying to tell you something about real life with this fantasy?

Wally Winkler went up to the roof one summer morning to feed his pet pigeons. He had climbed the stairs and was just picking up some grain when he heard a strange sound: "Woo-Woo-Wally! Woo-Woo-Wally!"

Wally looked up at the chimney above him and then all around the roof. At first he could see nothing. Then he saw something very thin and white at the edge of the roof. It made him think of a misty cloud. But as he looked, it seemed to grow until it looked like a tall, thin snowman with big black holes for eyes.

"Who are you?" asked Wally.

"I'm Spooky," replied the queer thing, in a voice that was half a whisper and half a sigh.

"What's wrong?" asked Wally.

Spooky sighed deeply. "I'm just a sad, lonesome ghost," he said. "I can't find any place to haunt." He shook as if he were crying. "And I haven't any friends or family. I'm all alone."

"Oh, I'm sorry, Spooky," said Wally. "It must be terrible to have no friends or family!"

Spooky stopped shaking and sighed a lonesome sigh.

"Can't you haunt around here?" asked Wally.

"No," said Spooky sadly. "Nobody except you believes in ghosts around here. I'll have to find a better place to haunt."

Wally thought for a minute. "I know!" he cried suddenly. "I know the place for you to haunt. Mother and Dad and I are going on a trip. We are going right through a ghost town. Wouldn't that be a good place for you?"

Spooky began to shake again. But this time it wasn't because he was crying. He was just excited. He wiggled up tall

and wiggled down short. Suddenly he looked like a very short, fat snowman.

"A ghost town!" he exclaimed. "That's woo-woo-wonderful! Could you take me with you?"

"Well, I'm not sure what my mother and father would think about riding with a ghost—," he began.

"They wouldn't need to know!" cried Spooky. "You see, you're a very special person. Only special persons can see me. And grownups are not often special in that way."

"Well, then," said Wally, "if you will be in the back seat of our car when we start out early tomorrow morning, you may go along."

"Oh, that's woo-woo-wonderful!" sighed Spooky. And he shot up into the air and sat on the chimney. He looked like a flat little cloud.

"I do hope there will be enough room," said Wally, beginning to worry. "They're sure to put some baggage in. I wouldn't want to crowd you."

The ghost laughed a strange, whispering laugh. "Oh, don't you worry about me," he said. "I can just kind of flow around things. I can sit on the ceiling until they get the baggage in."

"Then I will see you tomorrow morning." said Wally.

"All right—and I sure thank you, Woo-Woo-Wally!" the ghost called from the chimney. Wally threw some grain into the pen and went down the stairs.

Early the next morning Wally went out to the car. He unlocked the doors and opened the windows. There was the ghost, like a flat little cloud, sitting on the ceiling.

"Why, however did you get in?" asked Wally. "All the doors and windows were locked."

"Oh, I just flowed around the cracks," said Spooky.

Soon Wally's mother and father came out. The car was packed, and off they went. Spooky floated down from the ceiling to sit beside Wally. A sudden draft of wind seemed to go through the car.

Wally's mother turned around. "If that draft is too strong for you, you might close the window," she said.

"Oh, no, I like it," Wally called. Wally and Spooky giggled softly. "Are you comfortable?" whispered Wally.

"Oh, yes, I'm quite comfortable," whispered Spooky in answer.

That night they stayed at a small motel. Wally turned out his light and was just going to sleep when he saw the ghost sitting on the foot of his bed. When he saw that Wally was awake, the ghost said quickly, "Now, I'm not going to make any trouble, but I was just thinking I'd try a little haunting through these rooms. You don't mind, do you, Woo-Woo-Wally? I want to practice my haunting."

Spooky grew long and thin. "I haven't had a chance to haunt for a long time," he sighed.

"Well, be careful not to make any trouble," said Wally.

"Thank you," called Spooky, as he became a flat little cloud and floated out the door.

The next morning as they left the motel, Mrs. Winkler said to her husband, "Wasn't it windy last night! Did you feel that draft in our room?"

Wally and Spooky giggled again very quietly. "That was you," said Wally.

"Wally," said his mother, "why do you keep talking to yourself?"

"Oh, I'm just thinking out loud," said Wally. And he and Spooky laughed and laughed without making a sound.

They rode out over the prairies. They came to the mountains. At last they passed an old silver mine. They saw a big sign with an arrow at the top. The sign read, "GHOST TOWN AHEAD."

Spooky began to get so excited that he grew whiter and whiter and rounder and rounder and shorter and shorter. Just then Wally's mother turned around. "We are coming to the ghost town!" she said. Then she stopped. "Why, my goodness! I didn't know it was so misty this morning! There is mist all over the back seat of the car!"

Spooky made himself thinner and thinner. "Oh, I must have been wrong," Mrs. Winkler said then. "It must have been the way the sun was shining."

"Now you'd better be careful," whispered Wally. And Spooky nodded his head, but he didn't say a word.

On and on they rode. They went through the streets of the town. Mr. Winkler showed them an empty school, an empty church, and a big, empty station where the trains used to come in. An old engine still sat on the track. Something that looked

like little white clouds floated in and out of the engine windows.

Suddenly Spooky began to grow longer and longer. Then he grew smaller and smaller until he was a round, white ball. He bounced up and down on the seat in excitement.

"Loo-ook there, Wally," Spooky whispered loudly. "That's just the right place! And there are some ghosts like me. I won't have to be alone anymore!"

"Good-bye, Wally, and thank you," Spooky said in a thin voice as he flowed out of the car.

Wally watched the ghost rush toward the old engine. Two little white clouds came out to meet him. And then three little white clouds floated back to the station.

Mr. Winkler drove on down the street. All at once they heard a train whistle.

"That's strange," Mr. Winkler said. "Why, there haven't been any trains through here for years and years!"

They turned around at the end of the street and rode back. As they were going by the station, they heard the train whistle again.

"If I didn't know better," said Wally's father, "I'd think that whistle came from the old engine."

Wally smiled and stuck his head out the window. There on top of the old train engine sat a fat, happy Spooky with his two ghost friends. Wally grinned and waved.

Then Wally saw Spooky puff his cheeks out. "Who-oo, whoo-oo!" came a sound like a train whistle. "Whoo-oo-oo, whoo-oo-oo! Good-bye, Woo-Woo-Wally!"

Wally was a bit sad. But he was glad, too. Now poor, lonesome Spooky had a great big place to haunt and friends like himself to haunt with him.

The Sniffing Hound

Lloyd Besant

It is easy to see that Spooky is a make-believe character. The main character in the next story—a hound that sniffs—is also make-believe. Now a sniffing hound may sound real, but you'll soon see that this is a mighty special dog. Try to decide what makes this story a tall tale.

Sam lay in front of the general store in Parkersville. He had made a big, deep hole there, and he lay in it day after day with his nose on his paws.

While Sam lay outside asleep in the sun, Jed Coyle worked inside the store. He sold groceries, yard goods, and farm tools.

One morning Sara Flint came by and started to scold. "Well, I never!" she said. "That dog has made a hole so deep that a lady takes her life in her hands to come in here! If Parkersville had any other store, I'd stay away from your place, Jed Coyle!"

Jed didn't pay any attention to Sara Flint. She was always scolding about Sam. But anything Sam did was all right with Jed. You see, Sam wasn't just an ordinary dog. And the hole he lay in wasn't an ordinary hole, either. It wasn't even an ordinary dog hole. Sam hadn't dug it. He had sniffed it!

Yes, Sam was a sniffing hound. He was such a sniffing hound that he sniffed even in his sleep. All the time he was asleep he kept turning, until he had sniffed a huge hole around himself. The hole kept getting deeper and deeper. Some people said that soon it would reach to China!

In the store, Sara Flint kept on scolding. "Now listen to

me, Jed Coyle!" she said. "You'd better get that dog out of the way before someone tells the sheriff about him!"

Jed just smiled and said, "Someday, Sara, you're going to find out how important that dog is!"

Sara wrinkled her nose and stuck it in the air to show she didn't agree. She paid for the sugar she had bought and swished off home.

It wasn't long before Sheriff Bird dropped by to talk to Jed. "Jed," he began, "I've been hearing about that dog of yours. You ought to do something about him. That hole he's making is so deep that someone might fall into it and get hurt pretty bad."

"Now, Sheriff," said Jed, "everyone knows about that hole. No one's going to fall into it. Besides, Sam is my friend, and he loves that hole. You know, Sheriff, Sam's a very important dog. He's a sniffing hound, and sniffing hounds are worth their weight in gold."

"What good is a sniffing hound if all he can do is sniff a hole?" asked the sheriff.

"Oh, Sam can sniff other things, too. Important things," said Jed.

"What things?" asked the sheriff.

"Well, I haven't found out yet what special thing Sam can sniff," said Jed slowly. "But I will. Just any day now I'll find out. You'll see. Sam will be worth his weight in gold!"

The next day Jed got a big package of wrist watches. When he opened the package, he was excited. They were the kind of watches that shine in the dark. With one of them a man could always tell the time, day or night. Jed was sure he could make money on those watches. He put a sign in the window to let everyone know that he had them.

To Jed's surprise, the first one who came to see the watches was Sam. Sam came into the store with his head pushed forward and his nose stuck out. He went over to the watches and began to sniff. He lifted his nose and howled, "Ow-ooo-oo! Ow-ooo-oo-o!" It was a howl of joy that Jed had never heard before. Jed could tell that Sam was enjoying a real good sniff.

"I wonder why he likes to sniff those watches," thought Jed.

Sam sniffed the watches all day, as if he couldn't sniff them enough. Jed watched him and wondered.

The next morning, when Jed and Sam came to open the store, they found a broken window. And the watches were gone! Sam ran to the place where the watches had been. When he found that they were gone, he let out a deep growl. He began to sniff and growl around the store.

"Find them," said Jed. "Go on, Sam! Find them!"

Sam sniffed around and around the store. He sniffed his way out the door. He sniffed down the street. Jed followed him. People saw Jed and Sam and wondered what had happened. Soon there was a crowd following Sam, and Jed explained to the people what Sam was doing.

Sam ran this way and that and sniffed along as he ran. Every now and then he stopped and growled a deep growl. Then he ran ahead. Soon he was running fast right out of town. He turned into the first field he came to and ran around with his nose to the ground. All at once he lifted his nose high in the air and howled with joy. "Ow-ooo-oo-o!" said Sam. There in a hole at the foot of a tree was the box of watches.

"Good boy, Sam!" said Jed.

"What a sniffing hound that is!" people said.

So Sam was a hero. He had found the stolen watches. But he didn't seem interested in finding out who had stolen them. He just wanted to sniff them.

Jed put the watches back in the store where they belonged. Sam sat next to them and sniffed them all day.

Now everybody knew about the watches, and everybody wanted one. Very soon they were all sold. Sam was upset when the box of watches was empty. He walked around and growled. He wouldn't even lie in the hole he had sniffed. "But, Sam," Jed tried to explain, "that's what I got them for. I got them to sell so I could make money."

Sam was very unhappy. The watches were all gone. But that was not going to stop him from sniffing them. He ran after the men who had bought them and sniffed the watches. After a few days of this, the men who had bought the watches were angry.

"We'll bring those watches back, Jed, if Sam doesn't stop following us and sniffing them," they said.

Everyone had thought Sam was a hero the day he found

the watches. But a few days later everyone thought he was just a bother.

"Sam, you just can't do that," Jed scolded him. "The men bought those watches. And they don't want you running and sniffing after them."

Sara Flint brought back the watch her husband had bought. "Jed, you'll just have to give me Jim's money back," she said. "He doesn't want that silly old hound coming after him and sniffing all the time. I told you that dog would come to no good!"

Jed gave Sara Flint the money for the watch. He wondered how many other people would return the watches and want their money back.

"See what you've done, Sam," Jed scolded sadly.

But Sam paid no attention to Jed. He sniffed the watch Sara had brought back, lifted his nose, and howled with joy. When Jed saw that, he gave the watch to Sam. Sam carried it around in his mouth. He laid it in the hole and lay down beside it. And he sniffed it all day. He even sniffed it all night. Sam was so happy with his watch that he didn't bother the men who wore the others.

Sheriff Bird came in a few days later. "Some sniffing hound you have there, Jed," he said with a big grin. "Spends all his time sniffing a watch. He's nothing but a watch-sniffing hound." The sheriff roared with laughter. So did a lot of other people.

Jed wasn't too proud of Sam anymore. But Sam was his dog. Sam was his good friend. And it isn't fun to have people laugh at a friend.

A few weeks later two strange men came to town. They

came to Jed's general store for groceries. Jed asked them who they were and what they were doing in Parkersville.

"We're government men out here looking for uranium," said one of the men. "The government needs a lot of it. Anyone who can help us find it will be well paid."

Jed spread the word around. The next day, when the government men were ready to go into the hills around Parkersville to look for uranium, they found a large crowd of men at Jed's store. They were waiting to go with the government men and help them in their search.

Jed decided to go along. So he locked the door to the store and got into a car. Sam jumped in beside him and went, too.

Soon they came to a place that was full of rocks. The government men thought there might be uranium here. The cars stopped, and all the men got out. One of the government men told the Parkersville men about the kind of rock that was most likely to have uranium.

Now not one of the Parkersville men knew anything about uranium. They had just come along to see what was going on. But they walked around the place where they had stopped. They looked for the kind of rock they had been told about. Maybe they could make some money by finding it.

Sam went with Jed. In a few minutes Sam stopped and began to sniff at a rock.

"Stop that, Sam!" said Jed. He was a bit ashamed to have Sam sniffing rocks.

But Sam kept sniffing. All at once he lifted his nose high in the air and began to howl with joy, "Ow-ooo-oo-o! Ow-ooo-oo-o!" The Parkersville men laughed. That silly hound was sniffing at rocks!

But the government men didn't laugh. They rushed over to Sam.

"That's it," said one of them. "That's the kind of rock we're looking for."

The other man held a box next to the rock, and the box began ticking wildly.

"That ticking says there's a lot of uranium here!" the government man shouted. "This dog has found the kind of rock we want."

All the men stared at Sam. Just then he lifted his head and sniffed loudly. Then he ran over to another spot on the rocky hillside and howled again. Everybody rushed over to him.

Again the government man held the box next to where Sam was sniffing. The box almost went crazy with ticking.

"That dog made a real find this time!" the man cried.

"Listen to him howl!" said the other government man. "He seems to know he's found uranium."

"He's only howled like that over one other thing," said Jed. He told the government men about the watches.

"Did those watches shine in the dark?" asked one of the men.

"Yes," said Jed.

"Do you know what you have in that hound?" asked one of the government men. "Why, he is a special kind of sniffing hound. He can always smell uranium and other stuff that sends out rays. The stuff that's used to make watches shine in the dark sends out rays, too."

"Why, you have a real atomic-age hound," said the other government man. "With him we can find all the uranium the government needs for atomic power!"

"The government is going to want to use that dog," said the first government man. "We need this special kind of dog."

Jed stuck out his chest with pride. He had a special, sniffing hound that was worth his weight in gold!

"See, Sheriff," said Jed to Sheriff Bird. "I told you he was a real sniffing hound. Now we know what special thing he can sniff. He's a uranium-sniffing hound!"

The Knights of the Silver Shield

Raymond Macdonald Alden

Not all make-believe stories are funny. In some a character does great and daring deeds so that he can marry a princess or gain great wealth. Such fairy tales often tell about the struggle between good and evil, and magic is usually important to the plot.

We all like to dream of the brave deeds we would do if we had a chance. In the fairy tale that follows, you'll find out that it is not always the one who fights that wins the greatest battle.

There was once a great castle in a forest. The forest was dark and dangerous, and many cruel giants lived in it. But in the castle was a company of knights. They helped travelers in the forest and fought the giants whenever they could.

Each of these knights wore a beautiful suit of armor and carried a long spear. But the most wonderful thing about the knights' armor was their silver shields.

They were not like the shields of other knights. A great magician had made them many years before. Sometimes the shields shone in the sunlight with dazzling brightness. But at other times they would be clouded as though by a mist.

Now when each young knight joined the company, a new shield was given him. When the shield was new, it was always cloudy and dull. Then as the knight began to do service, his shield grew brighter and brighter. But if he proved to be lazy or cowardly, then the shield grew more and more cloudy until the knight became ashamed to carry it.

But this was not all. When any one of the knights fought a particularly hard battle and won the victory, something like a golden star shone in the very heart of his shield. This was the greatest honor that a knight could receive. The other knights always spoke of such a one as having "won his star." At the time when this story begins, the lord of the castle himself was the only one of the knights whose shield bore the golden star.

There came a time when the worst of the giants in the forest gathered together to battle the knights. They made a camp in a dark hollow not far from the castle. All the knights made ready to fight them. The castle was full of the noise of armor being made ready for use. The knights were so excited that they could hardly rest or eat.

Now there was a young knight in the castle named Sir Roland, who was among those most eager for the battle. His eyes shone like stars whenever there was anything to do in the way of knightly deeds. Although he was still quite young, his shield had begun to shine enough to show plainly that he had done bravely in some of his errands. This battle, he thought, would be the great chance of his life.

On the morning when they were to go forth, all the knights gathered in the great hall of the castle to receive their orders. Sir Roland hoped that he would be put in the most dangerous place of all so that he could show what knightly stuff he was made of.

But when the lord of the castle came to him, he said, "One brave knight must stay behind and guard the gateway of the castle. It is you, Sir Roland, being one of the youngest, whom I have chosen for this."

At these words Sir Roland was greatly disappointed. He bit his lip and closed his helmet over his face so that the other knights might not see it. For a moment he felt as if he must answer the commander angrily that it was not right to leave so eager a knight behind. But he struggled against this feeling and went quietly to look after his duties at the gate.

The gateway was high and narrow and was reached from outside by a bridge that crossed the moat. When an enemy came near, the knight on guard rang a great bell just inside the gate. Then the bridge was drawn up against the castle wall so that no one could come across the moat. So the giants had long ago given up trying to attack the castle itself.

Today the battle was to be in the dark hollow in the forest. It was not likely that there would be anything to do at the castle gate except to stand watch. It was not strange that Sir Roland thought someone else might have done this.

Presently all the other knights marched out in their flashing armor. The lord of the castle stopped only to tell Sir Roland to let no one enter until they had all returned. Then they went into the shadows of the forest and were soon lost to sight.

Sir Roland stood looking after them long after they had gone. He thought how happy he would be if he were on the way to battle. But after a little he put this out of his mind and tried to think of pleasanter things. It was a long time before any word came from the battle.

At last Sir Roland saw one of the knights come limping down the path to the castle. Now, this knight was not a brave one. He had been frightened away as soon as he was wounded.

"I have been hurt," he said, "so that I cannot fight anymore. But I could watch the gate for you if you would like to go back in my place."

At first Sir Roland's heart leaped with joy at this. But then he remembered what the commander had told him.

"I should like to go," he said. "But a knight belongs where his commander has put him. My place is here at the gate, and I cannot open it even for you. Your place is at the battle."

The knight was ashamed when he heard this. Presently he turned about and went into the forest again.

So Sir Roland kept guard silently for another hour. Then there came an old beggar woman down the path to the castle. She asked Sir Roland if she might come in and have some food. He told her that no one could enter the castle that day but that he would send a servant out to her with food.

"I have been past the hollow in the forest where the battle is going on," said the old woman while she was waiting for her food.

"And how do you think it is going?" asked Sir Roland.

"Badly for the knights, I am afraid," said the old woman. "The giants are fighting as they have never fought before. I should think you had better go and help your friends."

"I should like to, indeed," said Sir Roland. "But I am set to guard the gateway of the castle and cannot leave."

"One fresh knight would make a great difference when they are all weary with fighting," said the old woman. "I should think that you would be much more useful there."

"You may well think so," said Sir Roland, "and so may I. But it is neither you nor I that is commander here."

"I suppose," said the old woman then, "that you are one of the kind of knights who like to keep out of fighting. You are lucky to have so good an excuse for staying at home." And she laughed a thin and taunting laugh.

Then Sir Roland was very angry. He thought that if it were only a man instead of a woman, he would show whether he liked fighting or no. But as it was a woman, he shut his lips and set his teeth hard together. Just then the servant came with the food. Sir Roland gave it to the old woman quickly. Then he shut the gate that she might not talk to him any more.

It was not very long before he heard someone calling outside. Sir Roland opened the gate and saw standing at the other end of the bridge a little old man in a long black cloak. "Why are you knocking here?" he said. "The castle is closed today."

"Are you Sir Roland?" said the little old man.

"Yes," said Sir Roland.

"Then you ought not to be staying here when your commander and his knights are having so hard a struggle with the giants. You have the chance to make of yourself the greatest knight in this kingdom. Listen to me! I have brought you a magic sword."

As he said this, the old man drew from under his coat a wonderful sword that flashed in the sunlight as if it were covered with diamonds. "This is the sword of all swords," he said. "It is for you if you will leave your idling here and carry it to the battle. Nothing can stand before it. When you lift it, the giants will fall back. Your master will be saved, and you will be crowned the winning knight. You will be the one to take the commander's place as lord of the castle."

Now Sir Roland believed that it was a magician speaking to him. The sword certainly appeared to be a magic sword. He reached out his hand as though he would take it. The little old man came forward as though he would cross the bridge into

the castle. But as he did so, it came to Sir Roland's mind again that the bridge and the gateway were in his keeping.

"No!" he called out, so that the old man stopped where he was standing. But the man waved the shining sword in the air again.

"It is for you," the old man said. "Take it and win the victory!"

Sir Roland was really afraid that if he listened to the old man, he would not be able to hold himself inside the castle. For this reason he rang the great bell at the gateway. Instantly the servants began to pull in the chains to draw up the bridge. The old man could not cross it to enter the castle, nor Sir Roland to go out.

Then as he looked across the moat, Sir Roland saw a wonderful thing. The little old man threw off his black cloak. As he did so, he began to grow bigger and bigger. In a minute more he was a giant as tall as any in the forest. At first Sir Roland could scarcely believe his eyes. Then he knew that this

must be one of their giant enemies. The giant had changed himself to a little old man through some magic power, that he might make his way into the castle.

Sir Roland shuddered to think what might have happened if he had taken the sword and left the gate unguarded. The giant shook his fist across the moat that lay between them. Then knowing that he could do nothing more, he went angrily back into the forest.

Before long, Sir Roland heard a sound that made him spring forward with joy. It was the bugle of the lord of the castle. Then came sounding after it the bugles of many of the knights. As they came nearer, he could hear their shouts of victory.

Sir Roland gave the sign to let down the bridge again and went out to meet them. They were dusty and bloodstained and weary. But they had won the battle with the giants. It had been such a great victory that there had never been a happier homecoming.

Sir Roland greeted them all as they passed in over the bridge. Then when he had closed the gate and fastened it, he followed them into the great hall of the castle.

The lord of the castle took his place on the highest seat with the other knights about him. Sir Roland came forward with the key of the gate to give his account of what he had done. The lord of the castle bowed to him as a sign for him to begin.

But just as Sir Roland opened his mouth to speak, one of the knights cried out, "The shield! The shield! Sir Roland's shield!"

Everyone turned and looked at the shield which Sir Roland carried on his left arm. He himself could see only the top of it and did not know what they could mean. But what they saw was the golden star of knighthood, shining brightly from the center of Sir Roland's shield.

Sir Roland knelt before the lord of the castle. He still did not know why everyone was looking at him so excitedly. He wondered if he had in some way done wrong.

"Speak, Sir Knight," said the commander, as soon as he could find his voice after his surprise. "Tell us all that has happened today at the castle. Have you been attacked? Have any giants come here? Did you fight them alone?"

"No, my lord," said Sir Roland. "Only one giant has been here. And he went away silently when he found he could not enter."

Then he told all that had happened through the day.

When he had finished, the knights all looked at one another. No one spoke a word. Then they looked again at Sir Roland's shield to make sure that their eyes had not tricked them. There the golden star was still shining.

After a little silence the lord of the castle spoke.

"Men make mistakes," he said, "but our silver shields are never mistaken. Sir Roland has fought and won the hardest battle of all today."

Then the others all rose and saluted Sir Roland, who was the youngest knight that ever carried the golden star.

Why Red River Flows North

Lloyd Besant

Plot, characters, theme—you've looked for them all. You have also read realistic stories, a fantasy, a tall tale, and a fairy tale. Are you enjoying stories more than you used to?

Read the next story just for fun. What kind of story would you call it?

Red River is a queer one. It doesn't flow south like most other rivers. No, it flows north.

The Red River didn't always flow north. It used to flow south. But one day that was changed. It was changed because John Johnson had an idea.

John Johnson and his wife, Joan, lived on a farm in North Dakota. Their farm was on Red River.

One day Joan Johnson said to her husband, "John, that silly river keeps running south away from our farm. It takes all our good water with it. Why can't it run the other way and bring water to our land instead of taking it away?"

John answered, "Well, because—because that's the way it is!" He didn't know anything else to say.

Joan stamped her foot. "Well, do something about it!" she roared. "You're a big, strong man!"

John didn't dare say no. So he nodded and said, "Yes, my dear. But first I'll have to think about it."

John sat down in a chair and began to stare at the floor. He stared and thought, and he stared and thought. John stared and thought all summer and all fall. He stopped staring and thinking only when he ate and when he slept.

Joan took care of the farm and their cabin and fed John. At first she didn't talk to him. She knew it took time to think. But as the weeks rolled by and he was still thinking, she grew angry.

"John Johnson!" she roared one day. "Stop thinking and do some doing!"

John shook himself. He raised his eyes and gave her a hurt look. Then he sighed. He would have to start thinking all over again. He lowered his eyes and stared at the floor.

It was the coldest winter anyone had ever known. Every time Joan went out to get wood, she froze her nose.

One day she came in ready to roar at her husband again. She was waiting for her nose to warm up so she could shout louder, when John suddenly stopped thinking.

He raised his eyes. "I have an idea!" he cried.

Joan was so pleased that John had an idea that she didn't even ask him what the idea was. She just waited.

He took his coat from a hook on the wall and put it on. Then he wrapped a scarf around his face and picked up an ax. And out the door he went.

Joan didn't ask a question. She put on her coat and scarf and followed him.

John walked over to the river and out on the ice. He thumped on the ice seven times and listened.

"That's good!" he said with a nod. And he put his ax over his shoulder and walked off up the river.

John walked up that river for three days. Joan followed along behind him. She didn't ask a question.

When they came to the beginning of the river, John walked to one side. He chopped two holes in the ice. Then he crossed to the other side and chopped two holes there. He threw the ax on the riverbank and put his two hands into the holes he had just chopped.

"Put your hands in the holes on your side!" he called to Joan. She did as he said.

Then he shouted, "When I nod my head, lift as hard as you can!" He nodded his head, and they both lifted hard. With a loud crack the river came up from its bed. It was frozen so hard it looked like a long ice ribbon.

"Now pull!" shouted John. And they pulled together. They started around in a wide curve, pulling the beginning of the river toward the place where the end had been. The frozen river swung around as they pulled, bringing the end toward the place where the beginning had been.

For two weeks John and Joan walked in the wide curve. When they stopped at last, the beginning of the river was the end, and the end was the beginning.

Then John and Joan started for home. When they got there, John spoke. "I'm hungry!" he said.

"I am, too," said Joan. And she began to fix dinner.

They were both so hungry that they ate for two days without stopping even to talk. Then they slept for a week. They might have slept longer, but they were wakened by a noise. It was the river ice breaking up. Spring had come.

John and Joan rushed out of their cabin and down to the river.

"Oh, look, John!" cried Joan. "The river is flowing from south to north! It took a lot of thinking, but it worked! Now we'll always have good, fresh water!"

And ever since that day, Red River has always flowed north.

Afterthought

1. What realistic stories have you read in this book? What made them realistic?
2. Which story was a fantasy? What made it a fantasy?
3. Which story was a fairy tale? What made it a fairy tale?
4. Which two stories were tall tales? What made them tall tales?

You have read about several kinds of characters, both realistic and fanciful. So you know that hounds, people, ghosts, and giants can be characters. What else could be a character? There hardly seems to be a limit. The poem that follows tells a story, and some of its characters are strange indeed.

How Much Is True?

I'll tell you a lie, and it's almost true:
I met an oyster as big as you.
And boy-size oysters are very few.

Man-size oysters are even fewer.
You see—my lie's getting truer and truer.
That happens to lies, you may be sure:

You start to tell a terrible whopper,
Then all your fibbing comes a cropper,
And your lie winds up all prim and proper.

"Hello!" I said when we met, said I.
The oyster frowned and strolled on by.
(Now have I managed to tell a lie?)

The oyster's name was Snaggletooth.
He had a sister named Bluepoint Ruth.
They lived in a shipwrecked telephone booth.

—How do I know? Well, some I guessed,
And some I imagined, and the rest
My friend, the Oysterman, confessed.

The Oysterman's name is Rocky Ray,
The Champion Mudfoot of Chesapeake Bay.
He told me all this yesterday.

And his tears poured down like the morning tide.
"I stole them out of the sea!" he cried,
"Where they lay all cozy and side by side

In their well-kept shipwrecked telephone booth!
I sold the oyster named Snaggletooth!
And for lunch I had crackers and Bluepoint Ruth!"

That's what he told me—more or less—
And some say no and some say yes,
But true or not is anyone's guess.

—I say I said, "Hello!" said I,
And the oyster frowned and strolled on by.
And it's certainly true that he didn't reply.

He may not have *frowned*. When they come to town,
Oysters, strolling along, look down
With a strange expression. It *could* be a frown,

Or it could be a smile. It's hard to tell
An oyster's expression through his shell
Unless you know him especially well.

—And that's my story. You realize
It's bound to come as a sort of surprise
To meet an oyster of such a size

Just strolling along.—Well, maybe not
Exactly *strolling*. It looked a lot
As if he were strolling, and that's what *I* thought.

At first at least. But it just may be
The strolling was really done by me
And not by the oyster—Yes, certainly:

I remember now! It was where I ate
My lunch today—at Main and State—
And the oyster was on a dinner plate.

An *enormous* plate! And there he sat
As big as you and twice as fat!
—Well, maybe he wasn't as big as *that*.

I guess he was only just oyster-size.
And recalling his taste now, I realize
Oysters go down much better than lies.

And I'll tell you this: I never knew
Lies were *so hard* to make up, sir. And you
May believe it or not, but that's *certainly* true.

John Ciardi

Branches for Climbing

What do you like to do when you have time just for
yourself? Perhaps you read or collect baseball cards or build
models. If you like to see plants grow, you may raise flowers,
but if you're trying to become an artist, you probably
paint flowers. Maybe you dream about writing stories or
playing the guitar or being an actor. If you don't have a
special interest, perhaps now is the time for you to branch
out.

Tree Climbing

This is my tree,
my place to be alone in,
my branches for climbing,
my green leaves for hiding in,
my sunshine for reading,
my clouds for dreaming,
my sky for singing,
my tree, my beautiful tree.

Kathleen Fraser

A Tulip for Tony

Marietta Moskin

Why was Tony interested in a bulb that looked like an onion? Find out how it helped him solve a problem.

Tony sat on the stoop of his house, watching the boys play stickball in the street. It was an exciting game. Players ran in and out between the parked cars and sometimes they had to scatter in all directions when a car came through the block.

Tony wished he were playing stickball too instead of watching from the top of the steps. He spent a lot of time watching other children play, but he just never could make himself walk up to them and ask if he could join.

It was the same at school. Often when Miss Allen asked a question, Tony had the answer right on the tip of his tongue. But instead of raising his hand, Tony sat quietly while someone else spoke up and won praises from the teacher.

Tony liked Miss Allen and he wanted to please her by talking in class. He knew she would like him to talk, because she looked at him or even called on him from time to time. But as soon as Tony tried to say something, he would feel the other children staring at his back. He would grow red and squirm and the words just wouldn't come out.

His classmates didn't seem to have that trouble. Some of the children brought things to school and showed them to the class. They would stand proudly in front of the room and tell about their treasures—where they had come from, what they were used for, or any other interesting facts they knew about them.

Only last week Pedro had brought some special tropical fruit his aunt had sent from Puerto Rico. Ugli Fruit they were called, and after Pedro had shown them around, Miss Allen had cut the lumpy, green skin and given everyone a taste of the juicy pulp.

Betty had brought a pet mouse she was raising at home in a little cage. Miguel had brought a beautiful dagger that Miguel's grandfather had inherited from his great-grandfather!

Tony was sure he, too, could talk about things like that. But he didn't have anything special to bring to school. He had searched his whole apartment—both rooms and the kitchen —but all he found were pots and pans, cups and plates, and all kinds of clothes. There was nothing he would have been proud to show off at school.

He had looked over all his own treasures, too—the box full of odds and ends he kept under his bed. He saved boxtops in there and old bottle caps, pictures of rockets, an old flashlight, and a shiny length of broken chain. All kinds of things that might come in handy some day, but none were interesting enough to show at school.

Right now, though, Tony wasn't thinking about his problem. He had just heard a familiar clippety-cloppety sound coming closer and closer. Tony looked eagerly toward the end of the block. Sure enough, a moment later, the bright flower-wagon belonging to old Mr. Spinelli turned into the street, and of course Rosabella was pulling it.

80

Tony and Mr. Spinelli were good friends. The flower vendor often passed through Tony's street on the way to Rosabella's stable. Many times he had stopped so that Tony could pat the old horse. Rosabella was the only horse Tony had ever known. He was pleased whenever he saw her.

Tony started down the steps to meet his friends. But just as Mr. Spinelli turned the corner, something happened. One of the ballplayers hit a long straight ball. It streaked down the block. It whizzed past Rosabella's ear and smashed right into the neat rows of flowerpots on the wagon.

Bang, crash, went the pots as they toppled over against each other like ninepins in a bowling game.

For a moment Rosabella stood very still. The zing of the ball and the noise of the crashing flowerpots had scared her. Then, with a toss of her head, she charged forward, scattering more pots as the cart went zigzag down the street. Poor Mr. Spinelli had to let go of the reins. Rosabella ran too fast.

Without Mr. Spinelli's firm hand to guide her, Rosabella got confused. She tried to turn. Crash! went the cart, and the rest of the flowerpots slid to the pavement.

The ballplayers took one look at the damage they had caused and then they all ran off as fast as their feet would carry them.

"Hey, come back!" Mr. Spinelli shouted after the boys. "What do you think you are doing? I'll call the police—you'll have to pay for this. . . ." But by now none of the boys were in sight. Mr. Spinelli dropped his raised fists and let his shoulders sag. He looked very sad. "Young rascals," he muttered to himself.

"Can I help?" Tony asked timidly. Mr. Spinelli didn't

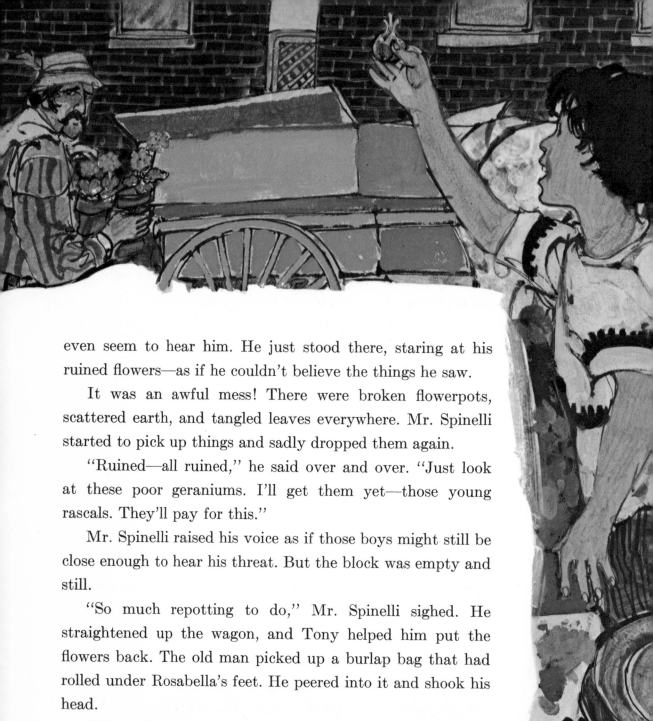

even seem to hear him. He just stood there, staring at his ruined flowers—as if he couldn't believe the things he saw.

It was an awful mess! There were broken flowerpots, scattered earth, and tangled leaves everywhere. Mr. Spinelli started to pick up things and sadly dropped them again.

"Ruined—all ruined," he said over and over. "Just look at these poor geraniums. I'll get them yet—those young rascals. They'll pay for this."

Mr. Spinelli raised his voice as if those boys might still be close enough to hear his threat. But the block was empty and still.

"So much repotting to do," Mr. Spinelli sighed. He straightened up the wagon, and Tony helped him put the flowers back. The old man picked up a burlap bag that had rolled under Rosabella's feet. He peered into it and shook his head.

"My tulip bulbs—all smashed. What can you expect—with Rosabella's big feet all over them. And such a good lot they were, too."

Mr. Spinelli tossed the burlap bag toward the nearest garbage can. He missed. The bag opened up and spilled its contents into the gutter.

"I'll pick them up," Tony said quickly. He ran over and began to push the pulpy mass back into the bag. He wondered what those tulip bulbs had looked like before Rosabella had trampled them. Then he saw one. Over there, under that car, was one lonely bulb. It didn't look damaged at all. Tony picked it up and looked at it to make sure. It reminded him of the onions his mother used in the kitchen every day.

Tony took the bulb over to Mr. Spinelli. The old man looked at it carefully. Then he handed it back to Tony.

"It seems fine to me," he said. "It might even grow. Why don't you plant it and see?"

Tony looked at Mr. Spinelli. "Gee, can I really keep it?" he asked.

"You found it!" Mr. Spinelli smiled. "Besides, you deserve something for all your help. It is good to watch things grow."

He searched among the broken pots. "This one is only a little chipped," he said. "I'll fill it with some earth. Just put the bulb deep down in it and give it water and light. If it is still any good, some green shoots will show in a week or so." He patted Tony on the shoulder. "Let's see if you are a good gardener," he added.

"I'll try," Tony told him. He held the bulb and the pot and watched Mr. Spinelli. As the old man finished putting his damaged plants back in the wagon, the smile faded from his face.

"Good-for-nothing boys," he muttered as he pulled on Rosabella's reins.

"Come on, Rosabella, old girl—let's see how many of these flowers we can save." The clippety-clop sounded sad this time as the man, the cart, and the horse made their way slowly up the block and around the corner.

For once Tony didn't watch them pass. He was looking at his tulip bulb. He'd never seen one planted—his mother didn't have time for potted plants or a place to put them.

Then a wonderful idea struck him. He had been longing for something special to take to school. Now he could take the tulip bulb!

Tony's brother Pete was home when Tony came upstairs with his treasure. Pete watched as Tony laid the pot and the bulb on his bed.

"What are you doing with that dirty old onion?" he scoffed. "You act as if it were a piece of gold."

"It's not an onion—it's a tulip bulb, stupid," Tony muttered. But he was worried. It did look like an ordinary onion—maybe they would laugh at him in school too.

"I'll plant it first. Then I can take it to school after the tulip has grown," Tony thought. That would also give him more to talk about.

He planted the bulb carefully in the black soil, the way Mr. Spinelli had told him. Then he searched the apartment for a place to put his plant. There were no safe or sunny places in the dark back bedroom he shared with his two brothers. There wasn't an inch of space in the other room either. His mother finally found a spot for Tony's plant on top of the refrigerator, next to the window. At least it was out of everyone's way up there between Dad's lunch box and the empty soda-pop

bottles. Besides, the kitchen was the lightest place in the apartment.

For the next week Tony couldn't keep his mind off that flowerpot. Twice a day he looked at it. At first nothing happened—or at least nothing showed. Tony began to worry. What if Rosabella's feet had damaged the bulb? Mr. Spinelli had not been sure. It was hard to wait day after day and see nothing but crumbly brown earth in the pot.

Then, one morning, a tiny light-green shoot had poked through the rough soil. After that Tony watered his plant even more carefully. It was good that Rosabella hadn't hurt his tulip after all!

He still needed to find out more about tulips for his talk in class. Mr. Spinelli hadn't been through their block again. Tony watched for him every day, but he never came. He must ask *someone*. Maybe the man in the flower shop near the school could tell him. One day Tony stopped in front of the shop. It took all his courage to go in.

The florist was putting flowers into a tall vase. He put down his work and came over to Tony.

"What can I do for you, young man?" he asked.

Tony wanted to turn and run out of the store but he remembered his tulip. He swallowed hard.

"I just would like to see what a tulip looks like when it is all grown," he stammered. "I'm growing one at home," he added, "but it has no flower yet."

Tony looked at the florist out of the corner of his eye. He hoped the man wouldn't be too angry at having his time wasted by a boy who didn't even want to buy anything.

But the florist gave Tony a big smile. "Well, well—a budding young gardener!" he laughed. "Come over here—I'll show you lots of tulips."

Sure enough, there were many potted tulips in the back of his shop—red ones and yellow ones, pink ones and white ones. They were the most beautiful flowers Tony had ever seen. He hoped his tulip would grow as tall and straight and bright.

The florist found a calendar which showed a large tulip field. There was a windmill in the picture and in front the flowers grew right to the edge of a narrow canal. The man told Tony this was the way tulips grew in Holland. Then he tore some pictures of tulips out of a seed catalogue and gave them to Tony.

"I wonder what color my tulip will be," Tony thought as he left happily with his pictures.

He didn't have long to wait. His plant had already shot up into a tall green stem with a pointed knot at the top and broad leaves at the sides. The very next morning Tony almost fell from the kitchen stool with excitement when he climbed up to water his plant.

"It's red," he yelled. "Look, Mom, come quick. My tulip is red!" Sure enough, the green knot at the top had opened slightly during the night and the pale-green petals were beginning to turn a bright red at the edges.

By that evening, the green leaves had turned completely and the small pointed red flower lifted its head proudly on the thin green stem.

"Now I can take it to school," Tony shouted.

Miss Allen was pleased when Tony brought his tulip plant

the next day. "How nice," she said. "You must tell us all about your pretty flower."

Tony could only nod. He didn't want to forget any of the things he was planning to say. He put the plant carefully on his desk. At last the time came for showing things. Tony's heart beat faster.

"Tony, I think you have something to show us," Miss Allen said. Tony stood up.

Once he started to talk, Tony forgot the staring eyes of the other children. He talked about Rosabella and Mr. Spinelli, about tulip bulbs and how to plant them. He showed the picture of the tulip field.

"Oh, how pretty," Juanita said. "I wish we could see the tulips grow like that."

David was more interested in the horse.

"I hope Rosabella wasn't hurt by the ball," he said.

"Didn't Mr. Spinelli catch any of those boys?" Sara asked.

Tony answered all the questions. In the end Miss Allen almost had to stop him from talking.

"We'll put your flower in a safe place until you can take it home," she told Tony.

Tony grew red and almost stammered again. He shook his head very hard. "It's for you," he told Miss Allen. "I brought the tulip for you!"

Miss Allen's big smile showed how pleased she was.

"Oh, what a nice present, Tony," she said. "Look, class, we can all enjoy Tony's tulip. We'll put it in the window and Tony can water it every day."

All morning, Tony could hardly keep his eyes off his tulip.

He was glad that it would stay here in class. It would get much more light and air here than at home in their apartment. Besides, every time he looked over at his tulip, it would remind him that he had given a talk in class. And it hadn't been so hard after all!

Afterthought

1. How was the tulip interesting just for Tony?
2. How was the tulip interesting for others?

THE FLORIST SHOP

Florist shops are beautiful,
All damply green and dimly cool,
And the men who keep them are sure to be
A little baggy about the knee,
With voices pleasant and rather low
From living along with things that grow;
For you can't stay noisy and hurried where
Petal on petal fills the air
With spiciness, and every tree
Is hung with gayest greenery.
Grocers bustle and butchers shout,
Tradesmen tramp noisily in and out,
But florists are quiet men and kind,
With a sort of fragrance of the mind.

Rachel Field

A Pot of Magic

*It might interest you to try
the flowerpot garden this article
tells about.*

How would you like to surprise someone with a pot of bright tulips or crocuses on a cold wintry day? Flowers in cold weather may be hard to believe, but you really can force spring bulbs to bloom in winter.

You must choose the bulbs in the fall. Tulips, crocuses, daffodils, and hyacinths are all bulbs that you can force to bloom in a pot. After you buy your bulbs, handle them carefully and don't let them get too hot or too cold. Keep them in a cool room at about sixty degrees until you're ready to plant them.

Your bulbs will grow in almost any container—a box, a can, or a clay pot—but it must have a drain hole in the bottom. And before you use any clay pot, soak it in water so that it will not draw water out of the soil you put into it.

Bulbs grow best in a loose, crumbly soil. Test your soil by squeezing some into a ball. If it sticks together, it is too firm for bulbs to grow in. You can make a good potting soil by mixing equal parts of soil, peat moss, and sand. Your bulbs will not need fertilizer.

Potting the bulbs is easy. Cover the drain hole with a small rock or pot chip to keep the soil in and to let extra water run out. Then partly fill

the pot; put in enough soil so that the bulbs, when set on the soil, will reach just to the rim of the pot. Press the bulbs into the soil gently, being careful not to damage them. Use as many bulbs as your pot will hold, spacing them so that they barely touch.

Finish filling the pot. Pour soil around the bulbs, and gently press it down. The top of the soil should be half an inch below the rim of the pot, and the tops of the bulbs should just show through the soil. Then water the pot well and set it aside to drain.

Now the potted bulbs must be put in a cool place where their roots can grow. All spring-flowering bulbs need thirteen weeks or more of cooling in order to root well.

Perhaps the best place to store bulbs for cooling is out of doors, near a fence or a building. Dig a hole about two inches deeper than your pot. Set the pot into the hole, water it well, cover it with a layer of sand, and put back the soil you dug out of the hole. Then mark the spot so that you can find it even under a blanket of snow. If the soil freezes deeply where you live, put a thick cover of leaves, grass, or straw over the buried pot. This cover will help keep the

ground soft enough for you to dig up the pot later.

You may also store your potted bulbs in the basement or garage. The place should be cold but not freezing, and bulbs stored there must be watered regularly.

Count out thirteen weeks on your calendar and mark the time for bringing the bulbs in from their winter cooling. After thirteen weeks have passed, check the buried bulbs. You can quickly tell whether they are ready to bring in. If they are, they will have sprouts about two inches high. If you buried your pot at the beginning of October, it should be ready to dig up soon after New Year's.

When you have brought the pot into the house, put it in a cool room away from the sunlight. Water the soil whenever it feels dry. After three or four weeks in the house, your plants should have begun to bloom. Then it's time to bring your colorful pot into the kitchen or the living room for the family to enjoy. They may think it's wintertime magic!

The Rebellious Robots

Deborah Newman

In this play you'll find out about funny Mr. Follansbee, whose special interest is inventing. As you read, think of how a play might interest someone who did not want to act a part.

Characters

AGATHA FOLLANSBEE	DAN
HENRY FOLLANSBEE	ELLEN
SIX ROBOTS	JOE
ANN	LISA
SUSIE	MAYOR PORTLY
TOMMY	

TIME: *The present.*

SETTING: *A gift shop. At one side there is a display of flowers, at the other, a display of jewelry, candy, and other gifts. Various signs are placed around the store, giving gift suggestions, price information, etc.*

AT RISE: AGATHA *enters, carrying a large box marked "candy." She puts the box down in the center of the stage.*

AGATHA (*Calling*): Henry! Henry, I need you. The candy is
here, Henry! Oh, where is that husband of mine? A fine help
he is—always in that workshop of his, inventing something
when there's work to be done. Well, I guess I'll just have to
open this myself. (*She takes a scissors from her apron pocket
and begins cutting the strings.*) This candy should have come
days ago. I suppose Henry forgot to mail the order again.
That man! All he thinks about are his inventions. (1ST
ROBOT *enters slowly, knocking down a chair as he comes
forward.* AGATHA *does not see him; her back is to him, and she
does not look up as she tugs at the strings.* 1ST ROBOT *stops near
her.*) Well, Henry, it's about time you got here. Now, you
just listen to me. I want you to stop all this foolish inventing
and get to work. This candy must be put on the shelves, and
then I want you to oil the door, and—Henry, are you listening
to me? (*She turns around, sees* 1ST ROBOT, *screams, and falls
to floor, covering her eyes. Then she slowly looks up and gets up
angrily.*) Henry Follansbee! You can't fool me. (*She goes over
and pokes at* 1ST ROBOT.) I know it's you. So *this* is your new

invention—a suit of metal to make you look like a robot. Well, you can just take the suit off right now and get to work. Our customers will start coming in any minute. (*She pushes* 1st Robot.) Go ahead, Henry! You heard me. (Henry *enters briskly. He carries some coiled tubing and some boxes with colored buttons on them.*)

Henry: Good morning, Agatha, my dear. It is a good morning, isn't it? (Agatha *stares at him, putting her hand over her mouth.*) The sun is shining, the sky is blue—and I'm really excited about my latest invention.

Agatha (*Pointing to* 1st Robot, *then to* Henry): Henry—I thought—Henry—who—who—

Henry: Now, now, my dear, stop saying "who, who" like an owl. As you always say, we have no time to play games when our customers will be coming any minute.

Agatha: Henry—who is that creature?

Henry: Why, that's my new invention, of course. I told you I was working on something wonderful. (*Pats* 1st Robot) Oh, you are a marvel, you wonderful creature.

Agatha: Henry, get it out of here.

Henry: Oh, my dear, I can't do that. We're going to sell these in the shop. As a matter of fact, I have a little surprise for you. Yesterday while you were gone, I sold two of them. And I'm sure I'm going to sell the rest today. We'll make a fortune. I'll bring in the rest of them now, my dear. (*He presses buttons on his boxes, and* 2nd, 3rd, *and* 4th Robots *march in and stand beside the* 1st Robot. Agatha *tries to get them to go out.*)

Agatha: Go away! Shoo! Get out of here! Henry, make them go away. I won't have them in the shop. (*She takes candy out of big box and puts it on counter.*)

HENRY (*Fussing over* ROBOTS): Agatha, my dear, you don't understand. These robots are marvels of science. Customers love them.

AGATHA: Last year you invented an electric back scratcher. How many of those did you sell?

HENRY (*Hopefully*): One?

AGATHA: You didn't sell any! The year before that, it was the automatic fire maker.

HENRY: Well, you must admit the automatic fire maker was a good idea. How was I to know I had invented matches?

AGATHA: Henry, I am going out to do the marketing. I want you to stay in the shop while I'm gone—and I want you to get those—those creatures out of here. Now! (AGATHA *goes out the door of the shop.* HENRY *dusts off* ROBOTS *as the door opens, and* ANN, SUSIE, *and* TOMMY *enter.* HENRY *greets the children happily, rubbing his hands.*)

HENRY: Aha! Our first customers today. Good morning, children.

ANN: Good morning. We've come to buy a birthday present for our mother.

SUSIE: We have three dollars. Each of us saved a whole dollar.

TOMMY: We'd like to buy the same candy we bought last year. It was delicious.

ANN: Tommy, we're not going to buy candy this year. Last year you ate almost the whole box, all by yourself.

SUSIE: He got sick, too.

TOMMY (*Indignantly*): I did not!

ANN: This year let's buy something just for Mother. I think she'd like some jewelry.

HENRY: Ah, my young friends, candy and jewelry are all very

nice, but this week the gift shop has something very special. (*He gestures to* ROBOTS.) This week, the gift shop is offering, for the very first time anywhere, the Mother's Mechanical Helper.

TOMMY (*Examining* ROBOTS): Mother's Mechanical Helper? What's that?

SUSIE: What can it do?

ANN: Does it do the dishes? Will it scrub the floor?

HENRY: Well, no. These Mother's Mechanical Helpers are the very first models, and they can do only one job. They pick things up off the floor.

TOMMY: Wow! Do you mean that if I left my pajamas on the floor, one of these robots would pick them up?

ANN: If I dropped my schoolbooks on the floor, would a Mother's Mechanical Helper pick them up?

HENRY: Yes, yes, of course! What bright children you are.

SUSIE: I'm not sure I understand how they do it.

HENRY: Let me give you a demonstration. Now, we'll need lots of things on the floor for the robots to pick up. (*He looks around, sees some large wastebaskets loaded with paper at one side of the stage.*) Aha! The wastebaskets! Now children, each of you take a wastebasket and throw the papers in it all over the floor. (*The children take the wastebaskets and scatter papers all over the stage.*)

TOMMY: Whee! This is fun.

ANN: I hope the robots really do pick this up. I'd certainly hate to do it.

SUSIE: The floor looks like my room when I've been making something.

TOMMY (*Looking around*): It sure is a mess.

HENRY (*Rubbing hands*): It's just fine. The messier the better, for my robots. Now, I wind up the robots. (*He turns a crank in back of each* ROBOT.) One—two—three. Then I press the button marked "Walk" and then the button marked "Pick Up." (*He presses buttons on the back of each* ROBOT. *As he does so, the* ROBOTS *set to work. They walk around the stage stiffly, picking up the papers and putting them back in the wastebaskets.*)

TOMMY: Wow! Look at them work!

ANN: They really do pick things up.

SUSIE: Mother would never have to scold us again when we leave things on the floor. (2ND ROBOT *picks up* HENRY's *coiled tubing and puts it in a wastebasket.* HENRY *gets it back.*)

HENRY: Now, now, now, I need this. (*When the* ROBOTS *have finished, they march back to their places and stand stiffly.* HENRY *smiles proudly.*) Well, what do you think of my robots?

TOMMY: They're great.

ANN: We certainly need one in our house.

SUSIE: But how much do they cost? We have only three dollars.

HENRY: Well, they would be rather expensive—but I'm anxious to have mothers try them out, so I'm offering them at a special price. They cost just three dollars. But if you buy one now, you must promise me that you'll let your mother try it out right away.

SUSIE: But we shouldn't give Mother her present before her birthday.

ANN: Just this once, we could. Besides, we could never hide the robot in a closet. It's too big.

TOMMY: Come on, girls. Let's buy one. (*He gives* HENRY *the money*.)

HENRY: Thank you. Now, which color belt would you like? All the robots are the same, but I've given them different belts.

SUSIE: I want the red belt. (*She points to* 3RD ROBOT.)

HENRY: Fine, fine. Now, just press the button marked "Walk," and the robot will come with you. (TOMMY *presses the button, and* 3RD ROBOT *begins to walk*.)

TOMMY: Come on, girls. We'd better go.

ANN: Good-bye.

HENRY: Good-bye—and let me know how your mother likes the Mother's Mechanical Helper. (ANN, SUSIE, *and* TOMMY *go out with* 3RD ROBOT. HENRY *rubs his hands happily*.) Well! Another sale already. My robots are a success. (*The door opens, and* DAN *and* ELLEN *enter with* 5TH ROBOT.)

ELLEN: Hello.

HENRY: What's this? Aren't you the children who bought the Mother's Mechanical Helper yesterday?

DAN: We certainly are.

ELLEN: We want to return it and get our money back.

HENRY: What's wrong? Did the robot break down? (*He turns the dials at the back of* 5TH ROBOT.)

DAN: It works all right, but our mother doesn't like it.

HENRY (*Astonished*): What? Your mother doesn't like the Mother's Mechanical Helper? I can't believe it!

ELLEN: My mother says we can't go through life expecting a robot to be around to pick things up.

DAN: She says we have to learn to pick up our own things.

ELLEN: So she told us to return the robot and get her something else for her birthday instead.

HENRY (*Insulted*): Very well. If that is the way your mother feels, I will certainly return your money.

DAN: Thank you. We'll buy Mom a box of candy, instead. (DAN *and* ELLEN *go to candy counter with* HENRY *and pick out a box of candy. He puts it in a bag, and* DAN *and* ELLEN *exit.* HENRY *goes to the* 5TH ROBOT *and brushes it off.* JOE *and* LISA *enter with* 6TH ROBOT.)

LISA: Good morning. We've come to ask you if we could return our Mother's Mechanical Helper and get our money back.

JOE: Our mother doesn't want the Mechanical Helper.

HENRY (*Annoyed*): Indeed! And *why* doesn't your mother want a Mechanical Helper?

LISA: Well—we've had the Mechanical Helper for two days. Every time something was dropped on the floor, we pressed the buttons and the robot picked it up.

HENRY: But that is exactly what the Mechanical Helper is supposed to do! What, may I ask, is wrong with that?

LISA: We have seven children in our family—and our mother is used to having things all over the place.

JOE: She says she can't stand a neat house. She likes to have stuff around.

LISA: Mother says she feels sorry for the people who have no children. Their houses are always neat.

JOE: She says children just naturally make things messy—but she *likes* it that way.

HENRY (*Shaking his head and pulling at his beard*): I just can't believe it! I just don't understand it!

LISA: So please, sir, could we have our money back?

HENRY: Very well. I certainly don't want any dissatisfied customers.

JOE: Thank you very much, sir.

LISA: Let's get Mom some flowers. She always likes lots of flowers. (*They go to flower display.*)

JOE: These are very pretty. (*He points to some flowers.*)

LISA: OK. May we have a nice big bunch, please?

HENRY (*Taking flowers and wrapping them*): Yes. I hope your mother likes these.

LISA: I'm sure she will. (JOE *and* LISA *take flowers and exit.* HENRY *straightens counter as* TOMMY, ANN, *and* SUSIE *enter with* 3RD ROBOT.)

HENRY (*Brightly*): Ah, children! What fine children you are! You promised to let me know how you liked the Mother's Mechanical Helper, and here you are back, good as your word. Well, how are things going? I'm sure you're delighted, simply delighted!

TOMMY: Well, no—we're not exactly delighted.

ANN: In fact, we don't like the Mechanical Helper.

SUSIE: I don't like it at all.

HENRY (*Bewildered*): You—you don't like it? (*The three*

children shake their heads "No.") Why—why don't you like it?

TOMMY: Well, you see, when we pick things up, we put them where they belong.

ANN: But the robot can't think. It just throws everything into the wastebasket.

SUSIE: I had a paper doll on the floor with all the scraps of paper from my cutting—and the robot threw the doll away with everything else. When my mother picks up, she always saves the important things.

TOMMY: The robot threw out my pajamas, my new baseball mitt, and my sneakers.

HENRY (*Stroking his beard*): Hm-m. I never considered this. I shall have to give it some thought.

TOMMY: While you're thinking, could we have our money back?

HENRY: Very well. (*He gives* TOMMY *the money.*)

ANN: I guess we should buy candy after all.

TOMMY: OK. Let's get a big box of chocolates. (TOMMY, ANN, *and* SUSIE *go to candy counter.* HENRY *sits sadly at center.*)

HENRY (*Gesturing to* ROBOTS): All of them—returned. All my wonderful, marvelous robots. My whole life's work—and no one wants them. (*He takes out a large handkerchief and dabs sadly at his eyes.* AGATHA *enters carrying a shopping bag, which she places on the counter.*)

AGATHA: Henry! I thought I told you to get those robots out of here.

HENRY (*Rising*): Yes, my dear. I'll take them back to my workshop now. You were right. No one wants to buy them.

AGATHA: Of course I was right. You and your inventions.

HENRY: I just can't understand it. I was sure I had invented something wonderful. (MAYOR PORTLY *enters.*)

MAYOR: Good morning, good morning. I've come to buy an anniversary present for my wife.

AGATHA: Good morning, Mayor Portly. I'm sure we can help you.

MAYOR: I've made out a list of what my wife needs. Let me see—where did I put that list? (*The* MAYOR *begins to pull papers out of his pockets. He reads from each paper, then shakes his head and pulls out another paper.*) "Bacon, lettuce, cheese. . . ." No, that isn't it. "New lights for the City Hall. . . ." No, that isn't it. "Dog licenses. . . ." No, that isn't it, either. Oh, dear, where is my list of presents? (*The* MAYOR *drops his papers all over the floor.*) Good gracious, now look what I've done! (TOMMY *runs up to* 4TH ROBOT *and presses the buttons. The* 4TH ROBOT *picks up the papers and starts for a wastebasket with them.* TOMMY *gets the papers from* 4TH ROBOT *and gives them back to the astonished* MAYOR. *The* 4TH ROBOT *returns to place.*)

TOMMY: Here are your papers, Mr. Mayor.

MAYOR (*Pointing to* 4TH ROBOT): What did that creature do? What *did* that creature do?

TOMMY: It picked up your papers. That's Mr. Follansbee's Mechanical Helper. It picks up anything on the floor and puts it in a wastebasket.

MAYOR: A Mechanical Helper? A Mechanical Helper? (*He smiles, jumps up in the air, and drops the papers again. This time* HENRY *pushes the buttons,* 4TH ROBOT *picks up the papers,* HENRY *gets them and hands them to the delighted* MAYOR, *who hugs* HENRY.) My dear Mr. Follansbee! My

dear, dear, dear Mr. Follansbee! How wonderful! How perfectly wonderful!

HENRY (*Sadly*): Your wife won't like a Mechanical Helper, Mr. Mayor.

MAYOR: Wife? Wife? Who said anything about a wife? These robots are just what I've always dreamed about.

HENRY: Your secretary won't like one, either.

MAYOR: My dear Mr. Follansbee, will you let me speak? Ahem! As you know, this town has a litterbug problem. Every town has a litterbug problem, but in this town, the litterbug problem is my problem because I am the mayor. Now, for years, I have tried to think of some way to keep the streets of our fair town clean. People do forget, you know. They drop papers, gum wrappers—oh, all sorts of things— on the streets of our town.

HENRY (*Becoming excited*): My Mechanical Helpers wouldn't stand for that. They'd pick up all the litter and put it in the wastebaskets on the street corners.

MAYOR: Exactly. We'll use your robots to keep our town clean. They'll be wonderful.

HENRY (*Excited*): They'll be perfect!

MAYOR: We'll buy all you have! We'll send them all over town!

HENRY: My Mechanical Helpers will keep the town clean! (HENRY *and the* MAYOR *shake hands and dance around happily. The children and* AGATHA *cheer.*) I'll rename the robots. Instead of the Mother's Mechanical Helpers, I'll call them the Mayor's Mechanical Helpers.

MAYOR (*Pleased*): Wonderful, wonderful! (*He stops and thinks.*) Now, let me think. Why did I come in here?

AGATHA: You came in to buy a present for your wife. (*She picks up various items from counters.*) Now, Mayor, your wife might like flowers, or jewelry, or—

HENRY: Agatha, my dear, I'm afraid that will have to wait. The Mayor and I have business to talk over. I know you will excuse us while we go to my workshop to make plans. (*He takes the* MAYOR's *arm.*)

MAYOR: Yes, yes, of course. We must make plans. (*They start off slowly, arm in arm.*)

AGATHA: Henry! Come back here at once.

HENRY: I can't do that, my dear. I must get back to work on my inventions. After all, *I* am the inventor of the Mayor's Mechanical Helpers. (*He bows to her, then leads the* MAYOR *off as she stares after him.*)

AGATHA: Well, I never! (*She drops the flowers and jewelry on the floor.*)

SUSIE (*Coming over*): I'll help you pick them up.

TOMMY: No, let the robots do it. (ANN, TOMMY, *and* SUSIE *quickly press buttons. The* ROBOTS *start over.* AGATHA *is already kneeling on the floor, picking up flowers. The* ROBOTS *pick up* AGATHA *and go toward the wastebasket with her, while she screams for help and the curtains close.*)

Myeko thinks American children do not like her because she is Japanese. Read to discover how an interest Myeko brought from Japan helps her begin to make friends.

A YELLOW PAPER FISH

Kay Haugaard

Then it was reading period. Myeko opened *Paths to Adventure*. She squeezed her eyes tightly together when she saw the picture of a yellow-haired girl and a boy with a spotted dog beside a white house with a white fence. It made her feel very lonesome. How she wished to run away from school down to the docks, and hide among the boxes on a ship that would take her to Japan and to the girls with whom she had gone to school and to Ojii-san and Obaa-san and their little paper house, which was the right size and had doors that slid and did not bang into one's face. There, one could sit on the floor and be comfortable in the proper manner. She would never like it here, never, never!

At lunchtime, Myeko waited until she thought all the children had gone into the cafeteria. She did not wish to be close to the others. She put her lunch box under her arm and walked through the empty hall to the cafeteria. How noisy it was, with laughing and talking and clicking of spoons and forks and glasses. Myeko got a paper napkin and a carton of milk. Then she looked around to find a bench upon which to sit. Perhaps she had waited too long, for there were hardly any places. At last she saw one and walked to it. It was near the wall that had the tank of goldfish. It would be nice to sit and watch the golden fish fan their petal fins through the clear water. They were so beautiful that Myeko picked up her yellow paper napkin and started to fold a fish. Then, she glanced up and was sorry she had not looked more carefully before she had chosen that bench.

Right across from Myeko, at the table next to the radiator, sat a few girls from her class. Carol sat in the middle of the group. She was talking and waving her hands and smiling, while Harriet and the others (Myeko thought they were called Margaret and Joanne) were watching her closely.

Then Myeko felt a hand on her shoulder and, turning around, she saw a lady with grey and white hair in a big knot on her head. Myeko had seen her in the hall, and knew she was a teacher.

"I'm sorry, honey," the lady said, "but this section is for Miss Price's class. The little children eat in that section." She pointed over by the window where the younger children were sitting.

The room had seemed noisy before, but now Myeko wished there had been much more noise, for all the girls sitting with Carol had heard the teacher. They laughed very loudly.

"Excuse me, honorable teacher, but I *am* a pupil from Miss Price's class."

The teacher looked puzzled. Then she smiled and kind of ruffled Myeko's hair with her hand. "Well, my goodness, you are a tiny, little thing."

Myeko did not feel hungry now. But she had promised Mama-san that she would eat her lunch so she opened her *obento*, took out a rice ball, and began to eat. Then she noticed the cod and she was happy. Now she would just forget what the teacher had said and eat her food with enjoyment.

"Wow!" Myeko heard Orville's voice close to her. He had come in late and was walking toward her. "What do I smell? Hey, did one of the goldfish die?"

Myeko looked up with surprise. Orville sat down beside her. The girls at the next table were sniffing and looking around. Harriet was looking under the table.

Orville pushed his glasses back on his nose and peeked into Myeko's lunch box. "Hey, what are those things?" He pointed to the rice balls. Then he said loudly, "It's over here . . . a dead fish! She's *eating* it."

All the girls started to giggle.

Two pools of tears burned Myeko's eyes, and her nose tingled as if little needles were going through it. If she did not rub her nose, it would drip and so would her eyes.

"Hey, kids, did you hear me? She's *eating* the dead fish."

Harriet laughed again, but Carol smiled at Myeko, and said to Orville, "What do you want her to eat, a *live* fish?"

Joanne, Margaret, Harriet, and Carol laughed so hard they nearly choked on their sandwiches, and Myeko laughed, too. She wiped her eyes and rubbed her nose while they were laughing so they would not notice the tears.

When the girls started to leave, Carol came over to Myeko and said, "Don't pay any attention to him, he's just a pest." Carol gave Orville a playful shove and Orville said, "Cut it out, Carol."

Then Carol looked at the little folded paper goldfish by Myeko's lunch box. "Boy! Did you make that?"

"Yes, I made it." Myeko smiled a small smile. It was the first time she had wanted to smile since she had started at the new American school. She picked up the fish by its back and set it on the palm of her hand. "It is, unfortunately, an ugly thing and the paper is poor and common, but I wish you to have it."

Carol took the tiny, yellow fish, and examined the fins and the flowing tail with her fingers. "Thanks! I wish I could make something like this."

Myeko looked up very quickly into Carol's face. "If you wish me to show you. . . ."

But the girls were waving from the doorway, and Carol was walking away so she did not hear. "Thanks a lot for the fish," she called and hurried off to catch up with the others before they left the room.

Myeko watched them and wondered how it would be to have many friends and not be afraid. She felt some of the strangeness of the new place melting. Then Myeko wondered what Papa-san would say; if he would think that a smile and a paper fish could be good seeds to plant for a friendship. Myeko hoped so, for it would make her very happy if the girls would invite her to sit with them at lunch.

PAPER-FOLDING

Florence Sakade

As you read the directions for paper-folding, remember how quickly Myeko folded the paper-napkin fish. How many times do you suppose she had practiced folding a fish?

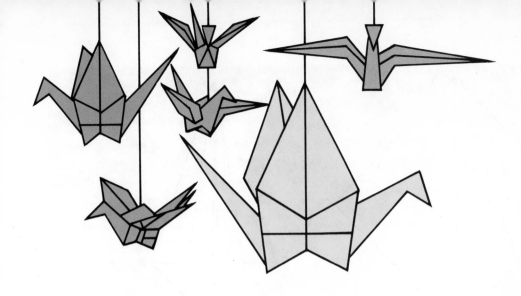

Origami, or paper-folding, is a favorite pastime with Japanese children. Some of the very difficult designs that can be made with only a piece of paper and nimble fingers are truly amazing. But it takes practice and patience to master this art, which has interested people in Japan for more than ten centuries.

One of the more difficult figures to make is the crane, but it is great fun, too. In Japan, the crane is a symbol of good luck and can be found almost any place. Often, folded-paper cranes of all sizes are strung on pieces of thread and hung from the ceiling to decorate a room.

Usually colored paper about four to six inches square is used for paper-folding. Sometimes two sheets of different colors are folded together. After Japanese children become very good at paper-folding, they fold designs out of papers only one inch square!

Why don't you try your hand at paper-folding? The diagrams on the following pages will show you how to fold a swan. Remember that five- or six-inch squares of paper are easiest to work with. Use thin paper, not heavy art paper. Practice with scratch paper so that you do not waste colored paper.

If the directions seem difficult, you can mark the corners of your paper like the markings in the diagram. The markings will help you fold your design correctly.

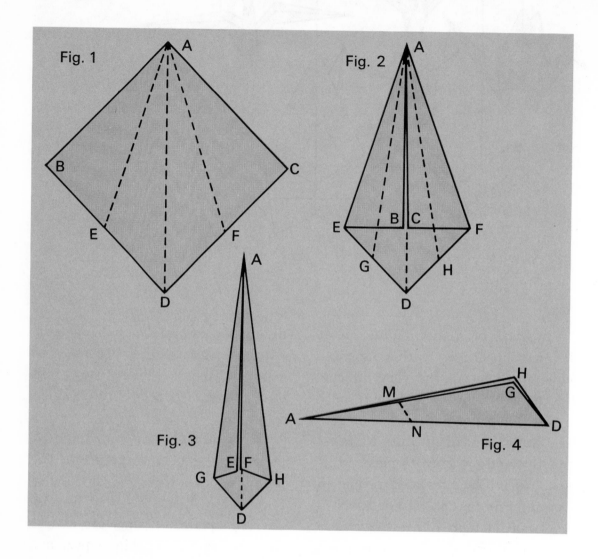

1. Crease a square piece of paper along line AD (Fig. 1) and then unfold.
2. Fold the edge AB forward to meet the center line AD. Do the same with the edge AC and you will have Fig. 2.
3. Now fold the edge AE forward so that it reaches the center line AD and then repeat with edge AF. You now have Fig. 3.
4. Fold along the center line AD so that AG is on top of AH as in Fig. 4.
5. To make the neck, pick up the paper with the open edge at the top and with corner A pointing to the left. Separate the two flaps slightly and bend back

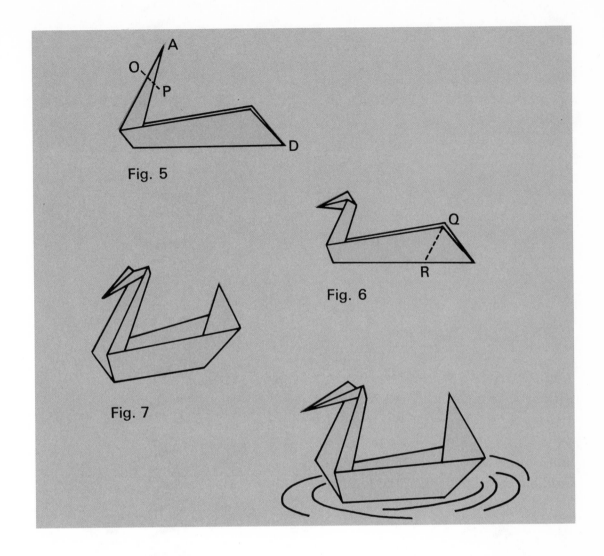

Fig. 5

Fig. 6

Fig. 7

the pointed end at MN as in Fig. 5, so that it is inserted between the body flaps. In doing so, the fold along the line AD in the neck portion will be reversed.

6. The head is formed in a similar way at OP. See Fig. 6.

7. The tail is formed at QR (Figs. 6 & 7) in the same manner as the neck and head. Follow the diagrams carefully to get the proper angles for the neck, head, and tail.

What Starts a Person Writing?

Marguerite Henry

Marguerite Henry was very young when she got the idea for her first article, but she already had an interest in writing. Today she is famous for her stories about horses. Find out how a corner of the kitchen helped her become a writer.

One merry Christmas my mother gave me a surprise to set the heart of a ten-year-old rejoicing. She had set up a bright red table in a corner of her kitchen, and on it were all the wondrous tools of writing. What caught my eye first was my own cream pitcher holding a bright bouquet of pencils—three reds, two greens, and a yellow. Brand new they were, with their erasers firm and unchewed, and all so freshly sharpened that to this day the memory of their cedarwood fragrance tickles my nose.

Beside the pitcher lay a gleaming pair of shears. They were tied to the table with a knitted string, just the way my mittens were fastened to my coat so they could never be lost. And there was an enormous jar of paste with the brush handle sticking straight up in the air, inviting me to grab it. And hanging on a hook by the side of the table was a punch for pressing holes in paper, and it too was caught fast with a red knitted string. And there was my mother's hand-painted pin tray that used to sit on her dresser holding a pansy brooch. Now it was mounded with paper clips. There was even a pencil sharpener!

But best of all was the stack of fat pads of paper, in every hue of the rainbow. They were from my father's office. On the top sheet, in his beautiful script, he had written:

Dear Last of the Mohicans,*
Not a penny for your thoughts,
but a tablet.
Merry Christmas!

Carefully I tore off the sheet and opened the one little drawer of my table. In it I laid the paper. Papa's beautiful handwriting must never get mixed up with my scrawling.

Tongue-tied with delight, I picked up each tool—a pencil first, and sniffed the newly shaved wood. I worked the shears, and smiled in joy because they were not blunt-ended like a child's plaything. From the rainbow of paper I tore off a pink sheet and snipped it in two. My shears cut sharp and clean, the way professional shears should. With the good-smelling paste I swabbed the halves together.

Everything was right! I tried hard to hold back the tears. At last I had a world of my very own—a writing world, and soon it would be populated by all the creatures of my imagination.

In the years that I scribbled and sketched at the little red table in the

*He called me that because I was his seventh and last child.

corner, I was never lonely. All about me were the most comforting sounds —an egg whisk beating against its bowl, soups and sauces purring and boiling, the clink of clean knives and forks dropping into their trays, and Mamma and the hired girl chatting away about things that didn't matter.

But what *did* matter was that they were there, and they were working, too.

Some people think writing is a mysterious trade. Yet with a tablet, a pencil, and a tabletop, anyone can write—as I discovered a year later. One of my mother's magazines invited its readers to contribute articles about any of the four seasons. I chose autumn because it was October at the time, and I had just come from a friend's birthday party. (Her name was Beth Berthelet and I have always thought it the most beautiful name in the world; I do hope she didn't marry a man with a less musical name than Berthelet.) Well, to get on with my story, Beth lived in the country, and we played hide-and-seek. Red and yellow leaves were thick on the grass, and the wind swirled them into corners, and they made a nice crunching sound as you scuffed through them. When it came my turn to hide, I buried myself under a pile of maple leaves, and I didn't think anyone was going to find me. Probably no one ever would have if Beth hadn't given her dog, Omar, one of my party gloves to smell, and he found me just in the nick of time; for the hot chocolate was ready, with marshmallows swimming on top, and the cake with frosting so thick you wished you had a long tongue like Omar's to lap it up.

So this is what I wrote about— "Hide-and-Seek in Autumn Leaves" —and when a check came from the magazine I was overwhelmed to the point of dizziness. Right there and then I decided that writing was a very pleasant way to earn a living, and I have been at it ever since.

If I had to pinpoint a time and a spark, I suppose it was the little red table that started me writing.

Afterthought

Good writers use words to please or excite or interest us. They often describe common things so that we see these things in new ways. Find the places where Marguerite Henry describes pencils and paper. What words does she use to make us see that these quite ordinary things are especially important and interesting to her?

Things Begin to Happen

Meindert DeJong

Lina
started writing
to straighten out her thoughts
about something
that
puzzled her.
What did writing her
composition
lead to?

To start with there was Shora. Shora was a fishing village in Holland. It lay on the shore of the North Sea in Friesland, tight against the dike. Maybe that was why it was called Shora. It had some houses and a church and tower. In five of those houses lived the six school children of Shora, so that is important. There were a few more houses, but in those houses lived no children—just old people. They were, well, just old people, so they weren't too important. There were more children, too, but young children, toddlers, not school children —so that is not so important either.

The six children of Shora all went to the same little school. There was Jella; he was the biggest of the six. He was big and husky for his age. There was Eelka. He was slow and clumsy, except his mind; his mind was swift. There was Auka, and right here at the beginning there is nothing much to say about Auka—he was just a nice, everyday boy. You could have fun with him. There were Pier and Dirk; they were brothers. Pier and Dirk looked about as much alike as second cousins. But Pier liked what Dirk liked, and Dirk did what Pier did. They liked to be together. They were twins.

Then there was Lina. She was the only girl in the little Shora school. One girl with five boys. Of course, there was also a teacher, a man teacher.

Maybe to begin with, we really should have started with Lina. Not because she was the only schoolgirl in Shora, but because she wrote a story about storks. There were no storks in Shora. Lina had written this story about storks of her own accord—the teacher hadn't asked her to write it. In fact, until Lina read it out loud to the five boys and the teacher, nobody in school had even thought about storks.

But there one day, right in the middle of the arithmetic lesson, Lina raised her hand and asked, "Teacher, may I read a little story about storks? I wrote it all myself, and it's about storks."

Lina called it a story, but it was really an essay, a composition. The teacher was so pleased that Lina had written a little piece of her own accord, he stopped the arithmetic lesson right there and let Lina read her story. She began with the title and read on:

DO YOU KNOW ABOUT STORKS?

Do you know about storks? Storks on your roof bring all kinds of good luck. I know this about storks; they are big and white and have long yellow bills and tall yellow legs. They build great big messy nests, sometimes right on your roof. But when they build a nest on the roof of a house, they bring good luck to that house and to the whole village that that house stands in. Storks do not sing. They make a noise like you do when you clap your hands when you feel happy and good. I think storks clap their bills to make the happy sounds when they feel happy and good. They clap their bills almost all the time except when they are in the marshes and ditches hunting for frogs and little fishes and things. Then they are quiet. But

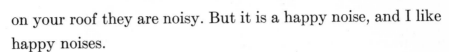

on your roof they are noisy. But it is a happy noise, and I like happy noises.

That is all I know about storks; but my aunt in the village of Nes knows a lot about storks, because every year two big storks come to build their nest right on her roof. But I do not know much about storks, because storks never come to Shora. They go to all the villages all around, but they never come to Shora. That is the most that I know about storks, but if they came to Shora, I would know more about storks.

After Lina had finished reading her story, the room was quiet. The teacher stood there looking proud and pleased. Then he said, "That was a fine story, Lina. A very fine composition, and you know quite a lot about storks!" His eyes were pleased and bright. He turned to big Jella. "Jella," he said, "what do you know about storks?"

"About storks, Teacher?" Jella said slowly. "About storks —nothing." He looked surly and stubborn, because he felt stupid. He thought he ought to explain. "You see," he told the teacher, "I can't bring them down with my slingshot. I've tried and tried, but I just can't seem to do it."

The teacher looked startled. "But why would you want to shoot them down?"

"Oh, I don't know," Jella said. He wriggled a little in his seat. He looked unhappy. "Because they move, I guess."

"Oh," the teacher said. "Pier," he said then, "Dirk, what do you twins know about storks?"

"About storks?" Pier asked. "Nothing."

"Dirk," the teacher said.

"Just the same as Pier," Dirk said. "Nothing."

"Pier," the teacher said, "if I had asked Dirk first, what would have been your answer?"

"The same as Dirk's," Pier answered promptly. "Teacher, that's the trouble with being twins—if you don't know something, you don't know it double."

The teacher and the room liked that. It made everybody laugh. "Well, Auka," the teacher said, "how about you?"

Auka was still chuckling and feeling good about what Pier had said, but now he looked serious. "All I know is that if storks make happy noises with their bills like Lina said in her story, then I would like storks, too."

The teacher looked around and said: "Well, Eelka, there in the corner, that leaves only you."

Eelka thought awhile. "I'm like Lina, Teacher; I know little about storks. But if storks would come to Shora, then I think I would learn to know a lot about storks."

"Yes, that is true," the teacher said. "But now what do you think would happen if we all began to think a lot about storks? School's almost out for today, but if, from now until tomorrow morning when you come back to school, you thought and thought about storks, do you think things would begin to happen?"

They all sat still and thought that over. Eelka raised his hand. "But I'm afraid I can't think much about storks when I don't know much about storks. I'd be through in a minute."

Everybody laughed, but the teacher's eyes weren't pleased. "True, true," he said. "That's right, Eelka. We can't think much when we don't know much. But we can wonder! From now until tomorrow morning when you come to school again, will you do that? Will you wonder why and wonder why? Will you wonder why storks don't come to Shora to build their nests on the roofs, the way they do in all the villages around? For sometimes when we wonder, we can make things begin to happen.

"If you'll do that—then school is out right now!"

There they were out in the schoolyard—free! Jella peered again over the roofs of the houses at the distant tower rising beside the dike. He couldn't believe it. But the big white face of the tower clock spelled out three—a little past three. "Boy," Jella said in wonderment, "he let us out almost a whole hour early, just because of storks." Jella was beginning to appreciate storks. "What'll we do?" he said eagerly to the other boys.

But Lina took charge. Since she had started it with her essay about storks, she felt responsible. It was a wonderful day, the sky was bright and blue, the dike was sunny. "Let's all go and sit on the dike and wonder why, just like the teacher said."

Nobody objected. They all dutifully set out for the dike, still feeling happy because of this hour of freedom that had so suddenly and unexpectedly come to them. Still grateful enough to the storks and Lina to be obedient to her and sit on the dike and think about storks. But Jella lagged behind, and that was unusual. Big Jella was generally in the lead. Going down the village street he stared at every house he passed as if they were something new in the new freedom. But he dutifully climbed the dike and dutifully sat down at the end of the row of boys. Lina sat at the other end.

They sat. Nobody seemed to know just how to begin to

wonder without the teacher there to start them off. Jella stared up at the sky. There wasn't a cloud in the sky. There were no storks. There wasn't even a gull. Jella looked at the sea stretching empty before him—there wasn't a ship in the sea.

Jella looked along the quiet row. Everybody was just sitting, hugging his knees. Everybody looked quiet and awkward and uncomfortable. Suddenly Jella had had enough. He looked along the row of boys at Lina. "The teacher didn't say we had to sit in a row on the dike to wonder, did he?"

"No," Lina said, "but I thought, well, he's never given us a whole hour off from school before, and I thought. . . ."

"Well, then," Jella said. . . . It just didn't feel right to sit when you were free. But the quiet sea and the quiet sky suggested nothing to him. Then fortunately a slow canalboat came pushing around a faraway bend in the canal. The two men on deck lowered the sail and the mast so the boat could slide under the low bridge. The men picked up poles to push the boat along under the bridge. Jella jumped up. Now he had an idea. "Hey, let's all go get our poles and go ditch jumping!"

All the boys, with the exception of Eelka, jumped up eagerly. Here was something to do—fun in the freedom.

"You, too, Eelka. Run and get your pole," Jella said. "And tell Auka to get mine, too. I'll wait here."

Lina stared at Jella in dismay. Even Eelka had to go. When it came to ditch jumping, Eelka generally was left out— he was too fat and slow and clumsy. "But I thought we were going to wonder why storks don't come to Shora?" Lina said. If even Eelka had to go along, she was going to be left behind all alone.

Lina glared down the dike after the running boys. "All

128

right for you, Eelka," she yelled unhappily. She looked darkly at Jella. "Boy, if the teacher finds out that you. . . ." She swallowed her words. It was a bitter, lost feeling to be left behind all alone in the surprise free hour.

Lina had a sudden hopeful thought. It must be that Jella wanted them all in on the ditch jumping, so that if the teacher found out, they'd all catch it together. Maybe he'd let her in on it, too! Maybe that was why he had stayed here with her on the dike. "Jella," Lina asked, "can I go, too? Why, if it wasn't for me, you'd be sitting in school right now. And I could get my mother's clothespole. It's long and smooth and. . . ."

"Naw," Jella said immediately. "Girls are no good at jumping. It's a boy's game."

"I'd be just as good as Eelka. Better even," Lina said indignantly.

"Yeah, I guess so. But Eelka doesn't mind getting wet, but girls worry about wet feet and their dresses flying. And they squeal and scream, and then they get scared and go giggly."

Jella seemed to have thought a lot about it. Lina could see it was totally no use wheedling or arguing. She drew her wooden shoes primly up under her, hugged her knees, and stared wretchedly out at the sea. "Teacher said we were to wonder why the storks don't come. He even said if we wondered really hard, things might begin to happen."

"We'll wonder while we jump ditches," Jella said shortly. He was a bit uneasy. But now the boys were coming back, Auka with two vaulting poles. Jella started to leave. "And we don't care if you do tell the teacher! He didn't say we were supposed to sit like dopes on the dike."

So Jella did care—he was even worried she would tell. She

was no tattletale! Lina did not deign to turn around to answer. But she couldn't help looking down the dike when Eelka came dragging his long vaulting pole. "All right for you, Eelka," she said stormily.

That was the trouble with being the only girl: you got left out of things. And if Eelka didn't also get left out, there was nothing for her to do but sit by herself or play with her little sister Linda and the other little children. What was the fun of that? Well, she'd show them. She'd sit right here and think and wonder really hard. Tomorrow morning when the teacher asked, up would go her hand, but there they'd all sit stupid and with their mouths full of teeth. It did not seem much of a threat. The excited voices of the boys came drifting back to her.

Lina fixed her eyes hard upon a distant hazy swirling far out above the sea, wanting it to be a stork but knowing all the time it was just a sea gull. She wouldn't play with Eelka again for a week! Maybe ten days even, maybe three weeks! Even if in all that time Jella and the rest left Eelka out of every one of their games. She wouldn't bother with Eelka either. She just wouldn't bother!

She stared hard at the gull. It was still a gull; it wasn't a stork. Suppose a whole big flock of storks came flying up out of the sea. The boys, jumping ditches, wouldn't even see them. But Lina had to admit to herself it wouldn't make much difference if they saw the storks or not. The storks wouldn't stay in Shora, and the boys couldn't make them stay, so what was the difference. Lina sighed. It was hard being the only girl in Shora.

She took off one of her wooden shoes and sat staring moodily into it. She caught herself doing it. It was a lonely habit. She often sat staring into her shoe. It somehow made her feel better and seemed to help her to think better, but she didn't know why. She often wished she could wear her wooden shoes in the schoolroom instead of just socks. The wooden shoes had to be left out in the portal. Lina was sure it would help no end if she could pull off one of her shoes and stare and dream into it awhile—especially before doing an arithmetic problem. Lina sighed. You couldn't dream with arithmetic. With arithmetic you could only think. It made arithmetic sort of scary. Hard and scary and not very exciting.

Storks were exciting! "Wonder why? Wonder why?" Lina said quite hard into her wooden shoe. The words came bouncing back at her out of the hard wooden shell. She whispered it into the shoe; the words came whispering back. She sat dreaming, staring into the shoe. And the sea gull was swirling and sailing far out at sea.

Still thinking and dreaming about storks, she got up in her nice hazy daze and wandered away from the dike, one shoe in her hand. She went slowly down the street, staring intently at the roofs of all the houses as if she'd never seen them before. The village street lay quiet and empty. Lina had it to herself all the way through the village to the little school. The school had the sharpest roof of all, Lina decided. All the roofs were sharp, but the school's was the sharpest.

A thin faraway shout and a shrill laugh came through to her. She turned. In the far, flat distance she could see the boys. Now big Jella, it must be Jella, went sailing high over a ditch. Hard behind him, first sprinting, then sailing high on their poles, came the other three boys. And then there came one more; it must be Eelka. But Eelka disappeared—he must have gone into the ditch. Now there was a lot of shouting and running. Lina caught herself waiting anxiously for Eelka to appear out of the ditch. Then she remembered that she wasn't going to play with Eelka for three weeks. She turned her back to the distant boys. "I hope he went in up to his neck," she heard herself saying half-aloud. It surprised her. For now it didn't matter whether or not Eelka went into the water up to his neck; it didn't matter that the boys were having fun. She knew why the storks didn't come to build their nests in Shora. The roofs were all too sharp! But not only did she know the reason why, she also knew what to do about it! They had to put a wagon wheel on top of one of the roofs—a wagon wheel just like her aunt in Nes had on her roof. Tomorrow morning she would spring it on them in the schoolroom. They'd be surprised!

Lina started to hurry back to the village, almost as if she had to hurry to tell someone. She put her wooden shoe back on to hurry better. There wasn't anyone there, she knew. The boys were playing in the fields; the teacher had gone. She could go home and tell her mother, but she would tell her mother anyway. It just seemed to her there had to be somebody *new* to tell it to—she had that feeling. There wasn't anyone like that. The whole street lay empty. It made her hurrying suddenly seem senseless. Lina slowed herself by staring at a house.

Once more Lina dawdled down the street, once more she stood a dreamy while before each house. Her shoe came off again. She was staring up at the roof of Grandmother Sibble III's house when the old lady came out. It startled Lina.

"I know I'm a nosy old creature," Grandmother Sibble III said, "but there you stand again, staring. I've been watching you wandering from the dike to the school and back again like a little lost sheep."

Lina laughed a polite little laugh. "Oh, I'm not exactly wandering. I'm wondering."

"Oh," said the old lady, mystified. "Well, I guess wondering is always better than wandering. It makes more sense." She chuckled a nice little old lady's chuckle.

They looked at each other. And Lina thought how she had never talked much to Grandmother Sibble III except to say a polite "hello" as she walked by. Now she did not know just what to say to her.

The old lady was still looking at her curiously. "Is that why you have your shoe in your hand?" she said gently. "Because you were wondering so hard?"

In surprise Lina glanced down at her hand holding the wooden shoe. She reddened a little and hastily slipped it on her foot. What must Grandmother Sibble think—not that she was her grandmother, she was just the grandmother of the whole village, the oldest old lady. It certainly must have looked silly, her hobbling down the street on one shoe, carrying the other. No wonder Grandmother Sibble III had come out of the house!

"I, . . ." Lina said, trying to explain. She giggled a little. "Oh, isn't it silly?" She fished in her mind for some sensible explanation. None would come. But Grandmother Sibble III wasn't standing there grinning in a superior, adult way. She just looked—well, mystified and inquisitive. Lina decided to tell her. "I guess it does look silly and odd, but it somehow helps me think better to look into my shoe. Then when I get to thinking really hard, I forget to put it back on again," she said defensively.

"Why, yes," the old lady said immediately. "Isn't it funny how odd little things like that help? Now I can think much better by sort of rocking myself and sucking on a piece of candy, and I've done it ever since I was a little girl like you." She carefully settled herself on the top step of her brick stoop. She looked as if she was settling herself for a good, long chat. "Now of course, I've just got to know what it was you were thinking about so hard it made you forget your shoe." She chuckled her little old chuckle again. "And if you don't tell me, I won't sleep all night from trying to guess."

They laughed together. Grandmother Sibble patted the stoop next to her. "Why don't you come and sit down with me and tell me about it."

Lina eagerly sat down—close, exactly where the old lady had patted. Old Grandmother Sibble was nice, she thought to herself. It was a nice surprise. She didn't talk to you as if you were a tiny tot, almost a baby, and miles of years away, the way grownups usually did. She even understood silly girl things like looking into a wooden shoe. She understood it the way a girl friend—if you had a girl friend—would understand. A girl friend who also had silly tricks and secretly told you about them. Aloud Lina said, "I was thinking about storks, Grandmother Sibble. Why storks don't come and build their nests in Shora."

Grandmother Sibble looked thoughtful. "Well, that is a thing to ponder all right. No wonder you had your shoe off. We here in Shora always without storks."

"But I figured out why," Lina told the old lady proudly. "Our roofs are too sharp!"

"Well, yes . . . yes, I guess so," the old lady said carefully, sensing Lina's sharp excitement. "But that could be remedied by putting a wagon wheel on the roof, couldn't it? The way they do in the other villages?"

"Yes, I'd thought of that," Lina said promptly. "My aunt in Nes has a wagon wheel on her roof, and storks nest on it every year."

"Ah, yes," the old lady said, "but doesn't your aunt's house have trees around it, too?"

"Yes, it has," Lina said, looking in surprise at the little old lady. Why, Grandmother Sibble must have been thinking about storks, too. It seemed amazing, the old, old lady thinking about storks. "I guess I never thought about trees. Well, just because there are no trees in Shora—so I didn't think about trees." Lina's voice faded away. Here was a whole new thing to think about.

"Would a stork think about trees?" the old lady wanted to know. "It seems to me a stork would think about trees. And it seems to me that in order to figure out what a stork would want, we should try to think the way a stork would think."

Lina sat bolt upright. What a wonderful thing to say! Lina fumbled for her shoe while she eagerly looked at the old lady.

"You see, if I were a stork, even if I had my nest on a roof, I think I would still like to hide myself in a tree now and then and settle down in the shade and rest my long legs. Not be on the bare peak of a roof for everybody to see me all the time."

Lina pulled her feet up under her and looked down confusedly at her wooden shoes. She really needed her wooden shoe right now. Her thoughts were racing.

"You see, years ago," Grandmother Sibble was explaining, "oh, years and years ago when I was the only girl in Shora, the way you are the only girl now, there were trees in Shora and there were storks! The only trees in Shora grew on my grandmother's place. My grandmother was then the only grandmother of Shora. She was Grandmother Sibble I, just like I am now Grandmother Sibble III and you would someday be Grandmother Sibble IV if your mother had named you Sibble instead of Lina. I asked her to! Oh, I had no business asking—we're not even related—but it just seems there should always be a Grandmother Sibble in Shora. But that's beside the point.

"The point is, my grandmother's little house stood exactly where your school stands now but, oh, so different from your little naked school. Really different! My grandmother's house was roofed with reeds, and storks like reeds. And my grand-

mother's house was hidden in trees. And storks like trees. Weeping willow trees grew around my grandmother's house. And in the shadowy water under the hanging willows, pickerel swam in the moat. And over the moat there was a little footbridge leading right to my grandmother's door. And in one of the willows there was always a stork nest, and there was another nest on the low reed roof of my grandmother's house. As a little girl I used to stand on the footbridge and think that I could almost reach up to the low roof of the little house and touch the storks, so close they seemed."

"Oh, I didn't know. I never knew," Lina said breathlessly.

Grandmother Sibble did not seem to hear. Her eyes were looking far, far back. She shook her head. "A storm came," she said. "As storms so often come to Shora. But this was a real storm. The wind and waves roared up the dike for longer than a week. For a whole week the water pounded and the salt spray flew. The air was full of salt; you even tasted the salt on your bread in your houses. And when it was all done, there were only three willows left at Sibble's Corner—that is what they called my grandmother's house, because everybody gathered there of a warm summer day to sit and chat and rest from work in the only shade in Shora, to talk and to lean their tired backs against the only trees. Then even those three leftover trees sickened and died. I guess their leaves had just taken in too much salt that long week of the storm.

"Later, after Grandmother Sibble I died, they came and tore down her house and chopped out the old rotted stumps of the willows and filled the moat with dirt. Then there was nothing for years and years, until they built your naked little school on the same spot. But the storks never came back."

Lina sat wide-eyed, hugging her knees, staring straight ahead, drinking it in, dreaming it over—the things the old lady had said—dreaming the picture. It sounded like a faraway tale, and yet it had been! Grandmother Sibble III had seen it! She had thought as a little girl that she could reach up and touch the storks, it had been so real and so close. Right in Shora!

"I never knew. I never knew," Lina whispered to herself. "And even a little footbridge," she told herself and hugged her knees.

Grandmother Sibble III roused herself. "So you see you mustn't think our sharp roofs is the whole story, must you?" she said softly. "We must think about other things, too. Like our lack of trees, our storms, our salt spray. We must think about everything. And to think it right, we must try to think the way a stork would think!"

Grandmother Sibble said "we"!

"Then have you been thinking about storks, too?" Lina asked in astonishment.

"Ever since I was a little girl. And ever since then I've wanted them back. They're lucky and cozy and friendly and, well, just right. It's never seemed right again—the village without storks. But nobody ever did anything about it."

"Teacher says," Lina told the old lady softly, "that maybe if we wonder and wonder, then things will begin to happen."

"Is that what he said? Ah, but that is so right," the old lady said. "But now you run in the house. There's a little tin on my kitchen shelf and in it there are wineballs. You get us each a wineball out of the tin. Then I'll sit on my stoop and you sit on yours, and we'll think about storks. But we'll think better each on his own stoop, because often thinking gets lost

138

in talking. And maybe your teacher is right—that if we begin to think and wonder, somebody will begin to make things happen. But you go find the candy tin; I can think much better sucking on a wineball. And you take one, too. You watch if it doesn't work much better than looking inside an old wooden shoe."

Lina had never been in Grandmother Sibble III's house before, never in the neat kitchen. There was the shelf, and there was the candy tin. There were storks on the candy tin! Pictures of storks in high sweeping trees were all around the four sides of the candy tin. On the lid was a village, and on every house there was a huge, ramshackle stork nest. In every nest tall storks stood as though making happy noises with their bills up into a happy blue sky.

Lina kept turning the candy tin to see the pictures again and again. Suddenly she woke up to the fact that she was staying in Grandmother Sibble's house a long, long time. Her first time in Grandmother Sibble's house, too! What would she think? She hastily shoved the candy tin back on its shelf and hurried to the stoop.

"Grandmother Sibble, storks on your candy tin! And on every roof a nest! Oh...." Suddenly Lina realized she'd forgotten the wineballs. She raced back. It was hard not to look at the storks, but she kept her face partly turned away and picked out two round, red wineballs. Then she ran back. "I forgot all about the wineballs," she apologized.

"Yes, I know," Grandmother Sibble said gently, for she saw that Lina—though looking straight at her while handing her her wineball—was not seeing her at all. Lina had dreams in her eyes. Lina was seeing storks on every roof in Shora.

The old lady quietly let Lina wander off the stoop and to her own house. Lina had dreams in her eyes and would not hear words anyway.

On her own stoop Lina looked back for the first time. There sat Grandmother Sibble III rocking herself a little and sucking on her wineball. But the dream Lina was dreaming was not just about storks—not directly. Later she would think about storks, try to think the way a stork would think, as Grandmother Sibble had said. But now she thought about Grandmother Sibble, who had a candy tin in her house with storks on it and who had known storks and who, when she was a little girl, had imagined she could reach up and almost touch the storks.

But that was not the wonder either, not quite. The real wonder was that, just as the teacher had said, things *had* begun to happen. Begin to wonder why, the teacher had said, and maybe things will begin to happen. And they had! For there sat Grandmother Sibble III on the stoop of her little house, and suddenly she had become important. She wasn't just an old person anymore, miles of years away, she was a friend. A friend, like another girl, who also wondered about storks.

Lina looked again at the little old lady, sitting there on the stoop. She marveled; she sat feeling nice and warm about a little old lady who had become a friend. It was a lovely feeling, as sweet as a wineball, as sweet as a dream. Lina took one shoe off and peered into it. Why, storks did bring good luck! The storks had made a friend for her. Why, now when the boys left her out of their games, she would go to Grandmother Sibble, and they would sit and talk and chat. Lina looked up out of the shoe triumphantly. Why, yes!

Afterthought

1. What are three or four good reasons for having a special interest?
2. How might a special interest be very important to you?

EVERY TIME I CLIMB A TREE

Every time I climb a tree
Every time I climb a tree
Every time I climb a tree
I scrape a leg
Or skin a knee
And every time I climb a tree
I find some ants
Or dodge a bee
And get the ants
All over me

And every time I climb a tree
Where have you been?
They say to me
But don't they know that I am free
Every time I climb a tree?
I like it best
To spot a nest
That has an egg
Or maybe three

And then I skin
The other leg
But every time I climb a tree
I see a lot of things to see
Swallows, rooftops and TV
And all the fields and farms there be
Every time I climb a tree
Though climbing may be good for ants
It isn't awfully good for pants
But still it's pretty good for me
Every time I climb a tree

David McCord

Swift and

Swift things are beautiful:
Swallows and deer,
And lightning that falls
Bright-veined and clear,
Rivers and meteors,
Wind in the wheat,
The strong-withered horse,
The runner's sure feet.

And slow things are beautiful:
The closing of day,
The pause of the wave
That curves downward to spray,
The ember that crumbles,
The opening flower,
And the ox that moves on
In the quiet of power.

Elizabeth Coatsworth

Beautiful

Swift or slow, animals are beautiful. Some are brightly colored; others have pleasing shapes; still others are graceful. But perhaps the most beautiful thing of all is how they are fitted for the life they live. The more you learn about animals, the easier it is to see this beauty.

Animal Clothing

George F. Mason

When you see an animal, its covering is usually one of the first things you notice. It may make the animal beautiful, but its use is far more important to the animal than pleasing your eye. Read the following article to find out how an animal's covering helps fit it for the life it lives.

All animals have some kind of covering, and this covering has the same purpose as the clothing that people wear. It protects the animal; so it may be called animal clothing.

One kind of animal has fur for clothing. Animals that have fur feed their young on milk from their bodies. All these animals are called mammals.

Fur is really hair. Most mammals have some hair growing out of their skin. Some have thick coats of hair, but others, such as whales and elephants, have only a few hairs. The few stiff hairs on the bodies of whales and elephants do not protect them.

Coats of fur are useful in several ways. One way is to protect animals from heat and cold. For when the weather is hot, fur keeps out heat. In cold weather it keeps heat in the body. In this way coats of fur act as insulation.

Heat cannot go through insulation very easily. That is why fur works just as well where it is hot as it does where it is cold. The hair of a deer in the north keeps him warm in cold weather. The hair of the lion in Africa helps him keep cool.

Some of the thickest and most beautiful furs are found on animals that live a good part of their lives in water. These animals have thick coats of soft fur to help keep water away from their skin. The beaver and the otter have fur like this.

When one of these animals goes into the water, the long hairs mat down over the fine underfur. Water never gets to the skin of a beaver or an otter, because air is trapped around the hairs of the underfur and keeps out the water. That is one reason why these animals can swim in icy water without getting too cold.

When animals with thick coats of fur come out of the water, they shake themselves. When they shake, they get the water off their long top hair. Soon their fur is dry and fluffy again.

Besides keeping animals warm or cool, hair is useful in other ways. Think of what might happen to fighting cats if they had no fur to stop the scratches of each other's sharp claws!

Sometimes the cat's hair also protects it against a dog. When a dog comes near, the cat is frightened. Its fur stands up on end. The cat seems to grow huge. A dog may leave a cat alone just because it looks bigger than it really is. In this way the cat is protected from injury.

Many animals have thick hair on their necks. This is called a mane.

The hair around the neck of a lion and the hair along the neck of a horse are manes.

Animals are often protected by this thick hair. An animal's neck is the place on its body where it can most easily be hurt. Some animals seem to know this, and they often attack that spot. A thick, long mane keeps the teeth and claws of fighting animals from cutting into the neck.

With the change in seasons there is usually a change in an animal's fur. Hair begins to fall out in the spring. In the fall it grows back as a heavier coat. But this change doesn't take place all at once. As old hairs fall out, new ones begin growing.

The fur of some mammals changes color for summer and for winter. The fur of some rabbits, for example, changes from a dark color to white for winter. This change happens as the old, dark hair falls out and the new, white hair takes its place. In spring the dark hair comes in again.

With this change in color comes another kind of protection for the animals. For example, the rabbit that has white fur in winter is the color of the snow around him, and because of this he is hard to see. The color of his hair helps him to hide from his enemies. Such protection may be thought of as camouflage.

Fur that is bright in color can be good camouflage in the jungle. Spots or stripes on animals make them hard to see against the leaves and grass. Their color may even help camou-

flage them in the dark. This helps
them hide from animals that can see
well at night.

Feathers are another kind of
animal clothing that can be useful as
camouflage. Birds are the only
animals that have feathers. Some of
their feathers help them fly, and
some make them beautiful. But all
feathers help the birds keep an even
body heat. Because of their feathers,
birds can be out in any kind of
weather.

Most of the animals that we know
have clothing of fur or of feathers.
But many animals have a shell or a
hard, shell-like covering on the outside of their bodies. Most snakes are
covered with scales. Also many fish
are covered this way.

Man is one animal that does not
have a thick covering for protection
against heat, cold, rain, and injury.
His skin and hair are not enough
protection. So he has to make his
clothing, while other animals have
the kind of clothing they need for the
place in which they live.

Marco and the Tiger

John Foster

A tiger's stripes are useful camouflage in the jungle. But they can be quite a surprise to a boy in the heart of a great city.

Marco stood on the sidewalk in front of 420 Royal Street, in New Orleans, gazing up at the door a moment or two before knocking. It was quite a door. It was the kind of door you didn't mess with. It was huge and black, with big square iron nails and heavy iron hinges shaped like spearheads.

Marco took a deep breath. Then he reached up and banged the iron knocker, which was shaped like a fist.

"Paper boy!" he called.

No answer. But from somewhere far beyond the door, came what sounded like a man, a large man, clearing his throat without much hope of success.

It was about four o'clock on a hot Thursday afternoon in March. And if you think New Orleans can't get hot in March, then you have never been in New Orleans during the month of March. It seemed pretty much like any other afternoon around that time of year. Of course, Marco, who was eleven, had no way of knowing that it would be an afternoon he would remember all his life.

Behind him, on Royal Street, a steady stream of cars went swishing past. Marco paid no attention. Nuts to them! He wasn't studying cars.

He took another whack at the knocker.

"I say again," he called, "it's Marco—Marco Fennerty, Junior, to be exact, collecting for the *States-Item*."

Then, glancing at his route book he yelled, "Hey, Perry!"

The owner of the house at 420 Royal, according to the route book, was Perry, O. K. Mr. Perry's full name was Oscar Kermet Perry. But Marco had it in his head that the man's first name was Perry and that he was one guy who was okay. Marco had been on the route only a month and this was his first day collecting, so there was a lot he had to learn. And he had never seen Mr. Perry.

Again no one answered Marco's call. But again that sound came from somewhere deep behind the door.

"If that *is* you, Perry, and you *are* clearing your throat," Marco said, "you don't seem to be getting anywhere, do you?"

He's probably got a cold, poor fella, Marco thought. But I *do* wish he would open up.

Marco squared his shoulders. He parked his bicycle and snapped the padlock on the rear wheel. Then he marched back to the door as though he carried a tomahawk instead of just his route book.

He was not a large boy. He was, in fact, rather small—if you didn't count his eyes and ears. But he was so quick and so fierce in combat that the bigger boys left him alone as a rule. Marco liked to think to himself that he carried TNT in both fists.

He was, as he also liked to think to himself, a boy without fear.

He gazed at the door and the hinges that were shaped like spearheads and at the knocker that was shaped like a fist. Then he looked at the doorknob, which was shaped like a doorknob.

He called out once more, giving briefly his name, occupation, and reason for being here. Then, taking hold of the doorknob, he gave it a turn, calling, "Perry, can I collect, please?"

There was a soft click.

Then, slowly and silently, the great black door opened wide. Marco leaped inside and the door shut behind him. He found himself in a carriageway that was like a long, dark tunnel. At the end of it was a large courtyard, lighted up by the afternoon sun.

In the French Quarter of New Orleans, there are court-yards, and there are courtyards. Marco had been around enough to know that this was not one of the best. Yet it had something. Yes, it did. It certainly did. His breath went out in a long, soft sigh.

"Gungah!" Marco said. It was an expression that made no sense whatever, but it was all his own.

The courtyard reminded him of a garden—a lost and for-gotten garden. Maybe, he thought, it's just seeing it this way, all bright and green at the end of the dark tunnel. It was like something seen through the wrong end of a telescope.

But there was something about this place that he felt more than he saw. What it was, he didn't know. But it had something to do with his heart beating so fast and the sudden dryness in his mouth. Somewhere ahead he could hear a foun-tain splashing busily to itself as he started down the musty carriageway, tiptoeing on the flagstones.

Why are you tiptoeing? he asked himself. You, a boy with-out fear (who carries TNT in both fists)? He had no answer to that one, but, for some reason or other, he could not stop walking on the tips of his toes.

He kept calling to Perry, but Mr. Perry didn't answer. . . .

Finally, Marco stepped out into the courtyard, blinking in the soft yellow light, and glanced around wide-eyed. He shook his shaggy blond head.

It's a pity, he said to himself, the way some people will let these fine old houses go to rack and ruin.

The courtyard had been pretty much left to itself for some time, maybe years. The big stone fountain in one corner was covered with black, evil-looking mold. A thick clump of bam-boo was growing every which way in the opposite corner. In the center of the courtyard, a huge concrete flowerpot had split open (maybe from last winter's freeze) and the big green plant growing there was half in, half out of the pot.

To the left, a rickety wooden staircase climbed, staggering, up to a second-floor balcony that went around three sides of the courtyard. Gazing up there, Marco saw broken black windows, like blind eyes, behind a railing with half its spokes kicked out.

On the fourth side of the courtyard was a high brick wall that seemed to be laced together with vines. It was topped with pieces of colored glass that glinted and glowed in the dying sunlight.

There was, or seemed to be, a curious hush in the patio. The sounds of the street—the roaring and snorting of buses, the impatient honking of horns as people rushed home from work—seemed to be echoing from far, far away.

Then again there came the strange noise Marco had heard before. It was coming from one of the two big wooden doors on the uptown side of the courtyard, where carriages had been kept in the old days.

The door on the left?

Or the one on the right?

Squaring his shoulders, Marco went to the door on the left. He knocked, then lifted the rusty iron latch.

For some time afterward, because he was a boy who thought about such matters, Marco wondered if all the things that started to happen to him then would ever have happened if he had opened the other door.

"Perry?" he said. "It's Marco the paper boy. . . ."

His voice, which wasn't much at this point anyhow, died off completely. It was even darker inside the doorway than the

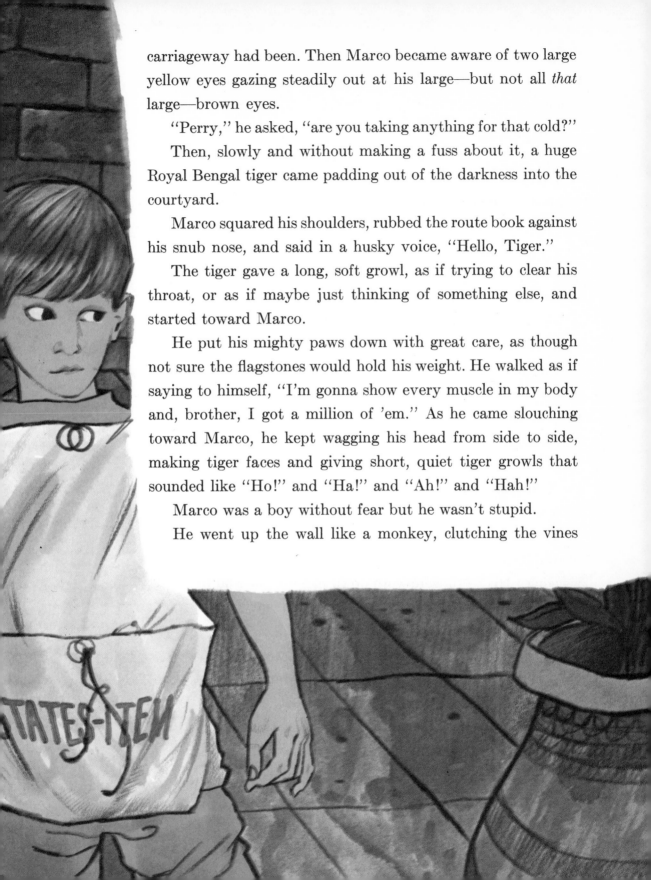

carriageway had been. Then Marco became aware of two large yellow eyes gazing steadily out at his large—but not all *that* large—brown eyes.

"Perry," he asked, "are you taking anything for that cold?"

Then, slowly and without making a fuss about it, a huge Royal Bengal tiger came padding out of the darkness into the courtyard.

Marco squared his shoulders, rubbed the route book against his snub nose, and said in a husky voice, "Hello, Tiger."

The tiger gave a long, soft growl, as if trying to clear his throat, or as if maybe just thinking of something else, and started toward Marco.

He put his mighty paws down with great care, as though not sure the flagstones would hold his weight. He walked as if saying to himself, "I'm gonna show every muscle in my body and, brother, I got a million of 'em." As he came slouching toward Marco, he kept wagging his head from side to side, making tiger faces and giving short, quiet tiger growls that sounded like "Ho!" and "Ha!" and "Ah!" and "Hah!"

Marco was a boy without fear but he wasn't stupid.

He went up the wall like a monkey, clutching the vines

hand over hand. Then he eased himself down on the top. The broken glass was worn down like old teeth and didn't hurt too much.

Marco and the tiger looked at each other a good long time.

"You're a handsome animal, Tiger," Marco said at last.

The tiger opened his great red jaws wide, wide, wide, and yawned. *"Um-ow-w-w-uhn-n-n-UGH!"*

It was, by far, the finest yawn Marco had ever seen. But, clearly, the tiger was telling him that flattery would get him nowhere. Yet Marco had felt that he must say *something*. The silence had become embarrassing.

What he had said was nothing but the truth, though. The tiger was more than ten feet long from the tip of his black nose to the black tuft on the end of his tail. He would have weighed more than four hundred pounds with a full stomach (which it wasn't). He was reddish orange, with neat black stripes. He had a fine, big head, and the hair on his cheeks was long and white, like a well-kept beard.

Yes, there was no arguing the point. He was a handsome animal.

He gazed up at Marco in an interested manner, switching his tail back and forth. (It *was* switching, Marco noticed. Not wagging.) His teeth were worn down like the glass on the wall, but they looked as though they could hurt plenty if he wanted them to.

Marco knew, of course, that the tiger was not the Perry, O. K., listed in his route book. Probably, Marco thought, good ol' Perry kept him as a watch tiger or a pet.

Then Marco noticed something else. The tiger was carrying his right front paw in the air.

Aw, Marco thought, he's got a thorn in his foot, poor fella.

If I take it out, I'll have me a friend for life, like that guy Androcles and the lion in *Aesop's Fables*.

But how long would that life last if he tried to get buddy-buddy with a tiger?

Angrily, Marco put the coward thought out of his mind. I can handle this, he told himself. I *will* handle it. I'm eleven.

Slowly, he climbed down the wall. He kept watching the tiger over his shoulder, ready to scurry right back up again if it seemed a good idea.

Watch the ears, he told himself. Watch those ears, boy. If they go back, you go up—fast—because he's going to spring.

Coming down, Marco had some bad moments, for the ears would twitch, twitch, twitch. And every time, Marco jumped, jumped, jumped. But then he decided that the twitching was just a nervous habit, which it was, and down he came with a thump.

He had never stopped talking on the way.

"Oh, now, look here, Tiger," he said. "I see by the way you're holding your right front paw in the air that you have picked up a thorn. I'll just take it out—or the piece of glass, as the case may be—and you and I will be lifelong friends."

"Ho! Ha! Ah! Hah!"

Patiently, the tiger waited as Marco, still talking, walked up to him. The boy knew he wasn't making a lot of sense. But he thought that, right now, the meaning of the words was less important than the sound of them. He tried, still talking, to think of words with soft sounds—words with plenty of *s*'s and *m*'s and *w*'s.

"Yes, sir," Marco said. "Yes, siree. Just you wait a second or so and I'll bring you instant relief. By the way, I'm Marco Fennerty, Junior. I just made eleven. I'm the son of Sergeant

Marco Fennerty of the New Orleans Police Department—only son and only child, I might add—so please keep that in mind, Tiger."

Easily, the tiger sat down.

"Ho!" he growled. "Ha! Ah! Hah!"

Gently, ever so gently, Marco took hold of his huge paw. Talking, talking about this, that, and the other, he turned the paw up and felt the rough black pad. Then he ran his fingers through the tufts of silky-soft black fur between the toes. He couldn't find a thing.

He pressed the pad, and the tiger's mighty claws slipped out like four ivory daggers. They were awful weapons indeed.

"Ah!" Marco said.

"Ho! Ha!" said the tiger.

Marco felt just the least bit silly. This was actually the first time in his life that he had held the paw of a tiger. But the main thing about the matter was that there was no thorn in the paw.

No glass, either.

Nothing.

Marco still held the paw while he tried to decide what in the world to do with it. After all, he thought, as silly as he felt now, he would feel a whole lot sillier if he just let go and walked away after making such a big deal about it to begin with.

Then he had an idea.

"Shake hands, Tiger," Marco said.

He took the big, heavy paw in both his hands and pumped it up and down. It was somewhat like working out with a furry barbell.

"You do that very well," he said. "I don't suppose you know any other tricks."

The tiger studied Marco with his great yellow eyes as if, hard as he tried, he couldn't quite figure this kid out. Marco was used to seeing such an expression on people when they looked at him, but the tiger had a way all his own. It was unsettling, to say the least.

For a moment Marco gazed deep into the tiger's eyes. Then he glanced away, rubbing his nose with the route book. For that moment it had seemed to the boy that he could see in the tiger's eyes the jungle, with all its wildness and awful power and raw beauty and its spookiness.

There was something else about those eyes. What was it? Marco could not decide.

"I'll bet you escaped from the circus, Tiger," he said. "And in the circus, tigers learn all the latest tricks."

Stepping back, he pointed one finger at the tiger.

"Roll over!"

The tiger made no move, no sound. But from the look on his face, he seemed to be saying, "Eh?"

Marco raised the finger and brought it down again.

"Play dead, Tiger!"

Watching Marco with polite interest, the tiger slowly lowered his right front paw to the ground. Then, slowly, he lifted his left front paw.

If only I had a whip, Marco thought. A whip to crack and a gun to fire in the air like the animal trainers in the circus have. Then, boy, I could make him jump through flaming hoops and everything.

"Come on, Tiger," he said, "I'm afraid we're not making our best effort. Now if you'll give me your attention, I'll try to show you what I mean. For my first trick I'll play dead. . . ."

Marco threw himself on the ground, then rolled over on his back with his hands and feet in the air. He gave the tiger an encouraging smile. "See? It's easy."

For maybe thirty seconds the tiger gazed at Marco lying there. Then he came up behind Marco and stared down at him for maybe another twenty seconds. Marco had to roll his head back to see the tiger. It is one thing to look into a tiger's solemn striped face. To look into a tiger's solemn striped face upside down is something else again—and hard on the neck muscles. But Marco did it.

Then the tiger took his left front paw, the one that was hanging in the air anyway, and gave Marco a swipe with it.

The courtyard, as noted, was large. Marco went rolling over and over and over and over until he bumped into the fountain in the corner. "Hey!"

Before he could get up, the tiger had padded over to him. Then, with another swipe of his paw, he sent Marco rolling over and over and over and over to the other side of the courtyard, where he went crashing and banging into the bamboo.

Marco jumped to his feet.

"Don't mess with me, Tiger!" he yelled. "I may appear small to you, but I am quick and I carry TNT in both fists!"

The tiger raised one furry white eyebrow. His feelings were hurt.

Marco, however, was feeling hurt all over. In his travels back and forth across the patio, he had scraped elbows and knees and had received minor damage to wrists, ankles, and nose. But his main problem was dizziness. You might think that rolling one way makes you dizzy, and rolling the other undizzies you. It doesn't.

Gungah!

He kept wobbling around in a very silly manner, like a top coming to the end of its spin. To keep from falling flat on his face, he grabbed a thick stalk of bamboo. Besides being dizzy, he was plenty mad. The tiger kept swimming past in a red haze.

Then Marco thought of school tomorrow.

"Hey, Marco, what happened to you?" the kids would say.

"Hmm?" he would ask.

"Where'd you get all the bobos?"

"Oh, *those.*"

"Yeah, those. How'd yuh get 'em, hey?"

"Romping with my tiger."

"Your tiger?"

"He doesn't mean to be rough, but"—and here he would give a shrug and a smile—"you know tigers."

Anger passed, then dizziness. When the tiger and the world were standing still again, Marco let go of the bamboo.

"Now, look here, Tiger," he said. "You're the one that's supposed to do the tricks—not me."

The tiger raised both furry eyebrows, as if to say, "Oh, really now?"

Then Marco had a thought.

"Well, after all, Tiger," he pointed out, "why should you do tricks, anyhow? You don't have to entertain me like that just because I'm your guest. We can have our romps and talks and all, but there will be no tricks. Agreed?"

The tiger smiled—or seemed to smile.

"I think we're going to be fine friends," Marco said. "But, really and truly, Tiger, you'll have to watch the rough stuff, you know? I bruise easily."

The tiger seemed sorry.

"And now it's getting late and I must go," Marco said. "Don't bother to see me to the door."

Then it occurred to him that he had better leave things as he had found them, the main thing being the tiger. Marco opened the door of the animal's quarters and got ready for an argument. But the tiger seemed glad to go back inside.

"Good-bye, Tiger," the boy said. "See you tomorrow."

From behind the door came what had first sounded to him like a man trying to clear his throat.

Marco went across the courtyard, now quite dark, and through the very dark carriageway. He let himself out, closing the heavy front door behind him. The Desire Street bus, all lighted up, roared past, then stopped at the corner with a hiss of air brakes. Cars went by, honking.

Slowly, deep in thought, Marco walked over to his bicycle and started to slip the key into the padlock. It was hard to believe, out here on the flashing, noisy street, filled with the

fumes of burned gasoline, that what had happened in the courtyard had really happened.

Suddenly, he turned around and went back to the door with the hinges shaped like spearheads and the knocker shaped like a fist and the doorknob shaped like a doorknob. Then, not taking any chances, he whispered, "Please," and turned the knob.

The door swung open silently and easily. Marco went through the dark carriageway and across the courtyard to the two big wooden doors. Everything seemed to be in order. He squared his shoulders, humming a little tune he had just made up. Then he lifted the latch of the door on the left.

"Tiger?"

Close to the ground, two yellow fires burned in the darkness. The tiger was lying down. The fires went out, then came back on again as he blinked his eyes. He was rather surprised to see his funny little friend again so soon and, if the truth were known, not too happy about it. The afternoon had been great but tiring.

With a grunt or so and a couple of groans and a creak and a pop of his bones, he started to get to his feet.

"Please," Marco said, "don't get up. I just wanted to be sure that you were really there. I was afraid that I had just imagined you, if you follow me, Tiger. I am said to have a vivid imagination."

Well, there was no question about it. The tiger most certainly was there. Marco watched the two yellow fires that went out and came back on and then went out again, like blinker lights. Dot, dot, dash, dot. . . .

He closed the door gently.

"Good night, Tiger," he whispered. "Sleep well."

The tiger gave a happy groan.

Animal Weapons

George F. Mason

A tiger in captivity has little use for its long sharp claws or fangs. But in the jungle it must use them to catch its food. In a similar way many other animals also rely on weapons. Read the following article to find out about some of those weapons.

Prizefighters use their hands as weapons. But hands aren't really the best weapons that can be used for fighting. There are many animals that have much better weapons.

Animal weapons may be used for different purposes. They may be used by the animal for protecting itself or for getting food. Since animals cannot make weapons to use in fighting, they must use the weapons that are parts of their bodies.

Some of the most beautiful and most deadly of all animal weapons are horns and antlers. These are used for fighting, but they may also make animals very beautiful.

Antlers are made of bone. Usually only the male deer grow antlers, and each will grow a new set of these weapons every year. When we see the great, branched antlers on the head of a deer, it is hard to believe that such huge bones are grown in only five months.

When the antlers have reached their full growth, the animals use them for fighting and protection. When a male deer uses his antlers as a weapon, he puts his head down and charges. He uses the points of the antlers to hurt the other animal. These points can kill an animal if they hit a tender spot on its body.

After about five months, antlers are scarred and broken. Then they fall off, and new ones grow in their place.

Some animals grow horns instead of antlers. These animals keep the same sets of horns all their lives. Horns are stiff and strong and not easily broken. They are useful for fighting at all times. Horns are grown during the first years of the animal's life, and both male and female animals may have them.

There are different kinds of horns, and the horned animals use these weapons in different ways. Animals with horns that point up charge as a deer does. Animals with curved horns use them to protect their necks by swinging their heads from side to side. In this way their horns can hurt an animal that charges them from either side or from behind.

The male sheep with heavy, thick, curled horns fight in a different way. They depend upon the heavy blows from their horns to stop their enemies. But the mountain goat has small, thin horns that he can use in charging. He is well armed and knows it. The goat can use his horns to protect himself against any animal his size.

There are other kinds of horns. Each animal has to use the kind it has in a way that will give it the most protection.

One animal, the giraffe, has horns that aren't weapons. The giraffe has short horns that are covered with skin and hair. These are not good

weapons. But the giraffes can fight. They fight among themselves, and one giraffe can even kill another. The weapon it uses is its neck. It tries to break the neck of the other giraffe with wide swings of its own head and neck.

Horns and antlers are well-known animal weapons. But there is another animal weapon that is little known. This is the tongue. Some animals can use this weapon to catch and kill insects.

The toads and frogs have tongues that they use for catching insects, which are their food. The tongues of these animals are attached at the front of the jaw instead of at the back as most tongues are.

When a frog or a toad wants to catch an insect, it actually spits out its tongue. The tongue is sticky, and the insect is caught on it. Then the frog or the toad flips its tongue back into its mouth, bringing the insect with it.

Another animal that uses its tongue to get its food is the chameleon. The chameleon's tongue is attached at the back of the mouth and not at the front like the frog's. But the tongue is very long. It may be as long as twelve inches when it is fully stretched out. It, too, is sticky and is used to catch insects.

When an insect gets close to a chameleon, this animal darts its tongue at the insect as fast as lightning. Just as quickly it pulls its tongue back with the insect stuck on it.

Horns, antlers, and tongues are only a few animal weapons. Every animal has weapons that are useful in its way of life. Now that you have read about these weapons, can you name others and tell how they are used?

The following story is about an otter family. Otters spend much of their time in water; they eat fish, crawfish, insects, frogs, and snails. They are playful animals and are often friendly, but they can protect themselves from an enemy when they have to.

A Brave Otter Family

Emil E. Liers

One cold, still day in late winter a red fox was running on top of a fallen log in a rocky pine woods. Suddenly he heard a squeaking and mewing. He stopped and listened, wondering what it could be. The sound seemed to be coming from a knothole in the hollow log he was standing on.

The fox smelled at the knothole, hoping for a good dinner of mice. But it wasn't the smell of mice that came to the fox. The squeaking seemed louder now. Mr. Fox sniffed harder and scratched at the knothole with his paw.

Suddenly the squeaking stopped. Then out of the far end of the log an otter poked her head. Her name was Beauty, and in her eye was an angry look. Without a sound she started for the fox.

Mr. Fox was so interested in the smells and sounds that came from the log that he didn't see her. Then he heard the crust of snow break. He looked up just in time to see a black streak dashing toward him.

Beauty was just six inches from his feet. She bared her teeth and screamed at him. Mr. Fox jumped back quickly from her fierce teeth. Then, his dream of a mouse dinner gone, he ran away over the snow.

When he was far enough away, the fox sat down to think the whole thing over. It must be otter babies that he had smelled in the hollow log. Well, well. He knew that he would not have liked the taste of otter. And anyway, he had just learned that it would not be easy to take them away from their mother.

Mr. Fox decided that he would just as soon be friends with his otter neighbors. He had often seen otters along the streams, and they always seemed like jolly animals. Sometimes he wished he could play with them.

Once Mr. Fox had come so close to some otters that one of them almost ran into him. But the otter had not tried to bite him. He just snorted in alarm, and all the otters splashed into the pool. Soon they poked their heads out, first one and then another. Then they began to play again.

Now that he came to think of it, Mr. Fox was sure that only the day before he had seen Beauty's mate, Ottiga. About three miles from the log where Beauty and her babies lived, Ottiga had been fishing for crawfish. The fox sat and watched. He wished Ottiga would catch a big fish and leave part of it for him.

Ottiga knew what the fox wanted. So, when the otter caught a fine blue crawfish, he walked to the shore where Mr. Fox was sitting. Dropping the crawfish, he began to roll in the snow. The fox ate the crawfish. After he had finished, he saw that the otter hadn't even stopped rolling. When the fox remembered all of this, he was sure he could not ask for nicer neighbors than Ottiga and Beauty.

After she chased the fox away, Beauty returned to her babies. As she crawled back into the hollow log, everything

was as quiet as it could be. Only a pile of leaves could be seen, but Beauty knew that right in the middle of the dry wood, grass, and leaves was a dear treasure.

When she had left the nest, she had covered her babies with leaves and grass. Now she pushed the covering away and looked down at the four bundles of fur. The otter cubs were four days old and about as large as very young kittens. There were three brothers and a sister. They were very cute.

The cubs had wide little heads and faces and big wide mouths. Beauty could not see their mouths unless she turned them on their backs, for their mouths seemed to open under their heads. Whiskers grew on each side of their chins, and there were whiskers over each eye. Each little cub had a black nose and tiny ears.

Like baby kittens, the otter cubs were blind at birth. Their eyes would not open until they were about five weeks old. Their fur was gray, and they each had a short tail. Their feet were webbed to help them in swimming.

Beauty curled up like a doughnut around her babies. The four little cubs were in the middle, where the hole of the doughnut would be. The cubs woke up, mewing and a little cold because their mother had pushed away the leaves that had covered them. But Beauty put her head over them so that no more cold air could reach them. The cubs ate hungrily. When they had all the milk they could hold, Beauty gave them a bath with her tongue. Then they went back to sleep.

Day by day the cubs grew. Even before their eyes were open, they were very playful. After Beauty fed them and washed them with her tongue, the cubs lay on their backs and played. They tried to bite one another. But they were too young to have teeth, and the bites didn't hurt at all.

After the cubs had eaten and played for a while, they would drop off to sleep. Then Beauty would slide out of the nest. After she had put some leaves and grass over her babies, she would lie near the door of their home to get some fresh air. And on clear days she would lie on top of the log in the sun.

As soon as it grew dark, Beauty would slip out to the stream. She would dive and swim in the water and eat her fill.

Sometimes Beauty would see her mate, Ottiga. They would chuckle softly to each other. But soon she would hurry home. Ottiga did not come too close. He knew that the cubs needed all of Beauty's care right now. So he stood guard over his family from a distance.

Early one morning, as Beauty was coming back from a feeding trip, she was frightened by the barking of an old hound. The hound was on her trail. Beauty's heart almost stopped beating when she thought how close the hound was behind her. Then she ran for home. She ran as fast as she could through the snow, thinking only of her babies.

Beauty reached the log just a little ahead of the dog. She popped into the opening and ran to the babies' nest. Everything was all right. The cubs were still sleeping under the leaves.

Beauty did not stop to push the leaves away. She ran back to the opening at the end of the log. Just as she reached it, the hound pushed his big head into the hole.

In a flash, Beauty clamped her teeth on his nose and held on for dear life. The dog howled in pain. He pulled and pulled as hard as he could. Now he was really angry. He leaped back and forth in front of the opening, barking louder than ever.

The hound jumped to the top of the log and ran along it. He was looking for another opening large enough for him to get through. He scratched and bit at the knothole.

Beauty lay just inside the opening of the log. But when the cubs woke up and began to whimper, she couldn't stand it any longer. She flew out of the log to drive the hound away for good. The dog saw her coming and jumped away. But he did not run as the fox had. He turned to attack Beauty.

On his first leap the hound missed Beauty. He tried again to bite her, but she sank her teeth into one of his long ears. He shook his head in pain and anger and soon got away. But then the hound made another leap at Beauty and grabbed her back. She twisted around and clamped her teeth on his nose again. The hound tore his nose away from her teeth and got ready to leap once more.

Beauty was very tired now. It seemed as if she could not live through another attack. But she would not give up. She stood still in the snow, ready to fight for her cubs.

She was waiting for one last attack when she saw a black streak rushing toward the hound. It was Ottiga, coming to defend his family.

From far down the stream he had heard the hound barking. Afraid that his family was in danger, he hurried to them. He swam like lightning through the water and raced along the banks of the stream.

Ottiga did not take time to call to Beauty as he flew over the ground to defend her. He shot toward the dog and clamped his teeth on the dog's mouth. The hound howled in pain.

With new life Beauty jumped on the hound's back. She bit him again and again. The three of them rolled over and over in the snow.

Beauty and Ottiga hurt the hound badly with their strong jaws and teeth. The dog didn't understand where the big otter had come from, and by this time the dog had forgotten to bite. All he wanted now was to get away. He stopped howling and waited for a chance to run.

At last Beauty, too tired to hold on, let go of the hound's ear. He was then able to throw off Ottiga. The dog leaped to his feet and ran away as fast as he could.

As soon as the hound left, Beauty returned to her babies. She was sore and tired. When she crawled into the log, all the cubs stood up on their tiny legs and made a fierce "tissing" noise. They had heard sounds of fighting and had smelled the hound. They were ready to defend themselves, too.

Beauty quieted the cubs with a soft chuckle and curled about them again. As soon as they were asleep, the mother otter went outside to roll in the snow. Her body stung from the bites of the hound. The cold snow made her feel better.

Ottiga had been waiting for Beauty. Now he scampered to her, chuckling his love. He knew that Beauty had been busy taking care of the cubs, but it had been a long, lonely six weeks since they had played together. He asked Beauty to take a little holiday. So the two otters swam in the stream. Then they rolled and played for half an hour, as gay as otter cubs.

Afterthought

1. What did you find out about otters in this story?
2. How were animal clothing and animal weapons important to the story?
3. Do you think fierce protection of the young is usual or unusual among animals?

Animal Tools

George F. Mason

Fur and feathers, teeth and claws—animals seem remarkably fitted for their lives. But they need more than clothing and weapons. Read the following article to find out about other wonders of the animal world.

When was the last time you did some work? What kind did you do? Did you use tools? You probably did. People often use tools. Sometimes they use their hands as tools. But most of the time they hold the tools with their hands and do the work with the tools.

Most animals use parts of their bodies as tools. Probably the most important tools animals have are their teeth.

Animal teeth are used for cutting and grinding food, but they may be used for other purposes, too. Animals such as foxes have long, sharp eye-teeth, which they use in killing or fighting. Beavers have long front teeth, which they can use to cut down trees. Rabbits and many other animals also have long front teeth. They are used to bite off bark and twigs.

The animals that eat grass have another kind of teeth. Their teeth are wide and flat and are used for grinding food. Cows and deer have teeth of this kind.

The largest teeth that we know of are the tusks of the elephants. The elephants use their tusks in digging for food and in fighting.

One strange set of animal tools is that used by a mosquito for getting

food. A mosquito doesn't really bite, as many people think it does. It can't bite, for it has no teeth.

If you watch a mosquito, you will see that it seems to push its beak into the skin, but this isn't what really happens. The mosquito's beak is only its lower lip. But inside the lip is a set of tiny tools. There are a pair of saws, a pair of tubes, and some tiny knives in this set of tools. The mosquito uses all of them when it gets food.

When a mosquito is hungry, it looks for a soft spot in an animal's skin. After finding this spot, the mosquito puts its beak on the skin and begins to cut. The tiny saws and knives in the set of tools quickly cut

through the skin. Then the two tubes in the beak of the mosquito are pushed in. One tube puts saliva into the blood to keep it thin. The other sucks up blood.

Only the female mosquito has this strange set of tools, for the male mosquito does not live on blood. It lives on plant juices instead. But the greedy female mosquito will suck blood until her body is red.

Another strange set of tools is the bittern's cleaning tools. This bird has powder puffs, shampoo powder, combs, and feather oil. On each leg the bittern has some soft, fluffy feathers that hold the shampoo powder. Under the middle toe on each foot there is a comb. And on

the top part of the tail there is a place where the feather oil comes out.

The bittern often feeds on fish or eels. When it catches and eats these animals, it gets slime on its feathers. The bird spends one to two hours cleaning up after each feeding.

First the bittern puts the shampoo powder on its feathers. The powder makes the feathers look as though they had been dusted with flour. The bird lets the shampoo dry on the slime. Then it uses its combs to loosen the dried slime. After much fluffing and shaking of the feathers, all the powder and the loose slime are gone. Next the bittern gets oil with its beak from its tail. The bird puts this oil over its feathers. Soon

the bittern is clean, and the feathers are shiny again.

Bitterns aren't the only animals that have combs. Beavers and a few other animals have combs, too. Beavers have a comb that is part of the nail on the second toe of each back foot. Since they are very clean animals, they spend a lot of time combing their thick fur and keeping it clean and soft.

Besides the tools you've just read about, there are many others. Can you think of any other tools that you have seen animals using?

Mike's Beaver Friends

Adapted by Lloyd Besant

The beaver has a remarkable set of tools. It uses its four front teeth as chisels to cut down trees. It dams a stream with the trees and builds its home in the water behind the dam. Read the following story to find out what happens when the beaver's tools get it into trouble with man.

Mike Gray lay on the bank of the stream on his father's farm. The hot sun warmed him. But Mike was not enjoying the warm feeling, for he was unhappy.

"You've got to go," he said sadly as he watched a family of beavers building a dam in the stream.

Mike was talking to the beavers. They heard him, but they didn't swim away.

Mike didn't frighten the beaver family. He had been there many times before to watch them work. For several weeks now he had been riding his pony, Dan, to this spot. Bizee Beaver and his family knew that Mike was their friend.

"If only you hadn't blocked the stream with your dam, Bizee," Mike sighed.

His father needed this stream to water his land. Mike knew this, but he hadn't said a word to anyone when he had first seen the beavers. He didn't want them killed.

But Mr. Gray found out about the beavers soon enough. The stream of water had slowed down because of the dam they were building. So one day he rode out to see what was the matter. He found the beavers and saw Mike watching them.

"Why didn't you tell me there were beavers here?" he asked Mike.

Mike answered, "I didn't want them killed."

Surprised, his father said, "I wouldn't kill the beavers, Mike. What made you think I would?"

"Well, Mr. Thompson did when he found beavers on his farm," Mike explained.

"But *I* won't," his father told him. "In the first place, we aren't supposed to kill beavers now. And besides, they do a lot of good."

Then Mr. Gray added, "Beaver dams keep soil from washing off the farms. The dams also slow up the water and cut down on flood damage. They help to store water in ponds for later use. The ponds make good fishing places. These things are helpful to us. Of course, beavers do some harm, but the good they do is far greater than the harm."

"I guess Mr. Thompson didn't know about the good that beavers do," said Mike. "But what are you going to do with these beavers?"

"I'm going to call Mr. Adams, of the State Game and Fish Commission. He'll trap them alive and take them up to a mountain stream where their work is needed. Maybe he can come to get them tomorrow."

Mike felt better when he heard this. But still, his beaver friends might be gone after today. This could be the last time he would see them.

After saying good-bye to the beavers, Mike got on Dan and rode slowly home. His father told him that Mr. Adams would be there the next day. As soon as it was dark, Mike went to bed. He wanted to be up early when Mr. Adams left with the beavers.

The next morning when his mother called him to breakfast, Mike rushed down the stairs. Mr. Adams was there. He had already trapped the beavers. When they sat down to breakfast, Mike asked Mr. Adams about the beavers.

"Oh, they're fine," said Mr. Adams. "They weren't hurt a bit. We put them in sacks and tied them on the packhorse. They'll be happy in the mountains. They won't bother anyone there, and no one will bother them."

After breakfast Mr. Adams and Mr. Gray went out to look

at the sacks of beavers. They wanted everything to be just right for the trip. Mike went along to watch Mr. Adams leave.

"Well, I guess that's everything," Mr. Adams said.

"Yes, I guess it is," Mr. Gray answered. But he had a smile on his face. The smile was one that Mike had seen often. It meant Mr. Gray knew something that he wasn't telling.

When Mr. Gray and Mr. Adams saw the puzzled look on Mike's face, they laughed. Then Mr. Gray said, "Just a minute, Mike." And he turned and walked to the barn.

Mike stood there and waited. Soon he saw his father coming out of the barn. He was leading Dan, and Dan was saddled. Mike was more puzzled than ever until he saw the bedroll and saddlebags on the horse. Then he understood.

"Oh, Dad!" he cried. "Am I really going with Mr. Adams?"

"Yes, if you want to," his father replied.

"If I *want* to!" Mike shouted in joy.

"All right," said Mr. Gray. "Run to the house and get the things your mother packed for you. But hurry! Mr. Adams wants to get started."

"Oh, Mother!" Mike cried as he ran into the house. "I'm going with Mr. Adams!"

"I know," said Mrs. Gray. "Mr. Adams wanted someone along for company." She added, "Now be careful, and be sure to do what Mr. Adams tells you to do."

"Oh, I will, Mother," Mike called, and he rushed outside.

"Thanks, Dad. Thanks for letting me go," Mike said. And he and his father put the things Mrs. Gray had packed for him into his saddlebags.

Quickly Mike and Mr. Adams got on their horses. And Mike waved good-bye and rode out of the yard beside Mr.

Adams. The beavers bounced along in the sacks on the packhorse. They were off to the mountains.

When they came to the foot of the mountains, Mike rode behind Mr. Adams up the steep path. Mr. Adams had told Mike that it wasn't far, but they had to go very slowly.

They stopped for lunch by a stream. Then they rode on up the path. That afternoon they passed some beaver dams. Mike was surprised to see how large some of the beaver dams and lodges were.

"Well," Mr. Adams told him, "the beavers just keep on building. When the family grows larger in number, they add more room. After the first two years of their lives, the young beavers leave and build their own lodges. But the old ones stay on as long as there is food."

Around many of the ponds Mike saw that the grass was very green. Mr. Adams explained to him that beaver dams held the water back to make the ponds and that the water kept the soil around the ponds moist. He also pointed out the aspen and other water-loving trees along the edges of the ponds.

"The bark of these trees is very tender. It is the food the beavers like best of all," Mr. Adams told Mike.

There were signs of other wildlife near all the beaver ponds. Mike learned that these ponds made good drinking places for deer and other animals. The plant life around the ponds was food for the animals and cover for birds and small game. There were also fish in these ponds.

"When the beavers make their homes, do other animals always come there?" Mike asked Mr. Adams.

"Yes, and that is how the beaver helps us save our wildlife," said Mr. Adams.

Soon the sun began to set, and Mr. Adams said that they had better make camp for the night. So they laid out their sleeping bags under a tree with great spreading branches. While Mike fed the horses, Mr. Adams carefully made a fire and cooked their supper.

Mike and Mr. Adams did not talk very much while they ate. Instead, they listened to the sounds in the mountains. They could hear the animals, the wind in the trees, and the gurgling of a mountain stream.

After supper they washed the dishes and got ready for bed. Mr. Adams carefully put out the fire. Then both of them crawled into their sleeping bags.

"Hear that stream gurgling?" Mr. Adams asked Mike.

"Yes," answered Mike, "it sounds like music."

"It does now, but in the spring it roars because of the melting snow and spring rains. Then it runs fast and takes good soil with it."

"It does?" Mike asked sleepily.

"Yes, streams do a lot of damage," Mr. Adams added. "This one takes water from land farther up the mountain. The land there is dry. When the stream floods in the spring, it damages land all the way down the mountain. We are going to put the beavers farther up on this stream. The dams the beavers build will help hold back the floods."

The day had started early and had been exciting. Mike was so tired that he fell asleep while Mr. Adams was talking about the stream.

The next morning, Mike got up as soon as the sun began to shine through the trees. Mr. Adams was already up and had a fire going. After a warm breakfast they saddled the horses and again started out on the trail.

Mike was a little stiff from the long ride of the day before, so he was quiet. For a while they rode on in silence.

Then Mr. Adams stopped his horse and said, "Well, we're here, Mike." Mike looked all around to see where "here" was. They were by the stream they had been following for a long time. There were many trees, and there was a pile of branches at the edge of the stream.

Mike and Mr. Adams got off their horses. Mr. Adams carried the sacks of beavers to the stream. He opened the mouths of the sacks, and the beavers crawled out. They looked around. Then they started toward the branches to hide.

"That pile of branches will make them feel at home," Mr. Adams told Mike. "Soon they will start building a dam, and there will be a pond here. The land around it will then become full of food for other animals."

"Who put those branches by the stream?" Mike asked. "Are there beavers here already?"

"No, I put the branches there," said Mr. Adams. "For a long time I've been planning to get some beavers and place them here. When your father called, I thought this would be a good chance to get them. I cut the branches so they would have food right away and some sticks to use when they started working on their dam."

It seemed strange to Mike that people should start a dam for beavers, but he didn't say anything. He just started looking for his beaver family. They were busy eating aspen and staying well out of reach of Mr. Adams.

"Come on, Mike, we'd better start back," Mr. Adams said, and he turned and walked to his horse. "The sooner we leave these beavers, the sooner they will look the place over and start to build."

After Mike got on Dan, he said good-bye to the beavers. He really hated to leave them. He knew he would never again have a beaver family all his own to watch. He took a last, long look at the place that was to be the beavers' new home. Then he turned the horse and followed Mr. Adams.

Suddenly Mike thought about something. "Mr. Adams, what do beavers eat in winter?" he asked. "Will they have enough food?"

"Sure they will. The beavers store branches in the mud at the bottom of the pond. They put these deep in the water to keep them from freezing. And they put rocks on the branches to hold them down," explained Mr. Adams.

"How do they get the food?" asked Mike.

"They swim down to their fresh-food locker every day and take what they need," Mr. Adams said with a smile.

At last Mike decided that the beavers could take care of themselves. He stopped worrying about them. But as he rode down the trail, he made himself a promise. He would come up here the very next summer to see how they were getting along in their new home.

Animal Behavior

Russell Freedman and James E. Morriss

How does a beaver know how to build its home? How does an otter know how to swim? You know that animals have built-in clothing, weapons, and tools. Now read the following article to find out why animals behave as they do.

The canary tilted her head. She looked closely at the grass and feathers on the floor of her cage. She pecked at a feather. Then she picked up a piece of grass, held it in her bill, and let it drop to the floor again.

Standing beside her cage was Dr. Robert A. Hinde. Dr. Hinde is a scientist who studies animal behavior. He had raised the canary without letting her see nesting materials or watch other birds building nests.

When the canary was grown, Dr. Hinde placed her in a cage with a young male canary. After the pair settled down together, the scientist scattered grass and feathers in their cage. Now he waited to see what would happen.

Would the canary know that grass and feathers were nest-building materials? Would she be able to build a nest without having a chance to learn?

At first, the canary seemed uncertain. She hopped across the cage floor, pecking at the grass and feathers. She picked them up, carried them about, and then dropped them again. Finally, she flew to a nest pan on a wall of the cage. Perched on the edge of the pan, she bent forward and looked inside.

Suddenly, she flew to the cage floor. She picked up a piece of grass and carried it back to the nest pan. From then on, the canary seemed to know exactly what to do.

To begin with, she spent her time carrying grass to the nest pan. When she had gathered enough grass, she began to weave it into the outer shell of her nest. Sitting in the nest pan, she grasped loose pieces of grass in her bill. She pulled them toward her, pushed them down under her breast, and pressed them into place. Then she turned in a circle to help shape the slowly forming nest.

Every so often she passed her bill back and forth along the rim of the nest, smoothing it out. And after a while, she began to line the inside of the nest with soft feathers.

The canary had never done these acts before. She had never seen them done. Yet without any chance to learn, she built a nest.

Animals can do many difficult acts without first having to learn how. A garden spider spins a web the first time it tries—exactly like those spun by other garden spiders. An opossum reacts to danger by going limp, closing its eyes, and "playing dead" —even though it has never seen another opossum behave like this.

These acts are instincts—behavior that is inborn and does not have to be learned. In ways we do not yet fully understand, animals come into the world already having certain built-in patterns of behavior. An animal gets this built-in behavior from its parents, just as it gets the color of its eyes and the shape of its body.

When an animal acts from instinct, it doesn't have to understand what it is doing or why it is behaving that way. A mother robin feeds her young because a "stuffing" instinct makes her react to the sight of wide-open mouths. If you place a wooden model of a baby robin's mouth in a mother robin's nest, she will feed the wooden model. If this model is sticking up higher than the open mouths of the robin's babies, she will blindly stuff all the food she gathers into the fake mouth.

A baby chick moves about the barnyard, scratching and pecking for food. Suddenly a bird flies overhead. At once the chick runs for cover.

This behavior might save the chick's life. The bird overhead may be a hawk or other dangerous enemy looking for its next meal. Yet a

chick reacts with fear to the sight of any bird flying overhead. It runs away from pigeons and sparrows. It even runs when it sees a falling leaf.

If the chick continued to behave like this, it would waste much of its time running away when there is no need. Luckily, the chick is able to change its behavior. It is able to learn.

Birds that often fly over barnyards are usually harmless. Before long, a chick gets used to seeing these birds. It loses its fear of them and goes right on eating when they fly past.

But the chick never gets used to seeing hawks and other dangerous birds. These birds are rare. Since they don't visit barnyards very often, a chick continues to run away from them—just as it runs from any other unknown bird.

By instinct, all young animals react to certain danger signals. If a young animal sees a strange moving object, hears a sudden noise, or senses a sudden change, it will freeze in its tracks or run for safety. Gradually, however, young animals learn to pay no attention to sights and sounds that don't promise real danger.

A puppy runs from the sound of gunfire. Yet an experienced hunting dog shows no fear. A kitten runs and hides when a vacuum cleaner is turned on. However, a wise old house cat refuses to budge from the carpet when the vacuum cleaner comes around. Squirrels and pigeons growing up in city parks get used to seeing people and hearing traffic noises, while their country cousins fear these sights and sounds.

Scientists have found that almost all animals are able to learn. By finding out about animal instincts and how animals learn, we hope to understand our fellow creatures better. We hope also to shed light on the behavior of man.

Coyote in Central Park

Jean Craighead George

This story is about Tako, a coyote from the desert Southwest. He has been brought in a cage on a freighter to New York City. A girl frees him, and he finds his way to Central Park. As you read, find out how Tako uses his instincts and his ways of learning to survive in a strange place.

When it was fully day, Tako peered out between the old stems of a ground-rambling rose. He was in a garden. Other flowers bloomed in beds beyond the roses. Fat pigeons cooed to each other beside a fountain. He stretched his toes and put his head down on his front paws. With ears and nose he investigated Central Park.

A squirrel chittered in a crab apple tree nearby. Birds called. These were comforting sounds to a coyote. He pressed to the edge of the roses and looked across to a wooded hill. He smelt the scent of lake water.

Tako lifted his head and peered upward. Somewhere above he heard the cry of a falcon. He saw it high above the city. The falcon closed her wings and dove toward Central Park. There was a burst of feathers beside the fountain, and a pigeon lay beneath the yellow talons.

Tako moved, and the falcon saw him. She covered her prey with her wings. Then she rose heavily over the garden, the

Central Park

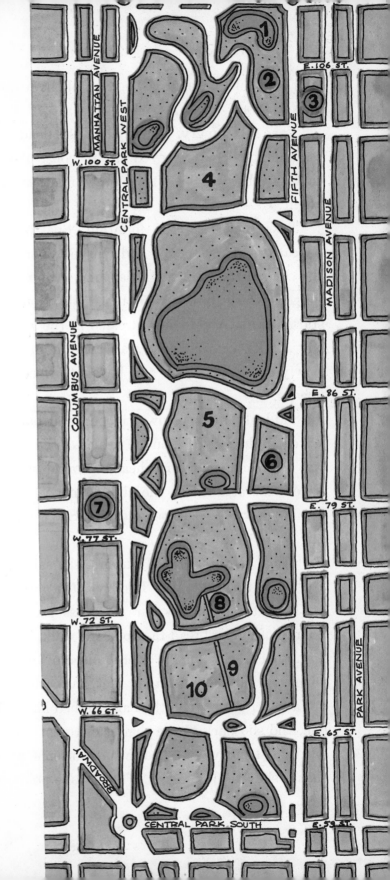

1. Harlem Meer
2. Conservatory Garden
3. Museum of the City of New York
4. North Meadow
5. The Great Lawn
6. Metropolitan Museum of Art
7. American Museum of Natural History
8. Fountain
9. The Mall
10. The Sheep Meadow

wall, and Fifth Avenue to the roof of the Museum of the City of New York.

Tako felt hungry. The smell of the dead bird had whetted his appetite. He, too, eyed the pigeons. They now flew in a tight, frightened flock this way and that. They would not alight.

Tako looked at the fountain. Sparrows were dropping beneath it. They fought and chirped. The coyote slipped to the edge of the garden. He lay under clumps of flowers as he judged which bird to snatch. Vibrations on the ground startled him. A gardener, dressed in the green uniform of the city Parks Department, was coming down the walk. He slowly got to his knees and began to weed the red and blue flowers.

Suddenly the sparrows chirped and bombed away. Tako watched them go. Then he realized the flight of the birds was a warning. They had heard a sound he had missed. They were more attuned to the city than he. An old woman was coming down the path toward him. She carried a brown paper bag.

"Good morning, Mr. Hansen," she said to the gardener.

"Good morning, Miss Landry," the gardener answered.

Tako threw up his ears as Miss Landry's bag rustled. Sounds of falling bread tattooed the walk. The sparrows came flying back. Two fought over a piece of bread. Beating their wings and jabbing with their feet, they whirled to the ground not a foot from his mouth. Tako arched his back, sprang upon one, and slid back to the shelter of roses.

Miss Landry clutched Mr. Hansen's arm. "What was that?" she asked quickly. "There!" she pointed.

196

The gardener parted the flowers. "I don't see nothin'," he said. He did not wish to alarm a bird lover.

"Did anything get loose from the zoo?" Miss Landry asked. "It looked like a wolf."

"Now, now, Miss Landry," the gardener said. "It's just the wind in the bushes."

Miss Landry walked around the fountain. The birds were now coming in flocks from all parts of the park. She tossed bread, looked into hedges, and glanced at the gardener.

He was staring into the roses. He turned and smiled. "Wind," he said, "a little whirlwind of leaves."

Miss Landry finished feeding the birds and left. The sun was touching the tops of the skyscrapers on Central Park West. When she had tapped away, Mr. Hansen got down on his knees. A red stain of blood colored the ground, and beside it lay a wing feather. But there was no bird. He weaved as he searched the roses.

"It wasn't no wolf," he said to himself, "and it wasn't no dog, either."

Tako, deep in the rose tangles, never took his eyes off Mr. Hansen. The man was hunting. Tako sensed this, and he crouched, ready to flee.

But the gardener got to his feet, turned his back, and went off to the iris bed. Tako worked his way through the roses to the far edge of the garden. He crossed the sidewalk and trotted into a flowering hedge.

Glancing back at the gardener, Tako went on, in the manner of all young animals seeking a territory of their own. If one spot has dangers, the wanderer looks further. The hunting eyes of Mr. Hansen were uncomfortable. Instinctively Tako moved away.

He trotted under trees, around bushes, over footpaths on his way to the lake. The water was low, dirty, and covered with scum. There would be no birds or frogs at its edges. Its banks would not make a good home. He sauntered on, listening to the city. It sounded like an insect chorus. Tako was not alarmed. These mechanical sounds of man came from streets and buildings. Being an animal of habit himself, he sensed that these were the trails of the people. He felt safe.

He noticed other matters of coyote concern. The earth between the trees was pounded hard by feet. The wildflowers had been replaced by papers, cans, and bottles.

One bottle smelled sweet. Tako tipped it with his paw, spinning the word "Coke" into view. It dripped and he tasted its contents. It was pleasant. He pushed his tongue into the bottle for more. It stuck. Tako pulled to get it out. It stuck tighter. Then he relaxed and his tongue slid out.

He dashed away. He would avoid bottles. This had been an unsuccessful experience. Tako learned from failure as well as success.

Trotting and running, he climbed a rock ledge and came upon a road. Cars poured along it. He lay down under a low-lying tree to judge his next move. Suddenly a blue jay announced him. Then another got the word and screamed, too.

Tako expected that people would be attracted to the sounds. No footsteps fell. He smelled each wind. They carried no human scents. And so it was printed on his mind that people did not understand animals.

Finally the traffic thinned. Tako saw a chance to cross to the wilder woods on the other side of the road. He dashed just as a mounted policeman rounded the bend. The horse saw Tako, shied, and whinnied. The coyote zigzagged into the grass and shot up the hill like a rifle bullet. He sped down a ravine into thick underbrush.

He stopped behind an oak tree and looked far down the hill to the man. Again, the speech of animals went unheard. The policeman's head was lowered as he tried to calm his frightened horse.

Tako forgot them. He pounced beneath a laurel bush. His paws sunk into the earth, and he began digging.

When he had a hollow deep enough to hide himself, he kicked leaves into it and lay down. Instantly he was asleep, for he had not rested completely since the last day on the freighter.

He did not sleep long. The birds that lived in the tops of the trees began to scold at him.

Tako got to his feet. He yawned in boredom at the frightened birds and stretched. Now that he was awake he felt restless. He must wander. His survival depended on knowing his territory, and so he must go on. He took a wooded path that led to an open meadow.

It was night when he got back to his den, for along the way he met a female German shepherd. Out of a downwind the shepherd lunged, taking him by surprise. Snapping the leash from her master's hand, she bore down on Tako. Dirt flying, she almost struck him before he sensed she was attacking. Usually males and females do not clash, but Tako was on her territory. He darted into the underbrush, then started north. He easily outran her.

At an inner signal, he turned and waited. He would not

give up the land he had explored this morning. He charged the German shepherd. She bristled her neck, barked, and turned back. She understood. The fight was over, the arrangement made. Tako's land lay to the north of the Great Lawn, hers to the south.

As Tako wandered home, he investigated another garden, the wading pool, and park benches. With nose, eyes, and ears he filled in the details of his territory. There were birds, mice, rats, snakes, and insects. Cats hid in the shadows.

Upon his return to his den he was satisfied that Central Park was good coyote territory.

The stars were only faint sparks above the city gleam as he put his nose in his tail. He had no sooner dropped off to sleep than a great rumble sounded in the earth. It roared and died like a thunder roll. He got up to investigate but stopped at some leaves nearby. He recognized the odor and whiskers of a brown rat. Tako watched her, but he did not pounce on her.

The rat came out of her burrow under an oak root. She glanced around and hurried down her trail. Tako stepped softly and followed her.

She crossed a sidewalk, went under a bench, and padded swiftly to a large iron grating. The thunder roll began again, louder than before. Tako drew back. The sound died, but the rat did not even slow her pace. Sensing that she was not frightened, Tako felt safe. He sniffed the grating. Drafts of warm air gusted out, bringing the odor of oil and people. Once more he hesitated. Below the grating lay a dimly lighted room.

The rat had disappeared. He tracked her to a hole at the edge of the grating, dug by rats and dogs. Tako pushed himself through and dropped down onto a narrow cement ledge.

He moved along carefully. Far below, tracks of steel shot under the earth. Tako looked for the rat. She was far ahead, running swiftly toward the room of light.

He hurried now. Tunnels in the earth were part of his desert memory. In the subway he began to feel safe beneath the city. The rat halted, stood up on her hind feet, and thrust her nose into a trickle of glittering water. She drank from a pipe. It had been chewed open by countless rats passing in the night. Tako waited until she had moved on, then he slid forward and drank also.

The thunder started again, louder and more terrifying than before. Suddenly a subway train sped out of the darkness and screamed through the tunnel below. Tako hugged the wall as the earth shook.

The train came to a stop. People got out. Others disappeared into it. Bells clanged, doors slammed, and the train sped off into the dark. The rat had not stopped. She was leaping down great blocks of cement to another ledge.

Tako balanced himself and jumped after her. He followed her to the subway platform.

He trotted down the platform, found stairs, loped up them, and rounded a corner. At the top of the next stairs the jagged silver skyline of the city was framed in the square subway entrance. Gingerly he climbed until he was looking down Central Park West. The avenue shone more brilliantly than the stars above the desert. It rumbled with sounds of automobiles. It smelled of dry cement.

Down the street stood the Museum of Natural History. Tako did not know, of course, that the museum had an exhibit of coyotes on the main floor. The sign under the stuffed

animals read: "Coyote (Brush wolf) *Canis latrans*. The coyote seeks irregular terrain with open fields, bushy edges, and woodland. It is at home in the deserts and mountains. Curiosity is one of its traits. It has a high degree of 'native intelligence' and is faster than a dog when running. On its home range of several hundred acres, the coyote often passes up food near the den and hunts far afield.

"The den is approached by a circuitous route. About three quarters of the coyote's food is rodents and rabbits."

The legend went on: "The coyote has moved to the east and is now established in the Adirondacks and Catskills. He is highly adaptive and thrives in western cities. None, however, is in New York City."

Tako was listening to sparrows. They had awakened and were arguing over roosts in the brightly lighted night. He followed their voices around the subway entrance to a newsstand. The birds were louder here. He looked up. Grass, newspaper, pins, and tinfoil were stuffed in the eaves of the building. An odor of oily dust told him he had nests on this part of his territory. He could not see the birds.

A low sound caught his attention. It began softly and rose. Music came from an open window across the avenue. The notes were strange but pleasant, almost as pleasant as a coyote chorus on the desert. The music did not speak of homes and territories and coyote pups, but it touched his memory. He drooped his head, his shoulder blades parted the fur on his back, and his tail hung low.

His homesickness passed. He found his way back to the grating, came out in the woods, and went home by a "circuitous route."

The route went around the Block House, the boat house, the garden, and finally to the laurel bush. He came toward it from the north.

As he slid under the laurel, a robin opened its eyes. The bird sat in silence as it slowly came awake. Then it moved, flitting from twig to twig to the top of the tall red oak. There it chirped brightly, announcing the dawn to other robins in the park. They answered back. The morning sang with bird talk.

Tako made himself comfortable as the falcon called above the city. She was peering down on the rooftops and parks in her daily hunting tour. The coyote slept as the city came awake.

Afterthought

1. Which of Tako's acts were instinctive and which were learned?
2. What information did you have about coyotes that the museum did not?
3. In what ways do you consider animals beautiful?
4. How is man fitted for the life he lives?

Night Writers

While we slept
rabbits leapt
across
the drifted lawn,
printing haiku
in the snow
for us to read
at dawn.

Edna Margaret Long

Ancient Song

along the battle ridge
wind
        and
               sage
repeat
their ancient song

Lance Henson

Ways of Life

Holling C. Holling

Think of America long ago—the
vast land stretching from sea to sea,
the forests and deserts, the mountains
and plains. Think, too, of the people.
The following article tells how
America's first settlers lived in
harmony with their land.

Indians lived in America thousands of years before Christopher Columbus reached the New World. It is thought that they came from Asia, crossing over from Siberia to Alaska. In America they found a good land. The rivers and lakes held fish, the air was alive with birds, and game was everywhere. At first the Indians were hunters, moving about the country in search of food. But when a group of people found a place they liked, they settled down and built homes.

America is made up of many different kinds of country. Some parts are covered with heavy forests. Other parts are open, rolling plains. Still others are hot, dry deserts. There are sections where great mountains tower to the sky, and others where the sea dashes against the coasts. In the days before Columbus, Indians lived in all these different kinds of country. Though there were many tribes, all the tribes in one kind of country lived in much the same way.

In the forest country of the eastern part of America there are many rivers and lakes. The Indians of this section traveled about in canoes. In the north where birch trees grew, they made their canoes of birch bark. In the south, they used "dugouts,"

made by hollowing out a tree trunk.

These People of the Forest built houses of poles covered with the bark of trees. They hunted and fished and planted small gardens for food. The decorations they painted on their deerskins or wove into their baskets or sewed onto their clothing came from the forests. The designs were of leaves, vines, and flowers.

West of the Forest People, between the Mississippi River and the Rocky Mountains, lived the People of the Plains. They had no deep woods. They knew only open prairies sweeping in every direction. These people built their houses of driftwood from the river bottoms and covered them with earth and grass from the plains. When the great winds blew across the prairies or blizzards howled in the wintertime, fires kept the people warm inside their houses.

The main food of the Plains Indians was buffalo meat. When they went on long buffalo hunts, they used small pointed tents made of skins. These tents were light enough to be pulled by dogs. After the white men came, bringing horses, the Plains Indians made larger tents and left the earth-covered houses. With their horses, they wandered freely over the open plains and far into the Rocky Mountains.

The Plains Indians knew nothing but great stretches of flat country, hot sun, round moon, bright stars, and jagged mountains. The designs they painted, wove, or sewed were straight lines and triangles, circles, and squares.

At the south end of the Rocky Mountains lived the People of the Desert. Water was hard to find, so the villages were always built near water. At first these people lived in caves in the canyon walls. Later they made great apartment buildings called pueblos. Pueblos were made

of rocks that were joined together with mud. One pueblo housed a whole city.

The Desert Indians were not wanderers as the Plains Indians were. They stayed at home and took care of their gardens. These early farmers grew such crops as corn, beans, squash, and peppers.

There were bright colors in the rocks and mountains among which these people lived. The decorations used on their pottery and in their weaving were copied from the things they knew best. Some decorations were rock designs. Some were clouds. Some were desert animals and birds. Most of the decorations were meant as good-luck signs to bring rain and good crops.

In the Northwest along the coast lived the People of the Sea. They lived where great cedar trees grew. Because they had a kind of stone that made fine, sharp tools, they liked working with wood. The cedar trees could be split easily, so these Indians built houses of cedar planks. Their canoes, cedar logs hollowed out, were large enough to go to sea. These people sometimes hunted land animals, but they lived mainly on fish and whale meat and seal.

The People of the Sea were fishing people. The designs they carved were like the animals and fish they found along their coasts. They carved and painted their histories on great poles which they set before their houses. We call them totem poles.

These were the ways of life of the Indians who lived in the forests, on the plains, in the desert, and by the sea. When the white men came, they found that the Indians had learned how to live well in all parts of this land.

The Raiders

Dorothy Harriman Leiser

Indians lived in harmony with the land, but they faced many dangers, too. In this story you will find out about one of those dangers and how a young girl faced it.

Kwala watched as her mother pulled at the bear grass. She wove the basket firmly. Willow strips lay soaking in a hard, watertight basket, ready for the weaving of new baskets. Her aunts and cousins were busy too, making baskets, stirring up the fire, heating stones on which to cook the evening meal. A little light came into the big lodge through the smoke holes in the roof and through the doorway. Kwala walked to the door opening and rested her hand upon the big cedar post. She stood quietly, looking toward the afternoon sun.

Kwala was a little Snohomish Indian girl who lived in a village on Upper Puget Sound. Her home was near the water, for that was where the men found most of the food for their families. The lodges, made of cedar logs placed upright and lashed together, were built near the beautiful bay which held salmon and perch and all the other fish which could be eaten fresh or dried.

Near the shore Kwala saw her older brother at work on the new canoe. Her father sat on the ground beside him, carefully carving with his sharp knife.

"Will it be finished soon?" she called.

Noonkwa, her brother, looked up scornfully. Already she had asked that question so many times! But her father smiled. "Tomorrow we will go out in it."

Kwala gasped. She had not really expected the beautiful long canoe to be ready by tomorrow. But Noonkwa's hands were skilled and almost as fast as his father's. She went to the beach where they worked to look at the design her father had carved. The face of a killer whale lay on the prow, part on one side of the canoe, part on the other. It was a big, beautiful canoe. She sighed.

"Why aren't you making a cooking basket?" taunted Noonkwa. But her father smiled again.

"Someday you may go fishing with us," he said.

"Tomorrow?"

"No," he shook his head. "The canoe will be full tomorrow."

She started slowly back to the lodge. Her older sister called to her from farther down the beach where Little Brother was digging in the sand.

"Tomorrow we will go to get the first salmonberries," she said.

Kwala had seen the soft orange-pink berries ripening. It was time to gather the first ones. Tomorrow! She sighed again. Tomorrow the canoe would dance over the water, while she and the women and children took their baskets to gather berries.

Inside the lodge she went to put new wood on the fire. On the shelves along the walls, the big baskets were stored with the deerskin bedding and the outer clothing of soft cedar bark. Tomorrow they would fill many of those baskets, and there would be enough fresh berries for all to have a feast.

Kwala woke before dawn. The fire was blazing, and her father and uncles and cousins were already gathering their fishing spears. She thought of the canoe lying new and beautiful on the beach. She slipped out of the lodge to go down to the edge of the water.

The sky in the east grew lighter. At her feet the little waves lapped gently. She touched the beautiful deep carving on the canoe.

"Go, go fast," she whispered to the carved whale. "Someday I will ride with you."

Her father and Noonkwa were coming.

"Here is the one who would go fishing," Noonkwa laughed.

"Ho, and I would catch a big salmon, too," she answered.

The men pulled the canoe into the water. She watched until they were seated and pushing off into the gray water. Then she went back to the lodge. The women were in no hurry. Even when the sun rose, the day would not be hot. There was time to laugh and talk as they broke up the fire and gathered the baskets.

The women in the three other lodges of the village were going berrying, too. Each family knew its own berrying place, and they would not trespass on the land belonging to another group.

As the sun rose, Kwala and her mother and sister and Little Brother and her aunts and cousins started off. They could see the canoes far out on the water. There was not a man left in the village.

They walked about a half mile up the beach and then turned inland at the mouth of a little slough, a stream formed by the water pouring in from the bay at high tide.

Tall cattails grew near the gray waters of the slough. Little Brother loved to hide among the cattails and leap out at Kwala, pretending he was one of the Wild Ones from the far north come down to capture her and make her a slave. It was a game that made her shiver. She had never seen one of these fearful men, but she knew better than Little Brother the reality of the men from the north.

Kwala had heard her father tell that in times past the Wild Ones had captured men and women and even children and taken them all away to belong to them. Her mother had told her that once, when she was a girl, she had hidden among the cattails in a place much like this one while an enemy canoe passed by.

Now they reached the place back a way from the slough where the berries were ripening. Little Brother picked berries and crammed them into his mouth, and Kwala began to fill her basket.

Suddenly she heard a frightened sound, a half whisper. It was her mother a few yards away. "The Wild Ones!" she hissed.

Quickly, so quickly the words were hardly spoken yet, all of them fell flat in the grass, then wriggled back behind the bushes.

The other berrypickers were across the slough, among the trees. They would be safely hidden. But suddenly Kwala saw her mother's lips form the words, "The boy?" Her eyes looked frantically all around. Panic tightened Kwala's throat until she felt she might choke as she looked up and down. There was no sign of Little Brother.

"Where are they?" she whispered.

Her mother pointed toward the mouth of the slough, where the water came in from the bay.

"I'll find him," Kwala whispered. "Don't worry. I'll find him."

Where could Little Brother be? Tired of eating berries, of his sister's silence, where could he have gone to play?

She did not know how far away the war canoe of the Wild Ones was nor how fast it was coming. She wriggled forward on her stomach, keeping herself hidden by grass and cattails. "Little Brother!" she kept whispering. Oh, where, where could he be?

At any moment he might spring out to surprise her. Surely he was hiding, watching her now as she crept forward, thinking how well big Kwala was playing his game!

Then she remembered. Little Brother did not really understand about the Wild Ones, but there was *something* he was afraid of. Most of all he feared the green water snake that slipped harmlessly through the water and among the brown cattails near the bank.

Now Kwala whispered piercingly, "Little Brother, the green snake is coming. Be quiet and crawl to me. Be quiet, Little Brother. Crawl fast to me." Over and over she whispered the words as she looked anxiously among the cattails. At last she saw that round head and those shiny dark eyes appear from behind a clump of thick grass.

She clutched him in her arms.

"Be still, Little Brother. Lie still here. I am not playing. Lie still and do not move."

At the solemn look in her face, Little Brother lay still and quiet. How long they huddled among the cattails she did not know. Finally she heard the swish of paddles, and through a far opening in the grasses she saw the dark shape of a canoe moving up the stream.

Swish, plop, swish, and the canoe was past. But still Kwala dared not move. Where were the strangers going, and when would they return?

Whatever the Wild Ones wanted, they did not find it. After a while Kwala heard again the sound of paddles as the canoe returned. Surely then her brother and father and uncles and cousins had been far away and not seen by these fierce strangers.

She lay cramped with inaction on the soft, marshy ground, her arms around her brother. Finally she saw her mother's face cautiously peering from behind a bush.

"They are out in the open water," her mother said in a low voice.

Kwala and her brother crawled stiffly back to the berry bushes. Her mother clutched Little Brother in her arms and rocked him back and forth, but her smile was for Kwala. "We will not pick any more berries today," she said.

The strangers were gone. They might go looking for other strangers to trouble, but they had not discovered her family. Kwala wanted to go home to see her father and brother and to sit by the fire and smell the roasting fish.

After a while they called softly to the women across the slough and heard answering calls. All of them waited until the

sun was high; then they came stiffly out of their hiding places. On the way back to their village there was not much talk, because no one knew yet if the men and boys were safe.

As they came close to the lodges, they saw the first canoe come calmly into the bay, as though nothing at all had happened, as though this morning had been the same as all others. Now the talk broke out. As soon as the fishermen had beached the canoes, they were told all about the strangers and how Kwala had saved her little brother.

"Ah," her father smiled at her. "I think tomorrow you will go fishing with the men."

Kwala felt that she might burst with happiness. Then she looked at Noonkwa holding a beautiful silver fish. She knew how he felt. How he wished he had been there; how he wished it had been he who rescued Little Brother! Many times she had looked at a big fish her brother had caught and wished she had been the one to hook that fish on a stout bone hook!

"Oh, such a fish! Look!" she cried.

Noonkwa, grinning, held up his gleaming halibut.

"And I am hungry," Kwala said.

Little Brother, his face still streaked with berry juice, ran to touch the fish. "Hungry!" he said as everyone laughed.

Afterthought

1. How did Kwala's people get their food?
2. What would Kwala rather do than pick berries with the other women?
3. How did Kwala show bravery? How did her father reward her?

The Boy Hunters

Mary Elizabeth Laing

When an Indian boy was grown, the tribe would depend on his hunting for food. So learning to be a good hunter was an important part of his training. But in the training, he often learned something besides hunting skills.

Once long ago a large tribe of Iroquois Indians grew tired of their old village in the forest. They decided to move to a new place on the top of a hill. The new village was near a river, and nearby there was a clear space in the forest where the people could plant corn. It was a good place for a village.

One day in early fall White Eagle, a boy of this Iroquois village, was walking in the forest. Suddenly he came to the old village where his people had lived before moving to the hill.

White Eagle paused at the door of the longhouse that had been his old home. He remembered how, as a very little boy, he had watched this house being built.

The young people of the village had cut down strong young trees, made them into poles, and set them in the ground. Upon these poles they had placed cross poles and fastened them with ropes made of branches. They had covered this frame with bark boards, fastening them over each other. Then they had set up a frame of poles along the outside of the boards and across the rafters. They had fastened this frame to the inner frame to hold the bark boards in place. When it was finished, it was a strong, well-built house.

The house was over a hundred feet long. It had to be long, because many families had lived there together. There was a door at each end of the house. Over each door was the sign of the turtle, the Iroquois family's sign. White Eagle remembered that in the long hall leading from door to door five or six fires had burned. Each fire had a family on either side.

When White Eagle's family had lived there, the longhouse had been a busy, happy place. At night the fires had burned brightly and had thrown interesting shadows on the walls. From the rafters had hung barrels filled with corn. But now the house was empty and still.

White Eagle entered the silent longhouse. He knew that the house would soon become the home of the owl and the snake. Outside, when the winter's snow came, the wolf would boldly prowl where the council fire had burned. And the deer would run through the old cornfield.

Slowly White Eagle went to the blackened fireplace that had once been his mother's. Out of the silence something whispered: "You have left the days of your childhood. Now it is time for you to begin learning to be a man."

As White Eagle came out of the empty longhouse, all the world seemed to call him to action. Loudly the forest spoke: "Come and find new adventure. Race with the swift deer! Try your arm against the bear! Try your mind against Jitso, the fox!"

As White Eagle looked and listened, he heard the distant call of an owl. He lifted his head and listened. The call was quickly answered by another call, and then another, and another. White Eagle knew they were the signals of his friends, the Boy Foxes. He turned toward the forest, gave the owl cry, and disappeared in the woodland.

The Boy Foxes were the boys of the tribe who were being trained to be hunters. Hodegweh, the best hunter of the tribe, was teaching them.

As young White Eagle swiftly and carefully ran through the forest, he silently and proudly sang the words of the Boy Foxes' song:

I am a Fox, a wise Jitso,
I am prepared to die;
If there is anything difficult,
If there is anything dangerous,
That is mine to do.

A little while later White Eagle was standing with his best friend, Sosondoweh, and the other Boy Foxes. They were listening to the words of Gayewas, their leader and the oldest of the Boy Foxes.

A bear had crossed the river a half hour before. He was slowly making his way toward a distant, rocky ridge. Hodegweh, the skilled hunter, had said that the Boy Foxes must follow the bear and kill him before he could reach his hiding place there. Gayewas named the boys who were to follow the bear. He named those who were to guard the left and drive the bear back if he tried to return to the river. He named those who were to run forward and head the bear away from the mountain.

Swiftly and silently they began the chase. Soon the distant calls of the owl were given and answered. The bear had been sighted.

White Eagle was the youngest of the Boy Foxes. But he ran so well that he kept beside Gayewas, the leader. They ran until the ridge was just before them. Suddenly there was the sound of snapping underbrush in front, and the bear came into sight. The two boys' hearts leaped as they looked. It was the largest bear they had ever seen. Both drew their bows, and two arrows pierced the bear at the same instant. The great bear turned in a rage to fight, but in a moment Gayewas sent an arrow that sank between his shoulders.

On all sides the Boy Foxes were closing in. The body of the bear was soon pierced by many arrows, but he was still fighting. He raised himself on his hind legs and with blazing eyes rushed at one of the boy hunters.

Then Gayewas, strong and fearless, ran swiftly to meet the great bear, calling, "Ho, grandfather!" The young hunter struck him a heavy blow with his club, a heavy maple club to which a deer's antler had been fastened. The antler broke the skull of the bear, and he dropped dead at their feet.

The boys gathered about the body in silence. Each paused, amazed by the great size of the bear.

Then Gayewas lighted his pipe and asked the dead bear to forgive them because in their need of meat they had taken his life.

The Boy Foxes turned toward the village, dragging the huge body. At first they were silent and careful, as they had been taught. But soon one of the boy hunters began singing their song. All the Boy Foxes joined: "I am a Fox, a wise Jitso." Over and over they sang it, their happy voices ringing all through the woodland.

Suddenly they heard the sound of heavy running behind them. They had scarcely grasped their bows when they saw another huge bear rushing upon them, her eyes blazing with

anger. In an instant the Boy Foxes had disappeared, and the raging bear was left alone with her dead mate.

Then Sosondoweh, White Eagle's best friend and a swift runner, came boldly out from behind a tree and quickly drew his bow on the raging beast. But before the arrow had left his bow, Sosondoweh was struck to the earth by the bear's huge paw.

That moment would have been the end of Sosondoweh if White Eagle had not boldly stepped from cover. The bear rose to fight. White Eagle ran forward and hit the bear a blow with his sharpened maple club. But White Eagle's arm was not strong enough. The bear was only dazed for an instant. Then she rushed at White Eagle with raised paws. White Eagle lifted his arm to strike again. But another club fell on the bear. It was the club of Gayewas. The sharp point of the antler on the club pierced the skull of the great bear, who fell backward and sank dead beside her mate.

But there was no joy in the hearts of the Boy Foxes as they paused to look at the two huge bodies. All their thoughts were for Sosondoweh, who lay badly hurt. Swiftly and gently they carried him to the village. Two of them ran ahead to tell the news, and another ran to call a woman who was skilled in healing wounds. Quickly she made a dressing of medicines to heal Sosondoweh.

Later the Boy Foxes gathered about their teacher, the skilled hunter Hodegweh. Quietly Gayewas told the story of their hunt.

When Gayewas had finished, Hodegweh spoke. "On the home path you should have kept silence, for only in silence can the ear warn you of danger. Remember that the eye sees the forward path only. The backward path must be guarded by the ear.

"The boldness of Sosondoweh was foolish, for his arrow could not hurt the bear. White Eagle was a true friend in defending Sosondoweh, but he has disobeyed my teachings. He is the youngest of the Boy Foxes, and his arm is not strong enough to break the skull of a bear.

"Remember my words, for soon you will have greater things to learn. See that you are ready. I have spoken."

In silence the boys listened to the rebuke of Hodegweh. They had killed the two huge bears, but they felt no pride. Had they not run away from the second bear? Had not a friend fallen? Each boy knew well that an older hunter would have quickly killed the raging bear in open fight. If they had been swift and sure with their weapons, Sosondoweh would not have been wounded.

That evening at the wood's edge a fire was lighted, and the people went out to look at the two dead bears. The old men told tales of their hunting. They told of huge bears killed by their fathers. But never before had boy hunters brought such a kill to their village.

But White Eagle did not listen to the old men's praise. His mind was filled with the rebuke of Hodegweh and with the sharper rebuke that would come to Sosondoweh when his wounds had healed. White Eagle knew that he had disobeyed. He would not do so again. He knew, too, that his blow had helped his friend only a little. But still he was glad that he had struck it.

Afterthought

1. What did White Eagle learn from the bear hunt besides hunting skills?
2. What differences can you find between the way of life of White Eagle's people and that of Kwala's people?

Chuka's Hawk

Elizabeth B. Whitmore

Big Brother was always saying that Chuka was too little. Read how a pet helped Chuka put a stop to that.

Chuka was playing on the roof of his mother's house, keeping well away from the corner where Big Brother's eagle was tied. The little Hopi boy looked at the sun. Only a small piece of it was showing above the mountains. Big Brother would come soon to feed the eagle.

Chuka stopped playing and stood watching the trail that led up to the mesa from the desert below. Soon he saw Big Brother coming, his bow and arrow in his hand, and his hunting bag full.

Big Brother climbed up the ladder onto the roof. His eagle pulled at the cord tied to its foot and screamed. Big Brother tossed meat to his eagle, and the eagle gulped it down.

Chuka hopped on one foot until his earrings bounced. "I want a pet eagle, too," he cried.

"Ho, you are too little." Big Brother laughed.

Mother was calling. They went down the ladder and into the house. Mother was dishing up stew from a pot in the fireplace. She handed a bowl to Big Brother, and he went to sit beside Father and Grandfather. She handed one to Chuka. He sat near the fireplace. He dipped a piece of corn bread in the stew and ate it. Hm-m-m-m, it was good. Chuka was very, very hungry.

When they were finished, Chuka helped his mother clear away the bowls and wash them.

"Little boys do women's work," said Big Brother.

Chuka brought his blankets from the storeroom and spread them on the floor. Every night Grandfather told stories about the Hopi gods or the birds and animals. Tonight Grandfather told about adventures he had had when he was a boy. Chuka liked these stories best of all.

In the morning the thump, thump of Father's loom awakened Chuka. He rolled up his blankets and took them into the storeroom. He took a piece of cold corn bread and went out to play with Grandfather's new puppy, Bakito. When Big Brother came along, Chuka called, "Take me with you to herd the sheep in the desert, Big Brother."

"You are too little to walk so far," said Big Brother.

Chuka watched Big Brother start down the trail; then he went to see Uncle, who was working at his loom.

"You do not look happy, Chuka," said Uncle.

"I want a pet eagle," said Chuka. "Will you help me catch one?"

"An eagle cannot be tamed," said Uncle. "Your brother's eagle will never make a good pet. You can tame a hawk, if you are patient. Tonight I will make some prayer sticks. Tomorrow we will take the prayer sticks to the bird cemetery and hunt for a hawk."

The next morning Chuka and Uncle walked and walked. When they came to the bird cemetery, they placed the prayer sticks on the rock and made a prayer that Chuka would catch a hawk to tame.

Soon, Chuka heard bird sounds from high in the air. He looked up. "Those are hawks," Uncle said. "We are in a good place. Look for a hawk's nest in a tree."

Uncle walked ahead, looking and looking. Chuka saw a young hawk on the lowest branch of a tree. He watched it fly to the ground, snap up a grasshopper, and then fly back to the branch again.

Chuka caught four grasshoppers in a bush. He held them in his hand while he wriggled out of his shirt. Then he threw the grasshoppers on the ground in front of the hawk. The hawk swooped down to snap them up, and Chuka threw his shirt over the bird and caught him. The hawk struggled, but Chuka held on.

When Uncle came back he asked, "What do you have there, Chuka?"

"A young hawk!" cried Chuka.

"You caught a hawk?" Uncle was surprised. "Our prayer and our prayer sticks were good."

They carried the hawk home and tied it by a cord on the housetop, as far away from Big Brother's eagle as they could. The hawk snapped its bill at the eagle.

"My hawk is not afraid of the eagle!" cried Chuka.

"Remember, you can tame him," said Uncle.

Every day Chuka went hunting. When he could shoot a mouse, he gave it to his hawk. When he couldn't, he caught grasshoppers. One day he stroked the hawk's head. It did not snap at him. After that, Chuka stroked the hawk's head whenever he fed him. The hawk liked Chuka. He rubbed his bill on Chuka's cheek and perched on Chuka's shoulder. After a while, Chuka untied the cord, climbed down the ladder, and took his hawk for a walk. The hawk perched on Chuka's shoulder. He was getting tame. The boy named his pet Wiki.

It was now time for Big Brother to learn how to weave blankets. Grandfather would teach him, and Father would herd the sheep.

"Come with me, Chuka," said Father. "It is time for you to learn to herd."

Every day Father and Chuka took the sheep out into the desert. Chuka learned to find grass and water for the sheep, and to keep the flock together. But he missed his hawk. He played with Wiki a little while every evening when he fed him.

After many weeks, Father said, "Bring the young dog Bakito today. He, too, must learn to work." As soon as Bakito had learned to herd, Father said, "Chuka, I am needed in the fields to plant the squash and corn and beans. You are big enough to herd the sheep. Bakito will help you watch over them."

Chuka felt very big and brave as he went down from the mesa with only Bakito. But when he was out in the desert, he did not feel big. He did not feel brave. The desert was hot and quiet and as empty as the sky. The day was as long as a week.

That night Chuka said to his father, "May I take Wiki with me when I go into the desert tomorrow?"

"Will you play with the hawk and forget to watch the sheep?" asked Father.

"Oh, no," said Chuka.

"Then you may take Wiki," said Father.

"Your hawk will fly away and leave you," said Big Brother.

The next morning when Chuka left the mesa, Wiki was perched on his shoulder. Every day Chuka herded the sheep, with Wiki and Bakito to help. Bakito chased rabbits and prairie dogs. Wiki found grasshoppers and snapped them up. Sometimes his sharp eyes saw a mouse, and he pounced on it. Once he heard other hawks high in the air. He left Chuka's shoulder and flew up, up until he was flying with them.

Chuka watched the hawks until he could not tell which one was Wiki. He was afraid Wiki would not come back. But soon a hawk began to fly down in big circles. When it was quite low, it swooped down and nipped Bakito on the ear.

Bakito howled, but Chuka was so glad Wiki had come back that he laughed and laughed.

One day while Bakito was chasing rabbits and Wiki was playing with the other hawks high in the air, an animal chased the sheep. It looked like a dog, but Chuka knew it was a hungry coyote! It wanted a lamb to eat—one of his father's lambs!

Chuka found a big stick. He waved the stick at the coyote and shouted, but the coyote did not run away. It snarled and dashed at Chuka. He yelled and tried to hit the coyote with the stick, but it was too quick for him and dodged aside.

The sheep ran wild, baaing and bleating in panic.

"Bakito! Wiki! Help! Help!" screamed Chuka.

The hawk heard Chuka. Wiki did not sail down in big circles this time. He folded his wings and swooped down from the sky like an arrow. He dug his claws into the coyote's back, and nipped and nipped. The coyote howled. It ran away. Then Wiki flew to Chuka and perched on his shoulder. He rubbed Chuka's cheek with his bill.

Chuka laughed, and rubbed Wiki's head. Then Bakito rounded up the sheep. When he had them all together again, Chuka praised him and petted him.

That evening Chuka ate two bowls of beans cooked with onions and peppers for supper. He ate three big pieces of corn bread. When the dishes were cleared away, Chuka looked at Grandfather.

"Tonight *I* have a story to tell," he said.

Then Chuka told about the coyote. He told about the big stick. He told about Wiki and Bakito.

When the story was finished, Father said, "My son, you

have done well. Tomorrow you may choose a lamb to have for your very own.''

Big Brother went into the storeroom. He came back with his best arrow in his hand. He gave it to Chuka. "I will help you make a bigger bow," he said.

Chuka is busy. He and Wiki and Bakito drive the sheep out into the desert every morning. They watch them all day and drive them home in the evening. They are not afraid. They know they can take good care of the sheep.

Indian Masks

Pat Ritzenthaler

You probably think of a
mask as something that
is fun to wear on Halloween.
But masks were more
important than that to
early Indians.

Hundreds of years before the white man arrived in North America, Indians used masks. In 1932 two clay masks were found in northern Wisconsin. These were used about 2,000 years ago by Indians of the Hopewell group. The Hopewell people had pressed clay onto the face of a dead man, pushing the clay closely all around the nose and eyes and mouth. When the dead body was burned, the clay mask became hard.

In Oklahoma, masks about 500 years old have been found. These were made of wood to look like human faces. Shells had been set into the eyes, mouth, and ears.

In 1897 some very unusual old masks were found on an island just off the west coast of Florida. They were small wooden masks, made to look like animal as well as human faces. One deer mask was seven and a half inches long, not counting the movable ears. The eyes had been made of tortoiseshell. This little mask was probably used about 400 years ago.

There are three sections of North America where masks were very important in the life of the Indians. These are the East, from New York to North Carolina; the Southwest, especially Arizona and New Mexico; and the Northwest Coast, mostly in Canada.

In New York the Iroquois Indians made strange-looking masks for their False-Face Society, a society that helped to cure the sick. The masks stood for strange beings without bodies. These beings were believed to live in the forest. In the old days the man who made the mask cut it from a living tree. He was careful to cut in such a way that the tree did not die.

The mask was carved with a long hooked nose, a big twisted mouth, sunken cheeks, and, sometimes, no chin. If the tree had been chosen in the morning, the mask was painted red. If it had been chosen in the afternoon, the mask was painted black. Then horsehair, to look like human hair, was added to the mask.

When the Indians began using metal, the carvers put metal strips around the eyes. Imagine how the eyes glowed when the men danced around the fire!

Another Iroquois society also used masks and helped to cure the sick. This group was called the Huskfaces. The men of this society made long cornhusk faces. They coiled the husks and then sewed them into masks.

The Cherokee Indians used masks in the Booger Dance. For this dance some of the men put on wooden masks. Then, acting like rowdies, they copied the actions of any strangers who had come into their territory. At other times, hoping to have good luck at hunting, the Cherokee wore masks made from animal hides.

The Delaware Indians also used wooden and cornhusk masks. But they wore the masks in a Corn Harvest Dance. Once a year they asked Mother Corn for good health. In the Big House ceremony only one dancer wore a mask. He stood for a spirit who had power over sickness. The same spirit gave good luck when the Indians hunted deer.

The Hopi Indians were people of the desert. They depended on farming for a living. Most of their religious ceremonies were based on planting, raising, and harvesting fields of corn, their main crop. Because rain was so important in their desert home, the Hopis held a Snake Dance. In this dance they prayed for rain. Designs that stood for rain, clouds, and lightning were painted on their masks.

In the Hopi kachina ceremony the Indians prayed for good health as well as rain. Kachinas were divine beings that acted as go-betweens for men and the gods. Though they could not be seen, the kachinas were loving and helpful. But they could become visible if men, properly trained, put on special masks.

Twice a year the men, dressed as kachinas, danced in a long line through the village. They danced in very old patterns that had been handed down over the years. The kachina masks they wore did not show human faces. They were covered with signs that showed the kachinas' power. These were signs of the good thing for which the people prayed— rain, crops, sunlight, growth.

On the last day of the ceremonies a sort of Santa Claus came to the dance square and gave each little girl a kachina doll and each boy a tiny bow and arrow. During the winter the men had carved these gifts for the children.

The Northwest Coast Indians were very good wood-carvers. Since they had plenty of wood, they made their masks of cedar. Here masks were used by groups of families, or clans. The Haida tribe, for example, had two clans—the Eagle and the Raven. Masks that stood for these birds were carved for clan ceremonies and dances.

If a little Haida boy became ill, his mother and father would ask the clan's medicine man to cure him. The medicine man would decide which spirit helper would cure the boy. Then he would put on a mask that stood for that spirit and enter the family's home. By the light of the fire he would do a curing ceremony over the child.

Some raven masks had movable jaws with strings on them. These masks must have looked frightening when the jaws moved up and down in the dim light.

Certain Northwest Coast masks were carved to look like men from old tales. One mask showed a wild man who had lost his wits after being bitten by land otters. Another showed a man with a hawk's bill. In

the story he had been changed by magic into a bird.

Though masks were different in different parts of the country, they were used in ways that were alike. The masks were usually made and used by the men, not the women. They were nearly always used for religious or curing ceremonies. Sometimes, however, they were used to entertain. Most of the time the masks were worn in groups, not by one man alone. But no matter how they were used, masks played an important part in the life of the Indians.

How Sand Painting Came to the Navaho

F. Bridges Angleman

People need more than food, clothing, and shelter. They need beauty in their lives. From this legend you can see how important art is to one group of Indians.

Long ago the Dineh came across the mountains into a new land. Dineh means "the people." It is still the name that they use among themselves. But we call them the Navaho.

The Dineh liked the new land. It was peaceful and big. There were softly colored deserts, and twisted cedars, and pink and red sandstone cliffs carved by the wind. In the deep canyons the Dineh found water, and shady groves of cottonwood trees, and deer and rabbits to hunt. There, too, were great shallow caves. In these caves the Dineh found ruined stone houses built by a people long since gone.

On the high mesa tops lived a farming people who grew corn and beans and squash. Their houses, of several stories, were built of stone. These people were called the Hopi, and they kept to themselves.

The blue sky covered everything like a great bowl, with drifting puffs of clouds, and black vultures sailing lazily on the warm air. The Dineh settled down at the base of the red cliffs. There they built their round houses, or hogans, of logs and earth. Soon the smoke of their fires rose in thin blue columns to the Sky Country.

It was a silent land, and nothing troubled the Dineh. They lived peacefully in their hogans, hunting and growing a little corn. For a while they were happy. But then a strange thing happened. They began to grow quiet and thoughtful. A great sadness came over them. They were lonely.

When their work was done, there was nothing to do but sit and look at the pink mesas and watch the clouds turn red and purple and gray in the glowing sunsets. All was beautiful. But the beauty made them sad because they were lonely. And they began to quarrel among themselves and to behave badly toward each other, as people will sometimes do when they need most to be friendly and kind. They stopped trusting one another and built their hogans farther apart. Soon no one would speak to anyone else.

Sky Father, who loved the Dineh, saw the columns of smoke growing farther and farther apart. He looked down and saw the unhappiness of the people. And he was sad.

Earth Mother, who was very wise, said to Sky Father, "Send down Thunderbird to teach the old men how to paint."

And Thunderbird, with a great

rush of wings, came down in a dark cloud. Lightning flashed from his eyes, and thunder rolled beneath his outstretched wings. The Dineh saw him coming. They were frightened, and they stayed in the hogans, peeping out from behind the deerskins that covered the doors. But the wise old men put on their best clothing and went bravely out.

At once Thunderbird folded his wings, and the lightning stopped flashing from his eyes. The Sky Father spoke through Thunderbird. He spoke kindly to the old men. He told them to build a great hogan, a House of Song, and to spread the floor with fresh sand and smooth it with a stick. The old men did as they were told. And from Thunderbird they learned songs to sing while they worked—a different song for everything they did.

Then Earth Mother spoke through Thunderbird. She told the old men where to look for brightly colored minerals and flowers and how to grind them between stones to make colored powders. And the old men obeyed, singing happily while they worked.

Now the people heard the happy singing. And because they were curious, they forgot their fear. They crept from their hogans and gathered in the House of Song. Thunderbird taught them songs to sing to help the old men at their work. And as they watched and sang, the colored sands ran through the fingers of the old men. Beautiful pictures took shape on the smooth sand floor. There was the white moon—and the red sun, He Who Carries the Day. And there were the holy *yei*, the children of Earth Mother, very tall, thin figures with happy faces. And there were the four mountains at the corners of the world, and the four holy plants: corn, beans, squash, and tobacco. There were many other things, all the good and beautiful things of Navaho land, pictured on the floor of sand.

Sky Father then spoke through Thunderbird. "Let white be the color of the east, and blue of the south. The west shall be yellow, and black shall be the color of the cold, dark north."

When the picture was nearly done, Earth Mother spoke through Thunderbird. "Let rainbow surround the picture on all sides but the east, from which no evil comes." And it was done. The painting was finished. And the singing and the pictures were very powerful magic.

Then the old men, singing, touched first the magic picture, then the bodies of the people who were sick and unhappy. And the sick were cured. All the Dineh forgot their unhappiness, because they knew that Sky Father and Earth Mother loved them and they were not alone.

Then Thunderbird said, "Before the sun has traveled to his hogan in the west, erase all that you have done. Take up the colored sand and scatter it to the west." And when this was done, the people were happy because of the good magic and the singing and because no evil man could steal the magic pictures made in sand.

And to this day, when there is sickness or unhappiness, the Navaho make the beautiful sand paintings, as Thunderbird taught them to do. In this way, the Navaho believe, peace is made again between the people and the gods. And happiness comes down from the Sky Country, not only to the Dineh, but also to everyone, everywhere.

A Navaho Chant

In the house of life I wander
With beauty before and behind me,
With beauty above and below me,
With beauty within and around me
To old age traveling
On the beautiful trail of life.

Ann Nolan Clark

Hunting

Alice Marriott

In the excitement of a first hunt, a young Indian might make mistakes or get hurt or embarrass himself. As you read this story about Eagle Plume's first hunt, notice the Indian sense of humor.

You never really knew what a man was like until you knew how he acted when hunting. That was the way to see what there was inside him and how it was going to come out. You might think lots of men were good if you knew them just around camp, but after you saw them hunting, you found out something. Even in the case of a young man on his first hunt, you'd know.

Sitting Bear's oldest son, Eagle Plume, was alone with his mother. Sitting Bear had taken some young men and gone down into Texas, and another son, who was named for him, had gone with him. Eagle Plume was at home. He was fourteen, and he could have gone with his father, but Sitting Bear said he wanted to train his sons one at a time in fighting.

Eagle Plume liked being the only man at home. He could sleep late, and when he waked, his mother would have meat roasted for him, not boiled. Then he could take his time eating it, and when he had eaten, he could rest for a while. Afterwards he might go to work making himself some arrows. He was almost out of arrows, and Standing Wolf was teaching him how to make them.

"You may be old sometime yourself," Standing Wolf had said. "When a man is old, that's when he needs to know how to make arrows. That way he can always get himself something to eat."

Eagle Plume went to Standing Wolf's tipi now that he had eaten. He took some of the roasted meat with him, and the old man said, "Thank you for food," and put it back until

From *The Ten Grandmothers*, by Alice Marriott. Copyright 1945 by the University of Oklahoma Press.

he was ready to eat it. They sat in the door of the tipi, where the spring sun fell full on them and the south wind blew on them crosswise, and worked on the arrows. It was still early, and their fingers made long shadows on their work, winding the sinew around the feathers.

Lone Bear came by and saw them there.

"There you are," he said. "Two old men sitting in the sun, when everybody else is going hunting."

Eagle Plume looked up at him. He had never been on a hunt alone yet, and he had no buffalo horse. The only horse he had was an old, bobtailed, yellow one.

Lone Bear saw the look, and a good smile came into his eyes. He let it slide over toward Standing Wolf, and said, "I think one of the old men can still sit on a horse."

Standing Wolf was pulling the sinew tight with his teeth, but he nodded his head back and then forward.

"I think that old man who can sit on the horse has some new arrows," Lone Bear went on, and Standing Wolf nodded again. Eagle Plume could feel his own eyes getting big in his head and his own breath getting big in his heart. Lone Bear looked straight at him.

"Go get your horse and come with me," he said. Eagle Plume went home, then, as if somebody had shot him out of a bow.

The old, bobtailed, yellow horse was grazing a little apart from the herd. Eagle Plume had been riding that horse for a long time and had trained it himself. It would stand where he told it to, and he could guide it without a rein, just by pulling on its mane. He jumped on its bare back, and headed it for Lone Bear's tipi.

This wasn't like one of the big hunts, when everybody went and the soldier societies had charge of things and you had to obey strict rules. This was just a few men, about six, going hunting to get something to eat. There were some more boys about Eagle Plume's age with them, and they were all riding easily, talking and singing and enjoying themselves. They went west from the camp, and the prairie swung and rose and fell away beneath the horses' hooves as if it were alive. There was a ridge behind the camp, and when they passed it, there was nothing but men and horses and the good smells of day in the world.

Lone Bear rode over close to Eagle Plume. He had a pinto for a buffalo horse. It wasn't very big, but it was light and quick, a nervous sort of horse, but strong. It was all excited now, so excited that it didn't want to come too close to the bobtailed yellow.

"Remember these things," said Lone Bear. "There are rules about hunting, just as about fighting. When you see the herd, you don't want to rush at them. Wait until somebody older than you are gives the signal. Don't kill more meat than you think you can skin and your horse can pack home. That way it won't be wasted and lie around rotting. If things get bad and there's an old bull after you, let your horse go. Let him run away. He knows more about hunting than you do."

The pinto was dancing up and down like a painted dancer by that time, so Lone Bear let him run. It was better to quiet him in that way than to make him more nervous by whipping him.

One of the other boys saw Eagle Plume and called to the

rest, "Look at the old man arrow-maker! Look at his bobtailed horse!"

They all came riding around him then, everybody laughing and making fun of the yellow horse. The horse knew it too, and he didn't care, but Eagle Plume cared for him.

"That's all right," he said. "Anyway, I'm riding my own horse. I didn't have to borrow one from my father's herd. Does your father know where his horse is now?"

That turned the laughing away from him and started it at the boy who had first been making fun of Eagle Plume. Everyone began to tease him about riding somebody else's horse and forgot about the bobtailed yellow. It didn't matter if he had borrowed a horse, because many men who weren't young lent their good hunting horses for a share of the meat the borrower killed; but riding along with the morning running over their bodies, the boys liked having somebody to pick on.

Lone Bear went up a rise ahead of them, stopped the pinto, and held up his hand for everybody else to stop. All waited there behind him, until he rode back and told them, "There's a herd there around the spring. Everybody come on when I give the signal."

He rode back up the hill and sat looking out at the herd, while the hunters all bunched their horses together behind him and waited for him to give the word. The men were still and the horses were still, and Lone Bear up ahead was stiller than all the rest. It seemed as if he had to be very solid to hold the pinto there where it ought to be. Then his arm went up and down, and they all went forward without knowing whether they started the horses or whether the horses saw the arm move, too.

Eagle Plume was riding with the main group. Two of the boys who had teased him were ahead, shouting and running their horses, but the men around him were riding quietly and letting the horses do the running. He tried to do the way the men did, because he knew that most of them were good hunters.

The ground went backward between the yellow's feet as if it were afraid of being kicked, and Eagle Plume went forward along the yellow's neck, with his bow in his hand and an arrow on the string. There was a calf ahead, a yearling, and he turned the yellow toward it. The horse ran up facing the calf and stopped. The calf just stood there looking at them.

Eagle Plume raised the bow and shot. He aimed for the spot between the shoulder and the ribs where the arrow would go into the heart, and he hit it, too, for he saw the arrow sticking out, but the calf just stood there. He tried again, for the eye this time, and hit the calf in the forehead between the eyes. The arrow hung down there like a dancer's headdress ornament.

He was out of arrows. He had just had two. The others must have fallen out when they were chasing. Here he had the calf, and the calf was shot; but it wasn't dead, and he didn't have another arrow to kill it. He tried to think what he had better do.

He slid off the yellow's back, and took his knife out of his belt. He hadn't lost that, anyway. If he could get close enough to the calf, he might be able to get one of his arrows back. The one in the forehead looked pretty loose. Maybe he could even get close enough to cut the calf's throat. He could try. He left the horse, and it stood there watching him and the calf.

The calf had its feet spread wide apart, and it let him get up close enough almost to touch the arrow. Then it jumped, and started after him. He ran back toward his horse, but before he could get close enough to mount, the yellow horse turned around and kicked backward. It kicked the calf in the head, and the calf dropped and lay as if it had been killed.

Now he was glad he had his knife out. It was ready for the skinning. Somebody was shouting behind him. It was Lone Bear, riding down to find out what had happened. He jumped off the pinto and started over.

"You got one already," he was calling. "That's good. That's the way to do when you go hunting." He was all excited and pleased as he came toward Eagle Plume and the calf.

That calf was as mean as a bear. They both thought it was dead and were all ready to skin it when up it jumped. It chased Lone Bear, who was so surprised that it knocked him

down. He lay there on the ground where he had fallen and the calf came up and began licking him all over. They never found out what it meant, acting like that.

It might go on licking him all day, or it might get tired and want to do something else. Eagle Plume thought he'd better make sure it didn't do anything else. He took his knife and got on the side of the calf opposite Lone Bear. Then he slit the yearling's throat. It turned around once, so that it faced east instead of west, fell down, and really died this time. It always happened this way. Buffalo always died facing east.

Lone Bear got up. There was so much blood on him you would have thought he was killed instead of the calf, but he wasn't even hurt.

"That's the way," he said. "That's what you've always got to do. Always remember if you help people in time of danger, they'll help you out when you need it. It's that way in life, not only in hunting. People who try the most deserve the best. That way everybody knows they're good, and they get the best, too."

He went over to the calf and got ready to help Eagle Plume skin it. "If a man helps his friends out and his horse out, why, then, they'll help him out, too. That way he will live like a good man with his friends and his horses and get a lot more from both of them. Always remember, hunting is like fighting and like living."

Afterthought

1. How did Lone Bear and the others tease Eagle Plume?
2. How were horses important to Eagle Plume's people?
3. What parts of the story would you especially like to read again?
4. What do you know about early Indians that you did not know when you began reading this unit?

THE FLOWER-FED BUFFALOES

The flower-fed buffaloes of the spring
In the days of long ago,
Ranged where the locomotives sing
And the prairie flowers lie low:—
The tossing, blooming, perfumed grass
Is swept away by the wheat,
Wheels and wheels and wheels spin by
In the spring that still is sweet.
But the flower-fed buffaloes of the spring
Left us, long ago.
They gore no more, they bellow no more,
They trundle around the hills no more:—
With the Blackfeet, lying low.
With the Pawnees, lying low,
Lying low.

Vachel Lindsay

Written in Stone

Stone

This is a stone, smooth and round,
And flecked with green, that I just found.
Where did it come from? Long ago,
Did a fierce volcano erupt and blow
This stone from its mouth—a red-hot glob
That slowly cooled to a stony knob?
Did waters wash it with millions of knocks,
Grinding it smooth against other rocks?
Was it part of a mountain's growth or fall?
Over its shape did strange things crawl?
It was old, I think, when bison and bear
Roamed the plains, and Indians were there.
Perhaps a child then, long ago,
Held it like this and wished to know
The story the stone keeps. Perhaps then,
  like me,
He sensed this stone's deep mystery.

Solveig Paulson Russell

The Revenge of Pele

His Hawaiian Majesty Kalakaua

Perhaps the early Hawaiian people did not know that their beautiful rocky islands were once volcanoes. But they wondered about a mysterious smoking mountain and its rivers of melted rock. The following legend is one they told to explain a volcano, a volcano that still lives today.

The people of Puna had met at the foot of a hill near the town of Kapoho. They were there to watch the games at the monthly festival.

The day was beautiful. A light breeze shook the leaves of the palm trees and blew spray from the waves of the sea as they broke on the shore of Puna.

While the people waited for the main part of the festival, all the children raced about playing games. Men and women danced, sang about legends of long-ago days, or watched the games of the children. Then they sat under the palms and ate coconuts and bananas and chewed sugarcane.

All this while, the crowd was waiting for something special. It was to be the holua race between Kahavari, the young chief of Puna, and his best friend, Ahua. The crowd grew excited as the time for the race drew near.

· In the game of holua the players slide down a steep hill on narrow sleds. The sleds are eight to twelve feet long but only six to eight inches wide. They have long wooden runners that turn up in front. These runners are tied at each end and have crosspieces for the hands and feet.

The players throw themselves face downward onto their sleds and dash headlong down the smooth holua track. The narrow sleds are hard to guide. Each player must be able to stay on his sled while it is gliding swiftly down the hill. It takes much practice to learn how to guide a holua sled and stay on it.

Kahavari was a very good holua player, but so was his friend Ahua. So the people knew the race would be exciting to watch.

Finally Kahavari and Ahua appeared at the foot of the hill. Behind each walked a man carrying a sled.

The waiting people greeted their chief with loud cheers and took their places to watch. The young chief smiled at them. He stuck his spear into the ground at the bottom of the hill to show the finish line of the race. Then he and Ahua took their sleds under their arms and climbed to the top of the hill. They stopped for a moment at the top before beginning their race downward.

Suddenly a lovely woman stepped from behind a bush and bowed to them. The men smiled at her and turned to start their race. But the woman stopped them.

"Chief of Puna," she said, "race with me instead of with Ahua."

The two men looked at her in surprise. Then they looked at each other.

"What!" Kahavari said with a laugh. "Race with a woman?"

"And why not with a woman if she can race better than you and if you are not afraid to race with her?" answered the woman.

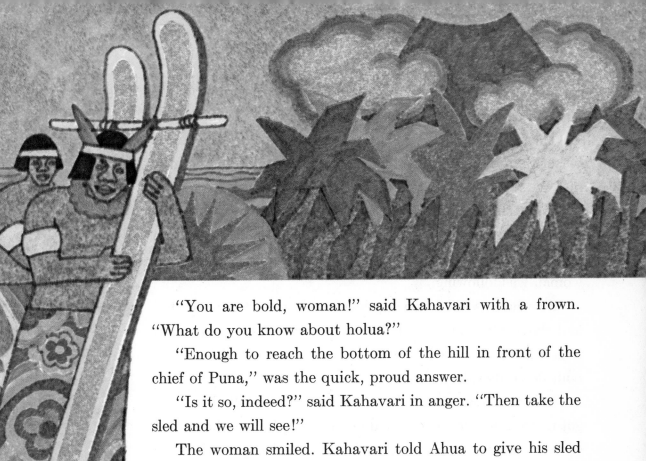

"You are bold, woman!" said Kahavari with a frown. "What do you know about holua?"

"Enough to reach the bottom of the hill in front of the chief of Puna," was the quick, proud answer.

"Is it so, indeed?" said Kahavari in anger. "Then take the sled and we will see!"

The woman smiled. Kahavari told Ahua to give his sled to the woman. And the race began.

Kahavari threw himself on his sled and plunged down the hill with the strange woman close behind him. On and on went the pair, around curves and over rocks, at breakneck speed.

Then for a moment the woman's sled began to sway, and she almost fell off. She righted it at once with a twist of her body. But this gave Kahavari time to flash past the spear a few feet ahead of her.

The people shouted and cheered because their chief had won. The woman frowned. Then without a word she pointed to the top of the hill. She was daring the chief to race again.

Kahavari smiled and nodded. He would race again. He was sure he was swift enough to win this race, too.

So the woman and the young man started back up the hill. They walked to the top in silence and turned for another start.

Then the woman spoke. "Stop!" she said. "Your sled is better than mine. If you would be fair, take my sled and give me yours!"

"Why should I?" asked the chief quickly. "You are neither my wife nor my sister, and I know you not. Come!" And he leaped onto his sled and dashed down the hill, thinking the woman was following.

But she was not following. She stood at the top of the hill and glared after him. Suddenly she stamped her foot in anger. And a river of melted lava burst from the hill and began to pour down its side.

Kahavari soon reached the bottom of the hill. When he got up from his sled and looked behind him, he saw the stream of lava rushing down the hillside toward the spot where he was standing. Riding on the stream was the strange woman!

Now the chief knew who she was. She was Pele, the dreadful goddess of volcanoes! Thunder roared at her feet, and lightning flashed from her flaming hair. Kahavari had made her his enemy, and now she was seeking terrible revenge.

Kahavari grabbed his spear and raced for his life to a hill nearby. Ahua caught up with him and ran beside him. As they looked back, the two young men saw a crowd of people suddenly covered by a sea of red-hot lava.

The glowing lava quickly spread. Kahavari knew that he had made an enemy of the goddess Pele and that she was using her strange power for revenge. The chief knew that the only way he could stay alive was to reach the sea.

With Ahua beside him, Kahavari dashed away. But right

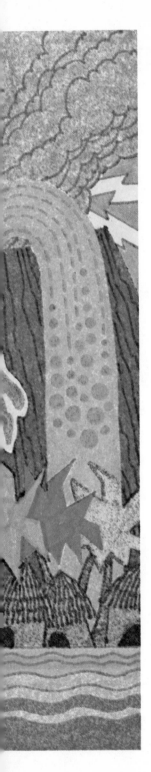

before them they saw a crack in the earth. And Pele was sending a stream of lava straight down the crack to cut them off from safety. With blazing hair the goddess rode on the lava stream.

Kahavari quickly laid his spear over the crack, and he and his friend crossed on it. They reached the sea with Pele close behind them.

On the shore the two young men sighted an empty canoe. They leaped into it. Using his spear for a paddle, Kahavari moved the boat swiftly away from the shore. Soon they were beyond the reach of the goddess.

The angry Pele rode the lava flow on into the water after them. But when she saw that she could not catch them, she glared and tossed rocks after them. The rocks were so hot that they hissed as they struck the water. At last Pele gave up and turned back.

Kahavari and Ahua finally reached the island of Oahu, where the chief of Puna stayed for the rest of his life. All of his family and hundreds of the people near Kapoho had been covered by Pele's lava flow.

Kahavari never went back to Puna. He feared that Pele would visit the place with another dreadful eruption.

Another lava flow now lies over the old one in Kapoho. Did Pele ride that red-hot stream of flowing lava? Perhaps she still seeks revenge against Kahavari, chief of Puna.

Fire-breathing Mountain

Frederick H. Pough

Mysterious mountains spewing steam and melted rock and dusty, smoky clouds—is it any wonder that early people made up stories about them? Scientists can explain the special mountains that volcanoes make. But what causes a volcano?

The mountain you see in this picture is not just any kind of mountain. It is a special kind that is found in special places. Look at the rocks and the steam and the dark cloud coming from its top. This mountain is called a volcano.

We may think of a volcano as a fire-breathing mountain. But it doesn't really breathe out fire. Inside the mountain is red-hot melted rock, called lava. The red glow from this lava looks like fire.

A mountain of this kind is built of the rock which has come out through an opening in its top, called a crater.

Sometimes the rock shoots out in the form of cinders, dark-colored bits of solid rock. But often it comes out as lava.

The dark cloud coming from the mountain looks like smoke, but it is made of dust, or powdered rock. When powdered rock, cinders, and lava are being forced out of a volcano, it is erupting.

What makes a volcano erupt? Is it possible that down under the crust of the earth the rock is melted and is waiting to find a weak place to break through?

We can't be sure what is going on

far below. We can't see through the earth's crust. Our deepest mine is only about two miles deep. The deepest hole we have ever dug is only a few miles to the bottom, and that's just a scratch on the earth's skin.

Through the years mountains wear away. Then we see rocks that once were five or more miles deep in these mountains.

Sometimes the rocks which have pushed high up from under the earth's surface crack and wear away. Then we can see what they look like inside. So we can say that we know what the earth's crust is like for the first five or six miles down.

What lies below? We can only guess. We can be sure that the rocks of the crust are solid but that every mile down they are a little hotter. Near the bottom of the crust the rocks must be pretty hot, hot enough to glow.

From mines and tunnels and deep wells we have learned about the heat inside the earth. Our deepest mine has to be air-cooled because it is so hot. As we go farther down, the heat may become many times greater than that of an oven. Surely this heat would melt rock!

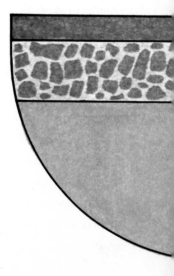

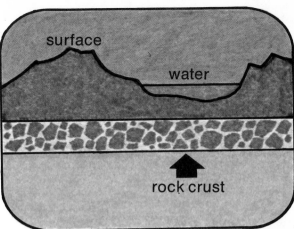

surface

water

rock crust

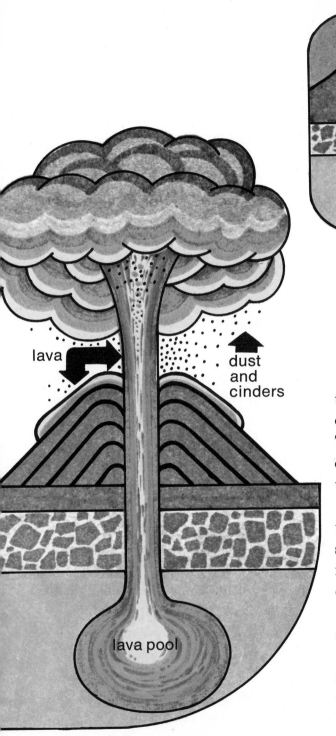

lava

dust
and
cinders

lava pool

How can we suppose, then, that the rock is really solid? Scientists once thought that it was melted. They thought the hot lava pouring out of volcanoes showed that this was true.

But someone made an instrument to help those scientists who were studying earthquake waves. This instrument showed that the earthquake waves pass through the first 1,800 miles of the earth as if it were solid.

That seems to settle the question for us. The rocks under the surface of the earth are hot enough to melt, but they don't melt.

Why not? Because they have no room to melt. Melted rocks need more space than solid rocks. And the crust of the earth is so heavy that the rocks can't push it up to find room to melt.

But what about lava? That is surely melted rock coming from inside the earth!

It isn't easy to explain how lava is formed. It may be that somewhere, for some reason, the earth's crust moves up a little and leaves some space.

Or perhaps the rocks are hotter in some places than in other places. The heat can't get out, so the rocks get hotter and hotter until at last the crust gives a little and makes room for them to melt.

So you see, we don't really know what makes the rock melt. We don't know what makes the lava rise. But we do know that the surface of the earth is weak where the lava breaks through. Volcanoes are formed at these weak places.

But heat alone isn't enough to make lava rise. Something else is needed. Perhaps that something else is gas.

You have all opened a bottle of pop. You have seen the little bubbles rush from the bottom to the top of

the bottle. They grow bigger and bigger on the way up. As they come to the top, they break, and they may splash a little of the pop out of the bottle. These bubbles are made from gas in the pop.

We know there is a lot of gas in lava. Perhaps the gas in lava acts like the gas in pop. The eruptions of volcanoes may be caused by this gas bubbling up through the lava. But the lava doesn't all come out at once. As it flows, it keeps bubbling quietly. And even after the lava stops flowing, it may keep steaming for months.

We think that is the way lava is pushed out of a volcano. The gas must have something to do with it. But gas alone wouldn't do it. The weak place in the surface must be there first. Gas may help the lava eat its way up through the weak place. Perhaps that's how a fire-breathing mountain works.

The Monster

Frederick H. Pough

What would you do if suddenly the earth
spit rocks and dust at your feet? Would you
stop to watch the birth of a volcano?

One February day in 1943, a man named Dionisio Polido started out from his home in the Mexican village of Parícutin. He turned and started down a worn path. He was going to plow his cornfield and get it ready for planting. He took along his team of oxen and a wooden plow.

When he reached the field, he looked across his land. It was a good field except for one low place where the corn never grew very well. But Dionisio always plowed and planted the low place. Maybe someday good corn would grow there.

At last he started to work. Slowly the two oxen pulled the wooden plow around the field. Dionisio walked along behind.

It was a good day to work, quite hot for February. The ground felt warm under his bare feet. It was very warm in the low place.

Up one row and down another went the oxen and Dionisio. But today each row seemed never to end. As he turned to come back across the field, Dionisio thought he saw smoke rising from the low place. Was something burning in his field? He stopped his team and went over to see. He leaned over to see more clearly, and his sombrero fell beside a crack in the ground. Something like smoke was coming from this crack. Dionisio stared at it.

Suddenly a great rumble came from deep in the ground, and the earth began to shake under Dionisio's feet. The oxen snorted loudly and stood swaying with the shaking of the earth. Then with a roar another crack opened in the ground, right by Dionisio's sombrero. The hat flew high into the air. Before it hit the ground, Dionisio was running for help.

Then he heard the oxen bellow. The poor beasts were trying to run, but they were still fastened to the plow, and they pulled in different directions. He ran to them and unhitched them from the plow. Away they tore across the field.

Dionisio turned and looked back toward the low place. The dark, smokelike cloud was still rising from the cracks. And now stones were shooting into the air. It looked as if someone inside the earth were throwing the stones. Dionisio didn't stop to watch. His legs had never carried him as fast as now. He ran straight toward San Juan, a village three miles away.

When he reached the village, the people were standing in the streets staring. Even here, three miles away, the rumbles could be clearly heard.

"What is it?" asked an old man as Dionisio passed. "What is that great noise we hear?"

"I don't know," Dionisio called back. "I just know that something terrible is happening!"

"Get the priest!" shouted a woman.

"That's where I'm going," said Dionisio, and on he ran to the church.

On his way other people called to him, "What is happening?" But Dionisio had no time to talk. He must save his breath for running.

"Father! Father! Come with me!" called Dionisio as he reached the church.

"Yes, Dionisio, I'm coming," the priest said quietly.

The people crowded around them as Dionisio poured out his story. The bursts of sound could be heard more often now, and in the distance a thin column that looked like smoke could be seen climbing high into the sky.

"I will go with you, my son," the priest said. Many of the men followed them as they walked the three miles to the cornfield. Dionisio was very tired now and could not hurry as fast as before.

When they reached the edge of the cornfield, they could hardly believe what they saw. In the short time since Dionisio had left, the field had changed. On the spot that had been the low place, a pile of black cinders stood as tall as a tree! A stream of rocks and dust shot high into the air from its center and settled back on the pile. As the rocks fell, they piled up around the opening and built a chimney. Through this chimney a great smokelike column of steam and dust kept pouring out.

"What is it, Father?" Dionisio asked in great fear. "What kind of terrible monster is it?"

The priest looked a moment in silence. Then he turned to the people about him. "It is a volcano," he said in a quiet voice. "It is a volcano being born."

"Volcano! Volcano!" the people said over and over. They knew about volcanoes. There were many near their village. But no one had ever seen one erupt.

The shape of the pile of rocks was still changing. Now the volcano began to look like a cone. More and more rocks flew into the air and fell back to build the cone still higher. The roar from the outbursts was so loud that the people could scarcely hear each other talk.

As the sun set and darkness came, the sight became more frightening. The flying rocks glowed like fire. When they fell back upon the cone, it was outlined in fiery red. As the dust and rocks blew out, the volcano looked like a huge torch blazing against the sky.

All through the night the people watched. What would happen next? How high would the monster build?

In the light of morning they could see that the cone was now two hundred feet high. But the fiery red was gone, and the stones looked black.

And now other people came streaming from far and near to see the wonder. Many cars jammed the road and chugged around Dionisio's cornfield. They called the volcano Parícutin after the nearby village.

Some of the visitors were scientists who came to study the

volcano. They were greatly excited. This was the first time they had been able to see a volcano being born. They knew they could learn from it many things about the action of volcanoes. They all watched in excitement as the rocks and dust flew into the air.

Day after day the people watched as the cone built higher and higher. Then something new happened. A stiff, doughy mass began to squeeze from an opening at the side of the cone. It was melted rock, or lava. It moved slowly down the side of the cone. Now and then splatters of the liquid rock fell on Dionisio's cornfield.

On the outside the lava was cool and black. But hotter lava below the surface pushed against the crust and cracked it. A red glow showed through the cracks, and the doughy mass poured out to spread down the cone. It was as if a great giant were pushing an endless pile of loose, red-hot rocks. Steam rose above it like a cloud.

The lava flow crept down the cone and onto Dionisio's cornfield. It moved across the land until the whole field disappeared under the great blanket of liquid rock. Then it spilled over into the forest beyond and stripped the branches from the trees as it went.

The fireworks kept bursting, with flashes like lightning and rumbles like thunder. The ground shook, and the lava poured on and on.

The village of Parícutin lay in the path of the flowing lava. Dust from the volcano filled the air and dropped on the streets and houses. The people could hardly breathe. They would have to move away and leave their homes to the monster.

Soon the people of Parícutin left their village. They moved to good farms they had chosen out of reach of the dust. Dionisio and his family went to a farm many miles away.

Slowly the lava took over the town. Now there was no village of Parícutin. It was swallowed up by the monster.

Still the lava kept moving. The people of San Juan were filled with fear. Would the monster take over their town, too? A government commission laid out a new town a safe distance from the volcano. But the people stayed in San Juan as long as they could.

When the dust came, they had to fight great clouds of it. They could hardly breathe. Many people left, but a few families stayed on.

Then a greater, stronger lava flow began to move straight toward San Juan. At last the few families that were left gave up. They piled their belongings into trucks and began their trip to the new town.

When the lava had covered San Juan, Parícutin had about reached the end of its powers. Then, a little more than nine years after the low spot in Dionisio's cornfield had begun to crack and send out smokelike clouds, the monster Parícutin died. Nothing was left but a giant black cinder cone.

Dionisio and his friends who had lived in the village of Parícutin never forgot those terrible days. In their new homes they told the story again and again to strangers. "The monster, the volcano Parícutin, swallowed up our homes," they said.

As Dionisio plowed and planted his new field, he often thought sadly of his old field with the low spot which was now the heart of a mountain. He was reminded of his home in Parícutin, which now lay deep under a solid mass of lava. And he sighed as he remembered.

Afterthought

1. In what ways is a volcano like a "monster"?
2. Why did the people leave the villages of Parícutin and San Juan?
3. What made this volcano of special interest to scientists?
4. Look back at what is said about the volcano in "The Revenge of Pele." What passages look as though they were told by an eyewitness?

The Great Spirit's Tower

Marion E. Gridley

Can you imagine a huge
rock that mysteriously
grows taller and taller?
As you read the following
legend, look for signs
that will let you know
whether or not the strange
rock is a living volcano.

Long ago a band of Indians wandered into a new country. They pitched their lodges close together in a camp circle. The chief told all the people to stay in sight of the tepees until the scouts could search the country and learn of its dangers.

It might be that wild beasts prowled over the plains around the camp. Unfriendly tribes might be near. And there might be many other unknown dangers.

Until the band of Indians could learn more about the country around them, they could not feel safe. So the scouts were sent out to hunt on the prairie, while the rest of the band stayed close to the camp.

But one day three young Indian girls wanted to go out onto the prairie to look for long grasses to use in making rugs. They asked if they could leave the camp.

"If you promise to be careful, you may go," the old chief told them. "But be sure to stay within sight of the camp circle."

The girls promised, and off they went. As they walked, they looked back now and then to see how far they were from the tepees.

But young people soon forget danger when their minds are filled with other things. The weather was sunny, and the country was beautiful. Flowers of bright colors grew all through the prairie grass. They were so lovely and their scent was so sweet that the girls began to pick them. On and on they went, for always just ahead there was one brightly colored flower sweeter than all the rest. Each girl picked and picked until she had an armload of the tender flowers and long grasses.

The girls did not mean to disobey the word of their chief. But as they laughed and talked, they were so happy that they forgot what he had said. They wandered farther and farther from the camp. Soon the smoke from the campfire was a dim shadow in the distance.

From his home beyond the clouds the Great Spirit who protected the Indians watched the girls wander far out onto the prairie. He had heard the old chief tell them not to go far from camp, and he knew of the dangers in the land. He saw that although the girls did not know it, danger was close to them. Three grizzly bears had seen them. The bears, hidden in the tall grass, began to move quietly toward them.

When the girls were too far from camp to call for help, the grizzly bears leaped toward them, growling and showing their teeth. The girls ran screaming. They could not decide which way to go!

The Great Spirit guided their feet to a large rock close by and helped them to its top. But even here they were not out of danger. The bears could climb, and they started up the sides of the rock. The girls could do nothing but stand close together in fear, watching the bears climb higher and higher.

The sides of the rock were smooth, and the bears dug their sharp claws into it to keep from falling. Sometimes they would slide back a little. But they climbed nearer and nearer.

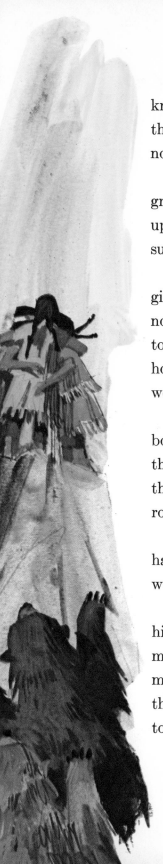

Now the Great Spirit helped the young girls again. He knew they had not meant to disobey. They had only forgotten the chief's words, and the Great Spirit was sure they would not forget again.

So he spoke to the rock. As he spoke, the rock began to grow. Higher and higher it rose, with the bears still climbing up its sides. Their claws made deep scratches in the smooth surface as they tried to climb.

Up, up the rock went, until it was a great tower. Now the girls knew the Great Spirit was helping them, and they were no longer afraid. They watched the bears fight their way almost to the top of the rock. Then suddenly all three bears lost their hold and fell. They were so high when they fell that they were killed when they struck the ground.

The girls knelt and raised their arms toward the sky. They bowed their heads to show the Great Spirit that they were thankful for his help. Then they took the grass and flowers they had picked and twisted them into a long rope. Down this rope they swung to safety.

The girls ran back to camp and told the old chief what had happened. The chief did not scold them, for he knew they would never disobey again.

The Great Spirit did not change the rock, so it stayed as high as a tower. All along its sides were the deep scratches made by the grizzly bears. Whenever the Indians saw the magic tower, they lifted their faces to the sky and remembered that there beyond the clouds the Great Spirit was watching to protect them.

Volcanic Wonders

Volcanoes in action are both terrifying
and exciting. But some of the most
interesting volcanoes are dead. They have
left volcanic signs, wonders written
in stone.

Mountains are made in different ways. Some are lifted up by forces under the earth which push against the surface. Slowly the surface gives until it becomes wrinkled. The huge wrinkles are mountains and hills. All this happens quietly, through many, many years.

But a volcanic mountain is built of rocks and cinders and lava that come out through its crater. Every time melted rock comes out of the crater of the volcano and flows down its side, the mountain grows a little larger. And every time rocks and cinders are forced into the air from a volcano, they fall back and become a part of the mountain.

With each eruption the volcano may grow larger and higher. Rocks and cinders may pile up to build a high mountain. Lava may flow out and cool as it stops flowing. When it is cool, it is solid rock.

Between its eruptions a volcano rests. It may rest for a short time, or for hundreds of years. So a mountain made from a volcano may also take a long time to build.

NOTE: The information about lava columns is from *The Sky Is Blue*, by W. Maxwell Reed. By permission, Harcourt Brace Jovanovich, Inc.

At last a volcano stops erupting. Then it is dead. It no longer grows larger. It loses its heat and becomes cool. After many years it may be just a sleepy old mountain covered with grass and trees. Little streams of water may flow down its sides.

But the volcano does not remain the same size. If it doesn't grow larger, it will surely grow smaller. The streams of water that wear away hills and other mountains will wear away its surface, too. In time a volcanic mountain may become very small, and it may even disappear.

When this happens, how can we be sure there ever was a volcano in that place? Scientists have studied some of our natural wonders. They have discovered a number of signs that tell them there was once a living volcano nearby.

Lava flows and lava structures are such signs. The beds of some lakes are made of lava, and old lava flows have been found along lake shores. In places solid lava has been discovered under the soil. And in some parts of our country huge lava structures may be seen rising high in the air.

Scientists have also learned that certain minerals are found in the lava and cinders that once poured from volcanoes. Rocks with these minerals in them may be colored by the special colors of the minerals. The sight of these colors in rocks is a sign to a scientist that the rocks once came out of a volcano.

Sometimes hills and parts of hills are made of dark-colored glass. A scientist knows that this glass was formed by the sudden cooling of melted lava.

Some of our most interesting natural wonders are found near the places where these signs of volcanic action have been discovered. Often the wonders themselves are really parts of dead volcanoes.

Whenever you see a hot spring shooting water and steam into the air, you can be sure that such signs are somewhere nearby. The shooting hot springs are geysers.

Here you see a picture of another natural wonder, Old Faithful, our best-known American geyser. In the land all around Old Faithful, there are hills of glass, rocks with bright mineral colors, and strange structures of lava. The heat in the crust of the earth comes close to the surface here, just as it does under a live volcano. So the same kind of heat that once caused volcanoes to erupt makes the water under Old Faithful hot enough for steam to form. The steam becomes so strong that it pushes the water into the air. Then the eruption dies back. Steam begins to build again, until it becomes strong enough to cause another eruption.

The heat under Old Faithful must be very great, for you can depend on the geyser to erupt about once an hour. That is why it is called Old Faithful.

First it gives a rumble. Then water begins to rise from it. Each gush is stronger than the one before it, until it leaps 120 to 170 feet into the air. The water is so hot that great steam clouds form when it reaches the cooler air. The geyser dies back in about four minutes, and steam builds up for the next eruption. This goes on hour after hour, day after day, in summer and winter.

Signs of old volcanic mountains are often found around lakes and streams. There is one quiet lake of a beautiful deep blue that lies below high lava cliffs. The cliffs rise all around it, so that the lake and its cliffs look like a giant cup half-filled with water.

Scientists who have explored the lake explain that the giant cup is really the crater of an old, dead volcano. That is why this lake is called Crater Lake.

Ages ago a huge mountain was built here by a steaming, roaring volcano with red-hot lava inside. Lava poured out until the mountain was nearly 14,000 feet high.

Years later the top blew off the mountain, and the rest of the lava flowed out through its crater. At last the top of the crater became weak—too weak to stand. Then the whole top broke loose and fell into its own crater.

Some people speak of this mountain as "the mountain that swallowed itself." It swallowed more than 7,000 feet of the crater at once. Rain and snow gathered in the great cup that was left and half-filled it.

But the volcano did not die when its top fell. It was alive even after water gathered in the bottom of the crater.

Scientists tell us that about a thousand years ago the old volcano erupted again. It forced up three small cones through the water at the bottom of its crater. Since then two of these cones have been covered with water. But the third and largest cone is still seen above the water. It is an island known as Wizard Island.

Wizard Island is really a little volcano—a volcano within a volcano. The top part of it is made of cinders and dust. It cooled long ago, and now it is partly covered with pine trees.

There is another island in Crater Lake. It is not a cone but an odd, twisted structure of lava from the old volcano. In the moonlight it looks like a ship under sail. But when the sun shines in a certain way, the island suddenly seems to disappear. For this reason the island is known as the Phantom Ship.

Some of the most unusual lava structures in our country are the lava columns that rise high into the air. Each was once the center of an old cinder cone. While the volcano was alive, its center was filled with melted lava. As the volcano died and lost its heat, the lava cooled into solid rock.

The busy little streams that flowed down the sides of the mountain went about their work of wearing away the surface of the cone. They wore it deeper and deeper, until at last nothing was left but the lava center, which was too hard for the streams to wear away very fast.

Today these structures stand, great columns of rock hundreds of feet high. No one can tell just how long they have stood there. But from the study of these and other natural wonders, scientists are able to tell many new things about volcanoes.

We all know that a big oak tree can grow from a little acorn that is planted in the ground. We know that after hundreds of years the tree falls down and becomes a part of the ground. Now we know that a huge volcano, also, can grow and die and that it can be worn away until it disappears. But instead of living hundreds of years as the oak tree does, a volcano may live for millions of years.

Afterthought

1. In what ways is a geyser a sign of volcanic action?
2. How do scientists think that lava columns such as the one in "The Great Spirit's Tower" became formed?
3. In what ways do you think the study of rocks from the moon is important?

Mountains

Mountains are the high places;
They reach up and up
To the blue-blue above.

They stand around us,
Looking down at the people
In the pueblo,
In the plaza,
In the fields.

I like to know
That mountains are there,
Around me,
So quiet,
So big
And so high.

I have heard
That the Thunder sleeps
In the mountains,
With his great bow
And lightning arrows
By his side.

I have heard
That clouds gather
In the mountains,
And that rainbows
Make bridges
Over them.

I have heard
That mountains
Are the home
Of the winds
And the night.

Perhaps
These things are true;
I have heard them.

Ann Nolan Clark

Proud Typhon

As you read the following story, you will likely be aware of many signs of volcanic action. But to the people of ancient Greece, these were signs of a fierce battle. In this myth the early Greeks see volcanic caves and mountains as places where their gods fought the giants.

Typhon fled through the sea, stirring a trail of angry waves. His hundred dragon heads bellowed to the skies. All the monster giants had been killed—all except Typhon.

He shook his heads. "There shall be another battle," he roared. "I shall prove that I am god of mountaintops and of all else that is high."

Typhon crawled ashore. He disappeared into the earth, where he lived in a deep, dark cave. A fire-breathing dragon hissed nearby. "Zeus, ruler of the gods, has slain all the other giants," he told the dragon guard. "But his rule shall not last. I am taller than any god on Mount Olympus, and I shall rule the skies!" Then he grunted, "Guard this place while I make ready to rise against Zeus once more."

Typhon was so tall that when he sat down in the great cave, his hundred heads remained outside. Each head curled

and hissed among the treetops. And the question in each head was the same—how to kill Zeus.

In the darkness Typhon stretched his snaky coils in the caverns. As water from the earth cooled his rage, steam rolled forth. Suddenly he cried, "I shall pull up mountains and a thousand rocks, and I shall hurl them at Zeus. He shall be pulled down from his throne and hidden in the earth. Now is the time!"

A dreadful noise echoed through the cave. Typhon broke off long rocks that hung from the ceiling. The earth groaned with pain as the hundred dragon heads pulled up great oak trees with their mouths. Then fire curled from the cave. And Typhon crawled to the top of its cliffs, pulling off hilltops as he went.

Now Hermes had heard all that Typhon said; so he rushed this news to his father, Zeus. There was panic among the gods. Zeus was their bright chief, god of all that is high. But the powerful Typhon might kill him!

Zeus was not afraid. He stroked the golden wings of Hermes and said, "Rest here. I shall return soon."

Then Zeus took thunderbolts in one hand and his iron sword in the other. On Mount Olympus he stood ready for his terrible enemy.

The tall Typhon came surging across the sea, and Zeus flung a thunderbolt. But Typhon only laughed. At once his hundred heads coiled and spit a hundred rocks at Zeus. Just as quickly the hundred heads coiled and spit again, flinging great oak trees. All the earth shook.

The chief god staggered. Typhon came closer, throwing whole mountaintops at him. But Zeus dodged them and took up his iron weapon. With this sword Zeus came down upon Typhon, beating his hundred heads with heavy blows.

The rocks on Mount Olympus piled higher and higher. Typhon and Zeus struggled closely, and the battle raged louder. Suddenly Typhon coiled around Zeus and squeezed him. Zeus was not able to breathe, and Typhon took the wonderful sword away from him. He swiftly cut out the power of the god's hands and feet. Then, with Zeus unable to move, Typhon carried him across the sea.

The giant was weak when he reached dry land. His wounds were bleeding. "Guard!" he bellowed. "Take Zeus to a dark cave. Bring down a rush of water so that he may not be seen or heard."

The dragon guard carried Zeus into a deep cave. He wrapped the power of Zeus's hands and feet in a bearskin. With a snort the dragon tore open the ceiling, and a river of water came forth. He then blew a fiery tunnel. Through this passage the dragon guard returned to Typhon's den.

But Typhon was so weak he could not crawl into his den. Instead he lay in the sun to heal his wounds. He was tired, and his heads were tired. Soon his eyes closed in sleep.

Now Hermes had followed Typhon across the sea. He waited a time, then passed through the falling river. There he found Zeus, powerless. With great care Hermes unwrapped the bearskin. Then he fitted the power back into the hands and feet of his father.

In a moment Zeus had his strength back. "I am healed," said Zeus. "No earthly giant shall rule the skies!"

He sprang from the cavern, grabbed thunderbolts, and raced to the top of the cliffs. Typhon, still lying in the sun, heard the thunder of Zeus rumbling nearer and nearer. But Typhon was still weary and did not flee in time.

Zeus chased him, hurling one thunderbolt after the other. Not far from the great cave, Zeus caught Typhon and flung him out to sea. With one last thunderbolt, Typhon fell. A fiery mountain shot up from the sea. Rocks and rivers of burning earth burst forth in fury.

For many years the last of the monster giants has sent flames and hot lava into the air. But Typhon never again rose against the gods.

A Cave Is Born

Dorothy Sterling and Winifred Lubell

You have read about Zeus and Typhon and some
volcanic caves. Caves, too, are signs written
in stone, but not all caves are formed by volcanoes.
The following article tells how another kind of
cave is formed.

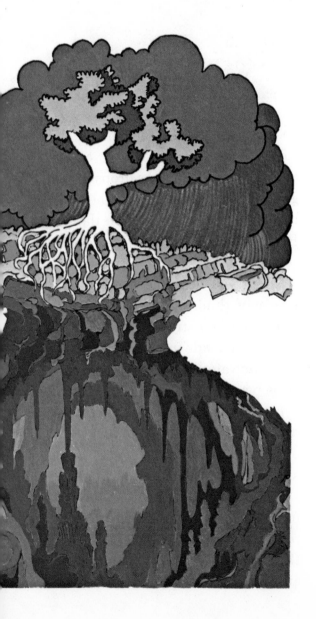

Did you ever stub your toe against a door? If you did, you may have yelled, "Ouch! That door's as hard as rock!"

But just how hard is rock? There are rocks that you can crumble in your hand or cut with a knife. There are rocks that can be broken with an ordinary hammer.

If you have ever watched men building a road, you have seen them digging into rock. Sometimes the rock is so hard that the workmen have to blow it to bits with dynamite.

Rocks differ in hardness. One of the softest rocks is limestone. Granite is one of the hardest. But even granite won't last forever. And its chief enemy isn't dynamite, either. Its chief enemy is water.

Water can eat away the hardest rock. It can wear down the tops of mountains. Water can crumble cliffs and grind up huge stones. It can hollow out the sides of hills as surely as dynamite can, though not so quickly.

"Oh, you mean waterfalls," some-one may say. "Roaring floodwaters, rushing streams, pounding waves."

Yes, and tiny drops of rain!

You don't believe this? Let us suppose there is a dripping water pipe outside your house. Day after

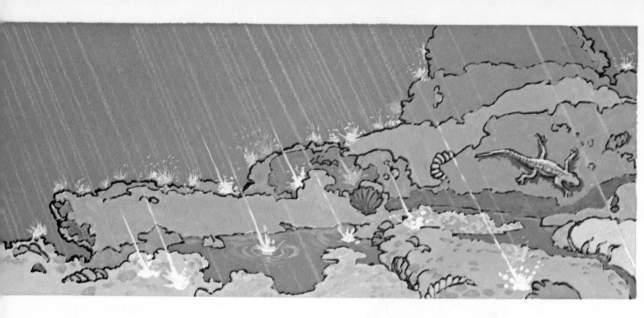

day, year after year, tiny drops of water fall one by one on a rock below the pipe. Plink, plonk, plink.

In a few years you will find that the rock is getting smaller. Each plink acts like a hammer, breaking up the surface of the rock into tiny grains. Each plonk carries away the grains. More and more rock is broken up. If you wait long enough, the rock will be gone, pounded to bits by the water.

This is what will happen unless— unless the rock under the pipe is limestone and the water is a little acid. Then the rock will not be broken into grains. It will be hollowed out instead.

One special thing about limestone is that the lime in it will dissolve in acid in much the same way that salt does in water. The acid that works on limestone comes from the air and soil. Falling rain takes in carbon dioxide from the air. As drops of rain go down through the earth, they take in more carbon dioxide from the soil. Rainwater with carbon dioxide becomes acid.

When you hear the word "acid," you may think of vinegar or something sour and strong.

The acid made from carbon dioxide and rainwater isn't like that at all. It is weak and pleasant to taste. Whenever you drink pop, you're drinking this acid. The bubbles that fizz as you take the top off the bottle are bubbles of carbon dioxide gas.

It's strange to think that the acid found in ordinary pop can break up rock. Yet this weak acid tunnels through beds of limestone until they are full of holes.

Whenever it rains, drops of water drip through the soil. Some are taken up by the plants that grow there. Some run off, filling lakes and making rivers deeper. But if it rains long enough, some water finds its way under the ground to beds of limestone.

The water trickles through tiny cracks in the stone. It dissolves the lime and makes the cracks larger. After a while two cracks meet, grow bigger, and form a hole. The hole becomes wider, deeper. More water trickles through the rock and moves downward, nibbling away at the cracks. It moves sideways between the layers of stone. The water is always moving, always dissolving lime, always making the holes bigger.

The cracks become wider and wider until they become tunnels. The tunnels meet, crisscross, and grow into rooms. The rainwater may gather until it becomes an underground river that fills the tunnels and floods the room.

It has taken a long, long time, but at last a cave is born. It will keep on growing—to giant size—as long as there is water running through the tunnels in the rock.

Strange Black Smoke

Adapted by Lloyd Besant

Today we do not believe that a volcano was caused by an angry goddess or a fiery giant. We know that a dragon did not spit fire to form a cave, and we know that an underground river was not formed by a dragon's snort. But earth's mysteries are not easy to understand. Fear of darkness and of the unknown has stopped many people from exploring caves. While you read the following story, think about how brave Jim White was.

Jim White had spent a hot, dusty day on the range. Now he was enjoying the ride home in the late afternoon. His horse walked lazily along.

Jim looked at the land spread around him. He never tired of seeing it. There was always some interesting sight in this part of New Mexico. Every time he saw the desert plain, the hills, and the Guadalupe Mountains, he found some new beauty. But the sight was never so beautiful as in the late afternoon, when the sun painted the high mountaintop and the foothills with warm colors. Then how far the Guadalupe Mountains reached! They seemed to grow larger and larger as the shadows added to their size and mystery.

Suddenly the cowboy brought his horse to a stop. "Look at that!" he cried in excitement. "There's smoke coming out of that mountain!"

For a moment he watched in silence. A great cloud of black smoke seemed to be twisting out of the foothills.

Jim looked away, then back again. Light and shadow often play tricks on the eyes when one looks at the mountains. But this was no trick, he decided. Heavy black smoke was certainly curling up from somewhere in the foothills. It rose as high as the mountain and swirled off toward the south.

"That's sure enough smoke!" cried Jim. "I wonder what's on fire!"

Jim started his horse at a gallop straight toward the smoke. Out here where ranch houses were far apart and there was little water, a fire could mean real trouble.

As Jim came close to the foothills, he could see that the smoke was even thicker than he had thought. It twisted and it turned as though it were alive.

"The whole hillside over there must be on fire!" Jim cried to his horse.

When he reached the top of the slope, Jim stopped his horse and stared in surprise. For it wasn't the hillside that was burning. No, the smoke was coming right out of a hole in the side of the mountain! Jim decided to go closer.

His horse snorted and stepped carefully as they moved down the hill toward the smoking hole. Above the sound of his horse's hoofs, Jim could hear a strange rustling sound, like the whirring wings of many birds. But he could see no birds at all flying overhead.

As Jim drew nearer to the mountainside, the sound of wings beating the air grew louder. It seemed to be coming right out of the cloud of smoke.

Then suddenly Jim stopped again. "That isn't smoke!" he cried. "It's bats! Thousands of bats flying out of that hole in the mountain!"

The bats poured out of the mountainside in a thick black stream and became a part of the cloud that rolled and twisted. They were coming out for food. Jim watched and watched. And still they kept coming.

"You stay here and nibble some grass," Jim said to his horse. "I'm going closer and wait until they all come out."

He sat on a rock and watched. An hour passed. Two hours. Still the bats poured out of the cave. After nearly three hours the cloud began to thin. Finally the last few bats came out to fly after the others.

Jim waited a few minutes to make sure they had all left. Then he walked to the cave and looked in. All he could see was a big black hole. He couldn't see the bottom of it. He needed a light. So he picked up some sticks and built a fire. Then one by one he tossed the lighted sticks into the hole. Each showed a little light for a moment, then disappeared.

He tossed some larger sticks. As they passed downward, he could see the walls of the hole. But the light the sticks made was soon swallowed up by the darkness. The bottom of the pit was too far down to be seen.

The sun had gone down, and Jim knew he must leave for home.

When Jim White reached the ranch, he tried to tell the other cowboys all about his wonderful discovery. But he was so excited that he could hardly get the words out.

"There must have been a million bats!" he cried. "Maybe two, three million! They looked like a great big cloud of black smoke!"

But the cowboys just grinned.

"Aw, sure," said Art Baker. "You saw a cave with some bats flying out of it. We've all seen bat caves! But millions of bats! That sounds crazy!"

"But there *were* millions of the bats!" cried Jim. "I watched for nearly three hours before they all came out."

"Aw, come off it, Jim!" said Shorty Long. "Three hours! It just seemed that long to you!"

"I tell you it *was* three hours!" Jim insisted hotly. But his friends just laughed and shrugged.

"You've been out in the sun too long," said Art. "Come on! Let's wash up for supper!"

Jim followed them slowly as they started toward the house.

They didn't believe him! He knew it was hard for them to believe his story. He knew that it sounded crazy. But he *had* seen the bats, millions of them!

A few evenings later Jim talked some of his friends into going with him to watch the bats fly out for food. The men went along just to please him. But when they saw the cloud of bats and heard the sound of their whirring wings, they were as surprised as he had been.

When they returned and told what they had seen, the rest of the men still wouldn't believe them. But the strange story spread. At last the owner of a fertilizer company heard it. He came out to see Jim White.

"If what you say is true," he said, "that cave must be thick with guano. The droppings from all those bats will make fine fertilizer. Will you show me the cave?"

So Jim took the man to the bat cave. And he became as excited as Jim. "I can hardly believe it!" the man said. "That guano will make money for anyone who can mine it. Do you want a job helping me, Jim?"

The cowboy was delighted. At last he would have a chance to go down into that pit and explore!

The fertilizer company built a passage far down into the pit. And Jim White was lowered deep into the ground. He found great deposits of guano.

For several years he was in charge of the men who mined the guano. As he looked for other deposits of fertilizer, he found that there were rooms both to the left and to the right of the passage. Because of the deposits of guano in the rooms to the left, he knew that the bats lived there. But to the right there was no sign of guano, only unknown darkness.

As he worked, Jim kept thinking about that dark, unknown part of the caves. He made up his mind to find out what was there. He didn't want to explore all alone, because there might be dangers. But none of his friends wanted to go with him. Finally he found a young Mexican boy who would go, and they began to make plans to explore the caverns.

One morning Jim and his Mexican friend took some food, lamps, balls of string, and long ropes. They set out to explore the mystery that lay hidden in the darkness. As Jim and the Mexican boy began their search, they found themselves in a world of wonder.

For thousands of years the caverns had been in darkness. Now, for the first time, they were lighted. And for the first time their beauties were seen. The light from their lamps showed Jim and the Mexican boy great stalactites that looked like huge icicles hanging from the ceiling.

The stalactites had been made by water trickling over limestone for thousands of years. Bits of lime in the water had stuck to the ceiling. More and more lime had been added through the years and had made these structures. Where the light fell on them, the stone icicles sparkled with rainbow colors.

In other places there were stalagmites of huge size like great forests of stone. These also had been made by water dripping over limestone. The water had fallen in drops onto the floor and had built up structures there. Some of the stalagmites looked like stalactites turned upside down. Others were dark-colored and smooth.

Many of the big stalactites and stalagmites met and formed solid columns that reached from floor to ceiling. In

some places both stalactites and stalagmites showed beautiful colors in the dim light of the explorers' lamps.

Jim and the Mexican boy could hardly believe that the things they saw were real. They stood and stared at the greatness and beauty of the rooms.

The explorers were drawn on and on, although it was hard to move about in the caverns. The rocky, uneven floor was hard to walk on. Water had worn it away so that it was rough and bumpy, with sudden slopes and drops. Sometimes the two explorers had to use ropes to lower themselves from one place to another. They often had to squeeze through narrow openings.

They had never seen strange rock structures like those the water had made in the caverns. They felt uneasy at the thought of what they might find in the rooms. Now and then they could see huge shapes through the shadows. In the flickering light of their lamps each of these seemed to be a terrible monster, ready to leap upon them.

The day passed, and the two explorers did not return. Their friends began to worry about them. But Jim and the Mexican boy were still going through the caverns.

Scared though they were, they were so excited by what they saw that they decided to stay and see how far the rooms went. Their supplies would last for another day if they were careful.

They lay down to sleep on a bed of stone. But now and again the silence was broken by sudden notes of ghostly music. There was little sleep for either of them that night. After a few hours, they got up to explore farther. But the caverns seemed to go on and on.

At last the explorers turned back. Their supplies would last only long enough for them to get back to daylight.

When Jim and the Mexican boy came out of the cave, they were tired and dusty but filled with wonder at what they had found. This time Jim White had seen some of the real beauty of the great caverns. His story was so strange that again people found it hard to believe.

"It was just like a new world!" Jim said. "We flashed our lights and saw the strangest things!"

"Sí, sí, it was beautiful," sighed his Mexican friend. "It was so big!"

"And the ceilings looked hundreds of feet high in some places," added Jim.

The ranch hands looked at one another. Who could believe such stories? But they listened as Jim told of more and more wonders.

"But why didn't you come back yesterday and go out again this morning?" Shorty asked. "You had us worried. We thought that something had happened to you."

"We wanted to find out for ourselves how far the caves

reached," Jim explained. "So we just kept going on. It was so dark in there that we couldn't tell when yesterday ended and today began."

"So we stay and sleep," the Mexican boy said.

Jim grinned. "You mean, we tried to sleep," he said. "But we couldn't. One minute it was so still that we could hear ourselves breathe. And then, in the silence, we would hear something that sounded like notes of music."

His friends looked at one another and shook their heads.

"Well, how far do the caverns reach?" asked Art.

"We still don't know," Jim said. "They just seem to go on forever! But we didn't dare stay too long today. We had a long way to come back. We knew our oil wouldn't last much longer, and we didn't want our lamps to go out. I wouldn't want to be left there in the dark!"

"Well, you thought up a good story this time," said Shorty.

Art shrugged his shoulders. He said, "Jim, you're the best storyteller I ever heard!"

"But it's all true, I tell you!" Jim shouted.

His friends just turned away. They still didn't believe him.

Jim and the Mexican boy looked at each other. How could they make the others believe what they said about the wonders in the huge dark caves?

In the next few years Jim made many trips into the caverns. Most of the time he went alone. He always took a rope, a lamp, plenty of string, and a wire ladder.

Many strange and fearful things happened to Jim on these trips. One time his string broke. When he found out that he had no guide string, he was frightened. He was lost and alone, and there were so many winding passages that it would be hard to find the way he had come. He must try to find his string again.

Jim started back slowly, looking every step of the way for his string. He tried to remember special structures he had seen. He saw two large stalactites that he remembered passing. When his light had struck them, they had looked like large, colored icicles reaching almost to the floor.

A little farther on he came to a room that had several openings. At first he could not decide which way to go. Then, turning his light this way and that, he saw a huge stalagmite that looked like a great monster. He had seen it before. So he went in that direction.

It led him to the largest room Jim had seen in the caverns. He remembered that he had crossed this room. He was sure that the ceiling was several hundred feet high. Yes, he was going in the right direction.

He tried to run down a slope, but his foot caught in a hole, and he fell. His lamp flew from his hand and dropped with a clatter to the floor. The clatter sounded all through the huge hall.

Jim lay there a minute with his eyes closed, breathing deeply. He must not let fear make him act foolishly. When he opened his eyes, he saw that his lamp was still burning.

He got to his feet and picked up the lamp. Then he went on carefully. He began to see more colors and more shapes that he remembered. He felt that he was on the right path now. And sure enough, just as he went around a turn, there was the end of the string! It had broken on a sharp rock. Jim laughed with joy. And his laugh came back again and again from the walls. The caverns seemed to be laughing with him.

For now it would be easy. The string would guide him back to the opening of the cave. Since he was safe, he could enjoy the rainbow colors of the stalactites and the stalagmites.

But suddenly Jim was in trouble again. His flickering lamp went out. Its oil was gone. Once more he was alone and frightened. But this time he had his string to follow. He would move slowly and carefully.

The darkness made him hear many things that he had not heard before. His footsteps sounded so loud that he stopped to make sure no one else was there.

Then he could hear strange rustling and whispering sounds and the drip, drip of water. Soft, ghostly notes of music sounded around him—one, then another, then several together. Some were like chimes or sleigh bells. Others sounded more like notes from a piano.

Now Jim felt sure he was hearing things that weren't there at all. Where could music come from in here? He quieted his fears and went on, step by step, following his string. It seemed days before he finally came to the opening in the cave. How good it was to see daylight!

Although fearful things happened on some of his trips, Jim White returned to the caverns again and again. He learned that there really were sounds like chimes or sleigh bells and piano notes in some of the rooms. He explored farther and farther into the unknown darkness.

Jim never reached the end of the caverns. No one has yet found how far they go. But all the world now knows that Jim White found something far more important than a bat cave. He was led by the strange black smoke to one of the great wonders of our times—Carlsbad Caverns.

Afterthought

1. How did Jim White manage to keep from getting lost in the cave?
2. Would you have been afraid to help Jim the way the Mexican boy did?
3. What do you think made the sounds that Jim heard in the caverns?

The Dream

One night I dreamed
I was lost in a cave,
A cave that was empty
And dark and cool,
And down into nothing
I dropped a stone
And it fell like a star
Far and alone,
And a sigh arose
The sigh of a wave
Rippling the heart
Of a sunless pool.

And after a while
In my dream I dreamed
I climbed a sky
That was high and steep
And still as a mountain
Without a cave,
As still as water
Without a wave,
And on that hill
Of the sun it seemed
That all sad sounds
In the world fell asleep.

Harry Behn

How Nature Decorates Her Caves

Dorothy Sterling and Winifred Lubell

Try to put yourself in Jim White's place. Imagine how you would have felt when the light from the lantern first caught the beauties of the dark caverns. Would your friends have believed what you told them? Perhaps, like the early people, you would have made up a story to explain what you saw. As you read this article, think of ways a story might explain the decorations in a cave.

Caves don't grow as quickly as Jack's beanstalk. It takes nature a long, long time to make caves. And it takes hundreds or thousands of years to decorate them.

When a cave is born, it may be filled with rushing underground rivers. Slowly the water in the passages flows away. Air rushes in through surface cracks and openings. The cave rooms begin to dry out.

While this is going on, rain and snow still fall on the surface of the land. Drops of water still make their way through limestone rock to the hollowed-out rooms below. Water trickles down the walls and drips to the floor, forming little pools on the uneven surface.

Let's suppose one drop of water sticks to the ceiling of the cave. It grows smaller and smaller, and at last it dries and disappears. But, although the drop of water has disappeared, it has left behind a tiny circle of lime.

What has happened? Do you remember that lime dissolves in acid in somewhat the same way that salt dissolves in water? When anything

dissolves, it is still there, even though you can't see it. If you dissolve salt in water, the salt seems to disappear. But when you heat salt water on the stove until the water dries up, you will see the salt in the bottom of the pan.

In the same way the acid rainwater dissolves lime. When the drop on the ceiling dries, a little lime is left. Another drop comes and dries, leaving a little more lime in the same place. A third comes, and a fourth, until over many hundreds of years the bits of lime grow into hard stone icicles. These structures are stalactites.

Stalactites in some caves grow quickly, and in others they grow slowly. It may take a year or a hundred years for a stalactite to grow an inch. The structures keep on growing as long as drops of water trickle down, dry, and leave lime behind.

Sometimes these drops of water splash to the floor. They begin to build a structure of lime on the floor like a stalactite turned upside down. This is a stalagmite.

At the large end stalagmites are usually wider than stalactites, and they are rounded at the top. They often look like candles with melted

wax dripping down their sides. But these candles are of stone, and they grow larger instead of melting.

Often a stalactite grows down so far from the ceiling that it meets a stalagmite growing up from the floor. Then a solid column of stone reaches from the floor to the ceiling.

There are many other structures in caves besides the stalactites and the stalagmites. New ones are being formed all the time. Nature keeps painting her caves with the lime dissolved in acid rainwater.

All the while that structures are growing in a cave, it is alive. It will live as long as there is water dripping from the ceiling and trickling along the walls. But when no more water trickles into the underground rooms, all the structures stop growing. Then the cave is dead. But the structures with their beautiful colors may still be seen.

Afterthought

We know that the earth is always changing. The changes usually happen so slowly that we cannot see what is taking place. A volcano may erupt quickly, but the forces which made it erupt have been in action inside the earth for many years. A cave may take thousands of years to be born. Even now new wonders are appearing, and old ones are disappearing. Do you think we will ever completely understand these mysteries?

To Tame a Land

Western Wagons

They went with axe and rifle, when the trail was still to blaze,
They went with wife and children, in the prairie-schooner days,
With banjo and with frying pan—Susanna, don't you cry!
For I'm off to California to get rich out there or die!

We've broken land and cleared it, but we're tired of where we
    are.
They say that wild Nebraska is a better place by far.
There's gold in far Wyoming, there's black earth in Ioway,
So pack up the kids and blankets, for we're moving out today!

We're going West tomorrow, where the promises can't fail.
O'er the hills in legions, boys, and crowd the dusty trail!
We shall starve and freeze and suffer. We shall die, and tame the
    lands.
But we're going West tomorrow, with our fortune in our hands.

Stephen Vincent Benét

Frontiersman

Adapted from Langston Hughes

All kinds of people helped settle the American West, even some who could never settle down. Find out why reckless, restless men like Jim Beckwourth were important in pioneering the West.

The first Yankee clipper ship that sailed around the Horn to California brought back tales of the riches to be had there. From that time on, Easterners began to head west. The West was a land where young men might make their fortunes, adventurers find adventure, and pioneers discover new wealth.

A sea voyage was long and expensive, so many people went west by the overland routes, and the going was rough. The northern routes across country led through high and windy passes and over snow-covered mountains. The southern routes lay across deserts, waterless and sunbaked. Either way hostile Indians threatened.

Across dusty plains and over rocky mountain trails went the wagon trains. Many were poorly supplied and had no guides. After a few years skeletons lined the way. Graves from Missouri to the Coast showed that only the most hardy of the travelers had managed to go on. Yet people kept traveling west. And among them was the Negro pioneer, James Beckwourth.

When Jim was a child, his family settled on a farm near a point where the Missouri River flows into the Mississippi. The place was known as

Beckwourth Settlement. Jim's father was a white man, and his mother a slave, so Jim was considered a slave. At the age of about twelve he was apprenticed to a blacksmith in St. Louis and worked for him for several years. But as Jim grew older, he liked to dance and stay out late. He often showed up late for work. One morning Jim and the blacksmith had a fight, and Jim fled into hiding. He got onto a boat and went down the river to seek work in the mines. Before long he became a hunter, supplying wild game as meat to the miners.

As soon as he had saved some money, he took a boat trip to New Orleans—just for fun. But Jim did not like that city. Perhaps his color had something to do with it. In New Orleans a Negro could not enjoy himself in as lively a way as a white man could. Young Jim began to dream of going west, to the Far West, as far as the Rockies.

He got a job with a fur company, in a horse and mule train heading westward from St. Louis. Jim's duties ranged from shoeing horses to Indian fighting, and from trapping beavers and skinning furs to hunting for game. No company could carry enough food to last for the whole trip across country. So the travelers

lived most of the time on deer, wild turkeys, and bear meat. Sometimes an enormous buffalo provided a campfire feast for the men. At other times they had to eat the stringy meat of a coyote to keep from starving. Jim's experience as a hunter for the mining company came in handy. He was a crack shot.

He was also, he said, good at horse stealing. Fur companies were always in need of horses, particularly since the Indians were good at horse stealing, too, and often raided white men's camps. Horses were the cause of many skirmishes with the Indians. The Indians cared little for furs, but they loved horses. Beckwourth could speak a little of several Indian languages, and he could sometimes bargain with an Indian for a horse. If he could not bargain, he could threaten with a rifle. Or he could lasso and steal a horse, riding swiftly away, perhaps with an arrow whistling toward him.

The fur company came back to St. Louis with a fortune in furs, but Beckwourth did not stay in St. Louis very long. The urge to travel came before everything else. He headed west once more, and it was fourteen years before he came back. Every one of those fourteen years had its share of danger and adventure, for most of each one was spent in the wilds among Indians and frontiersmen.

As an old man Beckwourth told some pretty tall tales, but there is probably some truth in most of his stories. Certainly he did turn up in many places throughout the Wild West, and he did pass a long and active life as a frontiersman. Danger was part of his daily living. Unknown dangers in mapless places kept alive his spirit of adventure. He loved the rugged life he lived. After fifty pioneering years he was still alive to tell about it in a book about his life.

In his book Beckwourth did not mention that he was a Negro. He was light in color, and on the frontier color did not matter much anyway. There a man was a man, and that was that. Frontiersmen had to be rough and ready fighters, quick on the draw. They had to defend themselves not only against Indians, but against each other. The men who went west in those days were tough, rugged, and self-reliant. If hungry, they would take food. If horseless,

they would steal horses. If challenged, they would fight back. Good men were all mixed up with bad men.

Jim Beckwourth appears always to have been able to protect himself. In skirmishes with Indians he was so successful that he began to believe that he could not be killed by an Indian. He never was.

One time Beckwourth was sent to start a trading post among the Blackfeet Indians. He knew that he might be scalped, but he was willing to try it. Since Jim had light-brown skin, he looked like an Indian. He could move among Indians without attracting too much attention. So until he opened his mouth to speak, the Blackfeet thought he was a member of their tribe. They let him stay. He lived as they lived, ate what they ate, and danced their tribal dances.

Later, among the Crow Indians, Beckwourth passed as a Crow. He made them believe that as a child he was captured by another tribe and had forgotten the Crow language. An old Crow woman claimed him as her long missing son, and he stayed

for some time as a member of the tribe.

For a time Beckwourth worked as a guide to wagon trains crossing the mountains to California. From coast to coast he wandered in one job or another, Florida to Mexico, Louisiana to the Rockies. Jim was hunter, trapper, guide, interpreter among the Indians, adviser to travelers, fur trader, and go-between in the problems of whites and Indians.

James Beckwourth was a man who could do many things. The pioneering age in which he lived gave him chances to do them all. But one thing he never did was to stay in one place and get rich. He was too restless for that. He cared less for money than he did for adventure. Time after time Jim came to the big cities, and time after time he left them for the plains, the mountains, and the wide, open prairies.

The Drake Players Go West

Edith McCall

Scattered settlers needed
entertainment, and they usually
had to make their own. Most of
them probably never saw a play
with real actors. But showfolk
needed audiences, so they pioneered,
too. In this light-hearted story,
you get a glimpse of how they
traveled as they took their shows
to the wild frontier.

Long ago, in the days when the whistle of the steamboat was a new sound and the puff and chug of a steam locomotive had not yet been heard in America, two creaky old covered wagons lumbered up a dusty road. They carried a company of actors and actresses to the Kentucky frontier, where they hoped to open the first theaters to bring shows to the pioneers.

"Whoa!" called out the driver of the first wagon. They had come into a little town. The horses stumbled to a stop in the shade of a tree on the roadside. It was a hot day in July and they had walked all day on that road in southern New York state, heading westward on the long journey from Albany to the Allegheny River.

"This as far as we go today, Mr. Drake?" called the driver of the second wagon. He had pulled his team in behind the lead wagon.

Mr. Drake leaned from the driver's seat to look back.

"Yes, Lewis. We'll post the bills for the show before we put up at the inn. Come on, boys!" He shouted to four young men who were walking up the road. *"Forty Thieves* tonight!"

Three young ladies climbed down from the rear of the lead wagon. They were Martha Drake, her young sister, Julia, and another actress named Fanny Denny. They were helped down by Joe Tracy, the only one in the party who was not an actor. Joe kept the wagons in repair, tended the horses, helped put up scenery, shared the driving, and made himself useful in many other ways.

From one of the wagons, Mr. Drake pulled poster boards advertising the play, *Ali Baba and the Forty Thieves*, from the *Arabian Nights*. As the young men reached him, he handed a bugle to one of them.

"Here, Noah. Give a few toots on the horn so the folks will come out to see what the hullabaloo is about."

To Noah Ludlow, even tooting the horn was exciting, like everything else in show business. The other three young men were sons of "Old Sam" Drake. Young Sam, Aleck, and James had grown up as members of the Drake Players and had been acting in plays ever since they were old enough to walk onto a stage. But to Noah, it was all new. He was nineteen years old, and had left his home the year before to learn to act in Albany. This was his first time on the road with the Drake Players.

Old Sam hurried ahead to the courthouse that stood in the center of the little business square. He wanted to use the courtroom as a theater that evening. In larger towns, the inn sometimes had a ballroom that made a better theater, but there would be no place that large until they finally reached Pittsburgh.

The young men knew what to do. Noah tooted the horn.

Young Sam and James took hammer and nails and put up some posters on the trees. Over his shoulders, Aleck hung the sandwich boards with the pictures of Ali Baba poking his head out of the great oil jar as the forty thieves raised daggers over his head.

Old Sam waved from the courthouse door that all was set. Noah tooted loudly to draw a crowd. Aleck marched back and forth. Then Old Sam shouted.

"Come one, come all, to the courthouse tonight, folks! See before your very eyes the wonders of the *Arabian Nights* of old! See Ali Baba outwit forty thieves! The greatest company of actors ever to come to your city will present the finest, the very finest show you have ever seen! See the great chests of genuine jewels, the silks and satins of the Orient—all before your very eyes! Tonight, one night only! Do not miss the greatest show of your lifetime, here at seven o'clock, tonight! Here in the courthouse, folks!"

The next two hours were busy ones. The men brought

rolled-up scenery, boxes, the curtain, and candle footlights. A plain little courtroom became a bit of far off Arabia.

Mrs. Lewis and the girls freshened up the costumes the best they could. In those days, it was hard to find bright-colored cloth that would wash, and the costumes looked dingy in the daylight. But at night, in the glow of the candle footlights, the dull, tarnished braid would become shining gold, the glass beads would be bright jewels, and the soiled costumes would become princely garments.

At seven, Noah peeked out through the closed curtains. The little courthouse was packed. The benches were filled to the last inch and there was standing room only for the latecomers. He remembered his first night as an actor. It had been in this same play, but he had been given only two words to say. Tonight he played the part of several of the thieves, popping in and out of sight often, each time with a different colored cap on his head to make it seem as if the four "thieves" in the company were really forty.

The clapping was loud and long when the play ended. To many in the audience, this was the only play they would see all year. The cities of the East now had a few museums, a small circus now and then, and theaters to go to most of the year. But on the frontier, such things had not yet come.

The next morning, the two wagons were on their way again.

"From here on, we'll be in the wilderness, almost until we get to Pittsburgh, folks," Old Sam said. "No more places to give a play for a while, so we'll travel all day."

They were all beginning to feel like frontiersmen by the time their wagon journey ended. They had reached the wild Allegheny River at the little settlement of Olean. There they were to trade the wagons and horses for a boat. The fact that none of them had ever been on a flatboat before did not worry them.

"You just let it float down the river. There's no place to go except between the riverbanks," said Old Sam.

Noah looked at the boat that was to be their home for a month or two. There wasn't much to it. It was about twenty-five feet long and fifteen feet wide, with board sides that rose five or six feet along most of its length. The sides were the walls of a roofed-over cabin. The roof curved a little so that water would run off it.

In the cabin, there was room to stow the stage properties and costumes and the few other things the company had, but there was room to curtain off only two bedrooms. Mr. and Mrs. Lewis would have one, and the young ladies the other. The Drakes, Tracy, and Noah would sleep wherever they could.

"What do they call a crate like this?" Noah asked Old Sam.

"It's a flatboat, boy, but the men here tell me this kind is called an ark."

On the roof, at the middle of the stern, was a forked piece of wood in which rested the long handle of the steering oar. It was just a long pole with a wide board at the end that went into the water. There were a couple of loose poles on the boat, too, and a pair of oars for the little skiff, or rowboat, that was tied to the larger boat.

"Yo, ho, ho! It's off to sea we go," sang Young Sam. He and the other young men pushed the ark out into the Allegheny River, while Old Sam struggled with the heavy steering oar.

Just then, a young man in the uniform of a soldier came running down to the riverbank.

"Hey, there!" he yelled. "Could you use a good hand aboard?"

Old Sam was making strange splashings with the steering oar.

"Reckon we could," he said. "If we can stop this dang thing."

The young men leaned on the poles. They had not gone far enough for the current to take hold of the boat; but even so, they had some trouble getting it close enough to shore for the young man to leap aboard.

"My name is Hull," he said. "I'm on my way home to Ohio after fighting in the war."

"Been on a riverboat much?" Old Sam asked.

"Not on the Allegheny, but twice up and down the Ohio, and down the Mississippi, too," said Hull. "Before I went into the army, I did a spell of keelboating."

"Good. We're actors, and not boatmen," said Old Sam. "I'll be obliged to have you take this confounded steering oar."

Hull took over, and soon the ark was following the channel of the river. The other young men saw Hull take off his jacket and shirt, and did the same themselves, for the July afternoon sun was very hot. Hull was brown to the waist, and his muscles rippled. The other boys looked white and thin beside him.

It was a very hot day, too hot to lie in the sun on the roof and too stuffy under the roof. They made an awning for themselves of some stage scenery. The breeze swept under it, and everyone on board stretched out in its shade. Even Hull, handling the steering oar, managed to lie down. He held the pole steady with his crossed legs.

Suddenly Mrs. Lewis screamed, "Look out, look out!"

Noah, without checking, jumped into the water, sure that one of the girls had rolled off the curved roof into the river. Someone was in the water, but it was not one of the girls. Mr. Lewis, startled by his wife's scream, had rolled into the river and was splashing about.

"A waterfall! A waterfall!" screamed Mrs. Lewis, pointing down the river. "We'll go over it in a minute."

Hull was on his feet. Ahead, he saw that someone had built a milldam right across the river. No boat could pass.

He shouted, "Every man who can swim jump overboard! Grab the boat and hold her with all you've got!"

Mr. Drake and Mr. Lewis leaned against the poles while all the young men jumped into the river. With all their strength, they pushed at the boat to stop its downstream drift. The dam made a little lake right there, and the current was not so strong as farther upriver. They managed to stop the boat just a few feet above the dam.

"Now, we've got to push or pull it upstream to safety," Hull said. "Can you hold it, boys, while I get a rope tied to her? We'll *cordelle* it back up the river."

The crew backwatered and pushed until they had the boat in shallow water at the stream's edge. Hull tied a heavy rope into a ring at the stern. While Tracy, Aleck, and James held the boat in place, Young Sam, Noah, and Hull got into the skiff and rowed upstream to where a tree overhung the bank. They took the coil of rope with them, letting it out as they moved away from the boat. When they reached the tree they wound it once around the trunk and beached the skiff.

"Pull!" called Hull. All three pulled with all their strength. Back on the boat, the other young men pushed. The boat began its upstream trip. When it was pulled up to the tree, the rope was taken upstream to another tree, and the job began again.

It was slow, hard work. The clumsy, square-ended, flat-bottomed ark was not built for upriver travel. At day's end, however, they were back at the point where they had begun the day's journey.

"Why in Sam Hill would anyone be allowed to build a dam across a river which is supposed to be open to Pittsburgh?" Old Sam growled.

Hull went ashore to find out. When he came back, he had the answer.

"We took the wrong branch of the river," he said. "There's a forking of the river here. That dam reached from a long, narrow island to the shore. We can get through by using the main channel."

"I've learned one thing," Noah said as he rubbed his aching muscles. "I am a better actor than a boatman."

As they moved the boat around to the main channel and began the day's journey, their young voices went up in song,

"Oh, fiddle dee, dee—

It's an actor's life for me!"

Poison Water

Evelyn Sibley Lampman

Wagon trains carried all kinds of
unexpected things across country. The
Luellings had trees and bushes in one of
their wagons. But before they could get to
the rich soil of Oregon, they had to cross
the desert.

"If this is a desert," said Peter in disgust, "I don't like them."

"It's not a real desert," objected Seenie thoughtfully. "At least, it's not like any I ever read about. The books never say anything about alkali in deserts, but they do talk about camels and oases. And here there's alkali and no camels and no oases."

"There's sure plenty of alkali," snorted Peter. "It's too bad it's not good for something."

Seenie nodded and frowned down at the toes of her dusty shoes. They were new shoes, although they didn't look it. They hadn't been intended for her in the first place, but she had worn out her other pair and these had fit. Mr. Luelling had brought a small stock of goods in one of the wagons, intending to open a little store in Oregon. However, it was beginning to look now as though there would be no goods left to sell. As their clothing and supplies gave out, his own family was dipping into the stock he had intended for trade.

All the children had been wearing shoes for some weeks now. In the first stages of the trip they had gone barefoot, but the sharp rocks in the mountains had put their shoes back on their feet, and the burning, stinging alkali dust of the desert was keeping them there.

The alkali was everywhere. It glistened on the ground like a fine powdering of fresh snow. Sometimes they passed dry lake beds of it, crusted hard and thick. It was beautiful to see, miles upon miles of dazzling white beneath a sky that was so blue it seemed unreal, but it was anything but pleasant to walk through. It burned their hands and faces; and when they perspired, the moisture mixed with the alkali dust stung as badly as a fresh cut.

Seenie considered Peter's last remark. He was right. There should be something to do with alkali, something useful. Suppose a fairy should fly by at this moment and invite her to make any wish she pleased. She might ask the fairy to turn all the white alkali into something pleasant like cake frosting. She imagined walking through acres of cake frosting, and whenever she was hungry stooping down to gather a handful. Then she decided against the idea. In the first place no fairy was likely to fly by, and in the second place so much sweet would only give her a stomach ache and leave her as thirsty as she was now.

My, how thirsty she was! How hot and sticky and thirsty! Too thirsty even to think up a good pretend story for her own amusement.

The extra water hidden in a bottle for the gooseberry bush had been gone a long time. If there were any left, she might be tempted to borrow just a small sip for herself right now. After all, the trees were getting more water than the people in this desert, which hardly seemed fair.

"Look," said Peter without much interest. "There's another one of them."

Her eyes followed his pointing finger across the glistening white flats and her heart pumped with excitement. Off in the distance and away from the trail was a river. It was calm and wide, its waters only a little less blue than the sky above it. No trees or bushes grew on either bank, but the cool, blue, tranquil stream threaded its way through the white stretches and disappeared into the horizon.

"A river," she gasped, her throat contracting with dryness. "Water!"

"That's the third one we've seen," he agreed. "And the best mirage yet."

Another mirage! Of course, he was right and she realized it instantly. If it had been a real stream the cattle would have smelled it, and it would have taken all the men could do to keep them in hand. The cattle were as thirsty as she. Even the gooseberry bush and the other trees were thirsty.

As they advanced, the cool thread of river running along beside them dissolved in a heat wave. It was funny how quickly it went. One moment it was there. Another step forward and it was gone.

She had heard about mirages and had always wanted to see one. Now she hoped she would never see another. They

were always of something you really wished for, like a settlement or a running stream, and it was heartbreaking to find they weren't real.

The oxen suddenly raised their drooping heads and began to bellow. Forgetting their tender, bleeding feet, they pulled at the wagon with renewed strength.

"They smell water," said Seenie.

"Poison water, most likely," muttered Peter. "You heard what your pa said. We can't hope to reach the Sweetwater till late tomorrow. And then only if we're lucky."

"Maybe he's wrong," hoped Seenie. "Come on. Let's look."

It took the restraining hands of all the elder Luellings and Hocketts to get the maddened cattle past the water hole. Their shouted command rose high above the reproachful protests of the oxen and the two cows following plaintively behind. Whips cracked in the heavy, hot air, and chains jangled protestingly. Seenie and Peter ignored all these noises which had become so familiar in these days in the desert. They hurried as fast as their tired feet would carry them to the side of the trail where the cattle turned glazed eyes.

"It's just like the others," said Peter. Although he had not expected good water, his voice was disappointed. This time he would have liked to be wrong.

In the dry dust and rocks there was a pool. It was shallow and stagnant, but it was water. No grass grew around the edges, but there were many scattered white bones. There were the skull of somebody's ox, leg bones, and a whole rib section, as well as smaller bones that had once belonged to lesser animals. On the white top of the ox skull someone had printed with black tar the words "Beware! Poison Water." It was almost an unnecessary warning. The drying animal bones scattered around told the story plainly enough.

From ahead, where he was still struggling to keep the oxen on the trail, Father's voice floated back to them.

"Any grass, Seenie?"

"No grass," she called back, as she and Peter wearily resumed their places in line.

"We'll reach the Sweetwater tomorrow," repeated Peter. "And Ma says there's just enough water left in the barrels for us tonight."

Seenie nodded, too hot and uncomfortable to speak. Warm

water from a barrel, when she wanted a whole, rushing river of it! She thought nostalgically of the Platte and the other streams they had forded. She hadn't minded walking then. Now it was hard to lift her feet. Wouldn't Mother ever call her to take her next turn in the wagon?

They traveled longer than usual that day, and the sun had disappeared below the alkali flats in the west when Father decided it was time to stop. They made camp a little distance from one of the poison pools, but this one had grass growing around it.

"Help with the watering, Asenath," said Mother wearily. "I'm spreading out supper right now. We'll eat as soon as the chores are done."

They had prepared for the desert crossing where the *Guide* had said they could expect to find no fuel, not even buffalo chips, by baking dried apple pies and biscuits and pots of beans. There were enough to carry them through. There had been no hot meals since they left the Big Horn, but no one cared. It was too hot for anything but cold food.

"Camp's so far away from the pool," complained Seenie irritably. "If we have to carry water to the tree wagon, we should have made camp closer."

"And have the cattle going crazy to get at the fresh grass?" demanded Mother shortly. "You know well enough the grass around the pools is as poisonous as the water itself. The cattle have to eat from the wagon, same as we do. Now do as I say, and don't argue."

Seenie shuffled over the dry, white soil, which lost some of its glitter when the sun went down. The smaller girls were already busy filling buckets and carrying them back across the hot, long way to the tree wagon.

This pool did not look nearly so menacing as the one they had passed earlier in the afternoon. It looked almost inviting. True, the water was sluggish and brown, and there were the scattered telltale bones lying around, but there was green grass at the edge. The warning left by previous wagons was posted on a stake stuck in the ground. It had been written on a piece of cloth with tar, and the cloth hung limp and bedraggled in the windless air.

"Hurry up, Seenie," ordered Mary, dipping her bucket in the pool. "The sooner it's done, the sooner we can rest."

"I am," snapped Seenie, but her motions became even slower and more deliberate. She lowered her own bucket into the water and allowed it to slosh around a little before she drew it up. The cool liquid splashed on her hand, and at the time it was pleasant although she knew she would be sorry later. Water mixed with alkali made lye which burned and stung. For now, the water felt soothing to her hot skin. Surely there was nothing the matter with this pool. She wondered what would happen if she took off her shoes and waded.

Finally she withdrew her bucket, and stepping slowly, carefully, she started toward the tree wagon. Rachel and Hannah passed her on their way back.

"What are you walking so slow for?" demanded Hannah critically.

"You don't think I want to spill it, do you?" she snapped.

"My bucket's full to the top. Water is precious around here."

Alfred, on top of the tree wagon, reached down to take the heavy bucket from her.

"Don't pour it," she shrieked. "Just hold it a minute. I'm coming up. I've got to water my gooseberry bush myself."

"For Pete's sake," objected Alfred. "I can water it. Besides, there's more than enough here for your bush. We've got to spread it around."

"Don't you dare use that water, Alfred Luelling," she warned. "And don't you water my bush. It's mine. It expects me to take care of it. If there's any left over you can have it."

"We'll be here all night," he complained. "And I'm tired."

But he didn't pour the water. He held the pail until she was in the wagon bed, and then watched disapprovingly as she watered her bush. The trees looked dry and unhappy. Some of them had shed leaves in the arid heat, and Father said he was afraid they were done for. But the greatest number of them still lived, and among these was Seenie's gooseberry bush.

"Don't drown it," said Alfred sarcastically. Everyone's temper was at the breaking point with the heat.

"I know what I'm doing," she said loftily. "Here, you can have the rest."

A scant quarter of a bucket remained after she watered her gooseberry. Alfred took it with a black look, pouring it around one of the small trees.

"Alfred," she said seriously, making no motion to get down from the wagon, "how does Father know it's safe to use water from poison pools on the trees?"

"He doesn't," said Alfred shortly. "He just has to take a chance. The trees will die without any water."

"So will we."

"You get water. Out of the barrels. Now, go on and fill that bucket again."

"I will. In a minute. I want to ask you something first. Do you think the poison water is hurting the trees? We don't let the oxen eat the grass around the poison pools."

"The trees will have a chance to get over it," he said thoughtfully. "I don't think it will hurt them. Father's very careful about which pool we use the water from. If there's no grass growing around it, then maybe the water's killed the grass. We don't use that water. If the grass is living, then there's a good chance it might be all right for the trees."

"But he doesn't really know? I mean, he didn't know till he tried it?"

"Of course not. But he had to try it, and so far everything's all right. Now, will you get more water."

"I'm going," she agreed meekly.

She got down, avoiding her sisters' reproachful eyes as they handed up their third buckets. She started back; but hearing a protesting bellow from the direction of the oxen, she told herself she ought to investigate that first.

Father, Mr. Hockett, Charley, and George were all busy around Berry, and it was Berry who was making all the noise. Father seemed to be thrusting something down the ox's throat while the Hocketts held him. As Seenie watched, Father withdrew his hand, the Hocketts let go, and Berry gave a great shudder.

"There," said Father. "Either that will cure him or finish him off. We'll have to wait till morning to find out."

"What's the matter with Berry?" called Seenie. "What are you doing to him?"

Father turned and looked over his shoulder. He seemed to

have grown older on this trip, but after all he was in his thirties. Thirty, Seenie remembered, was pretty old.

"Berry's sick," he explained. "Been dragging behind all day. Nathan heard about a treatment of raw bacon that cured a sick ox back home, so we tried it."

"What did you do? Make Berry eat some bacon?"

"Wrapped a hunk of it in a cold pancake and put it down his throat. We stroked his throat to make him swallow. That's all we can do."

"Will it make him feel better?" she demanded, feeling sorry for patient old Berry.

"We hope so. It's an experiment. We'll never know till we try."

"Like watering the trees with poison water from pools that have grass?" she demanded. "That's an experiment?"

"That's an experiment, too," he smiled. He didn't look quite so old when he smiled. "But I think it's working. The trees are standing up. You never know about anything till you try. Why aren't you helping with the watering?"

"I am," she said quickly. "I have been. I just wanted to see what was the matter with Berry. Father, do you suppose these pools with grass around them aren't really *very* poison? Do you suppose they've got over being poison, and nobody knows it?"

"I doubt it," said Father shortly. "Go back to your work, Seenie."

When Father used that tone, he didn't expect an argument. She turned hastily and started back to the pool, but her mind was busy. You never know about anything till you try it, she thought. Father hadn't been sure about using the water for the trees until he tried. He wasn't sure about doctoring poor, sick Berry, but he had to try. Perhaps the water in some of these pools marked poison wasn't really bad. Perhaps someone with a dreadful sense of humor had put up that sign for a joke. No, no one could be that mean. But perhaps the water had been poison once and it had changed. She didn't know what made it poison in the first place, but perhaps the poison had disappeared or lost its strength. No one would ever know it until it was proved. Someone would have to experiment and find out.

She took a deep breath and tried to put the idea from her mind, but it was too strong for her. It would take a very brave person to make the experiment, but think what it would mean. Why, it would be the greatest blessing that covered-wagon trains had ever had. She imagined hot and thirsty trains passing over the dry, alkali deserts and coming upon one of these pools.

"Another poison water hole," someone would say. "Hold the oxen. Don't let them get away. Drive on!"

And then someone with keen eyes, someone with dry parched lips, would see a sign above the pool:

"This pool tasted by Asenath Luelling in 1847
and found good! You may drink with safety!"

That's what the sign would say. All up and down the line of march, men and women and children would pour out of the wagons. The cattle would be unrestrained and allowed to quench their great thirst. Then, when everyone was refreshed, they would raise their eyes to the blue, blue sky above them and with a mighty shout their voices would rise above the alkali flats.

"God bless Asenath Luelling! Three cheers for that brave, brave girl!"

She hurried her steps. Almost, but not quite, she forgot how hot and tired and thirsty she was. The bucket bumped against her legs as she ran. The pool was deserted now. Perhaps the little girls had carried up enough water to satisfy Alfred. Or perhaps they were all handing up filled buckets and would return. She had better hurry if she wanted to make this experiment by herself.

She lowered the bucket and brought up just a little water in the bottom. The pool was roiled now, and somehow it did not look quite so harmless as before. There were bones about it, too, but she told herself stoutly they were very old. They had been there a long time.

Cautiously she raised the bucket to her lips, and hesitated a moment as she took a final deep breath.

"Seenie Luelling! Are you crazy?"

Peter had come up behind her unobserved. He stared at her with amazed and scornful eyes.

"I—I thought I'd try an experiment," she stammered.

"After all, we can't be sure these pools are all poison. You shouldn't believe everything you hear. And maybe the poison has got out of them."

"Maybe not, too," he snorted. "Well, if you want to try to kill yourself, go ahead. I'll just tell your ma what you were up to, and she'll make you drink mustard water till you throw it all up again. Drinking water from a poison hole! What a baby trick!"

"But we can't be sure it's poison till we experiment," she protested feebly. "Somebody's got to take a chance."

"Somebody did," he agreed, pointing to the limp cloth sign. "That's why they left that for other people to read."

"I guess you're right," she agreed hastily and emptied the water back into the pool. "I guess there's no need to try an experiment twice. Not after it's once been proved out."

Afterthought

Find two places in the story that tell you of Seenie's imagination. How was her imagination helpful to her on the dreary journey over the desert? How did her imagination lead her into danger?

Johnny Appleseed

Anne Malcolmson

Unforgettable Jonathan Chapman wandered the frontier for forty years. He was a gentle man, but he was as restless as Jim Beckwourth. Read to discover why this gentle pioneer became an American legend.

This is the story of Johnny Appleseed, as strange and lovable a man as ever lived in the American wilderness. Some say that his ghost still lingers in the apple orchards of Ohio and Indiana.

Appleseed, of course, wasn't his real name. His parents proudly named him Jonathan—Jonathan Chapman. Young Johnny Chapman spent his boyhood playing in the woods and on the farms near his Boston home.

As he grew sturdy and brown, two things became clear to all who knew him. First, he was a born orchardman. He understood trees, especially fruit trees. Second, he was going west. He had heard tales of the wonderful rich country behind the Pennsylvania mountains, the country of Daniel Boone and the pioneers. He was going to see it. As a young man he went to Pittsburgh, bought himself a little farm, and planted an orchard.

At that time Pittsburgh was West. Nevertheless it wasn't far enough west for Johnny. Day after day, people passed his farm. They came on foot, on horseback, in rickety farm wagons, in handsome coaches—all bound for the wilderness of the Ohio Valley. Some of them stopped at his door to ask for water, or food, or a night's lodging. To all of them Johnny gave what he could.

Johnny felt sorry for these people. He knew how lonely they were going to be without the towns and pleasant farmlands they had left behind. He wanted to help them. But how could he, a poor nurseryman, do it? Sometimes he had hardly enough to eat himself.

One night his question answered itself. He'd give them all apple orchards. So he did. To every traveler who stopped at his cabin, he gave a bag of apple seeds. The pioneers were nearly always grateful. They wrote home to their friends about the generous man near Pittsburgh. Soon Johnny had given away all the seeds he could spare. He started bothering his neighbors. Most of them were gruff Pennsylvania Dutchmen. They thought their young friend was a little crazy. But they were glad enough to give him the mash that was left in their cider presses, if he could use that.

Patiently he worked all winter, picking out the seeds from the sticky mess. He dried them with care and sewed them into little deerskin pouches, to be ready for the rush of spring travelers. When spring came, he left his own farm and went to the waterfront with his treasures. Here, where two rivers meet to form the great Ohio, came the travelers from the East. Some came to ferry across to the dark opposite shore, others to pile their belongings on flatboats which would carry them down to the unknown West. And here Johnny stayed, giving away his "orchards." People soon forgot that his name was Chapman. Along the levees and highroads they called him Appleseed.

Soon Johnny began to worry. If these orchards were really going to grow, they needed a trained orchardman to take care of them—someone who knew how to plant and prune. Who could do that? The answer was simple—Johnny himself. He sold his farm and bought a couple of flimsy canoes. He heaped them full with the cider mash, tied them together with a piece of rope, and went west.

For the next forty years until he died, Johnny had no home of his own. He paddled his little canoes up the creeks and backwaters. Wherever he found a likely spot, he stopped. He cleared away the underbrush and planted the seeds from small deerskin pouches. Then he built a fence around his plot to keep the deer from nibbling the first tender shoots—and off he went again. Several times he ran out of seeds. He had to go back to Pennsylvania for more cider mash to be dried and sorted and packed in pouches for more orchards.

Now and then when new settlers

moved into the countryside, Johnny "sold" them the saplings from his forest plots. If they had money he charged "a fib-penny bit" for each tree. But more often than not he took old clothes as a swap, or let the pioneers "buy" the orchards with promises to pay him later.

As you can see, he didn't make much money this way. That didn't worry him. He didn't need much money. He liked sleeping out in the open. He never wore shoes, even in the worst blizzards. At first he wore the cast-off clothes he received for his young trees. After a while, even these became too civilized. So he begged an old coffee sack from a storekeeper, cut a hole for his head and two for his arms, and let it go at that. Hats were a nuisance, too. Since he had to carry a kettle to cook his cornmeal in, he solved the problem by wearing the kettle.

He had no gun and no hunting knife. Not even the Indians, those master woodsmen, could understand this fact. Johnny, however, lived well on berries and apples and roots and the cornmeal mush he stirred up in his hat. As for shelter? Many an old settler will tell you that when Johnny was invited to spend the winter night in front of his cabin fire, he shook his head politely. He said he'd rather sleep out in the open with his friends the animals.

This strange little man with the odd outfit and the scraggly beard was a welcome guest in all the tepees, lean-tos, and cabins in the Ohio Territory. Wherever he went, he managed to carry little presents for the settlers. These were usually trees and "yarbs" for the grownups, bits of calico for the little girls, and odd pebbles and shells for the boys.

But best of all he had a stock of stories. In the wilderness, news was

scarce. The pioneers rarely had news of the neighbors who lived five miles away, news from back home, or news of what was happening in the world. Johnny talked and listened to everyone he met. In time he became a sort of living newspaper and postman for the people in the wilderness.

But the news he liked best to tell was his news "fresh from heaven." After he had shared a supper with a family in some lonely clearing, he sat before the hearth and read aloud from his Bible. Sometimes, in his own strange Biblical language, he told about his visions. One granny who listened to him when she was a little girl said he used to make the cabin "blossom with the roses of Galilee."

The boys, of course, liked most to hear him tell about his life with the Indians. The Shawnees, a fierce tribe, were still the terror of the Ohio country. Not many of the white settlers had much to do with them. But Johnny really lived with them. It is hard to understand how he escaped harm at their hands, going about unprotected as he did through the forest. But when you understand the Indians, you can readily see why. The Shawnees thought he was a medicine man. Woe to any brave who touched a hair on the head of a

holy person! Once, while camping in the forest, Johnny had met an Indian who was suffering from a fever. Johnny knew well what plants could be used to cure illnesses. In a day or so he had cured the brave. From that time on, the Indian was his devoted friend. He even asked the white man to visit him in his camp.

At first the other Indians were suspicious. They made Johnny prove his worthiness. His body had been so toughened by his life in the woods that he was as strong and courageous as a red man. He stuck pins through his flesh without flinching. He walked barefoot through the snow in the bitter cold weather. He could tell direction by instinct, and he knew as much wood lore as his hosts. In fact, he knew more than they did. He knew ways of planting corn to make it grow better. He knew how to cure sicknesses and wounds. The red men were amazed when they saw him take a red-hot iron and burn the ragged edges of a gash he had received from a sharp stone. Everyone knew that this was a good way to keep out infection. But how many had the courage to do it?

Johnny was as good an Indian as any of them. So he was made a member of the Shawnee tribe. Throughout the whole West he was known as the Indian's friend.

Many of the stories he told the settlers were about his adventures with animals. He dearly loved all living things. He considered it a sin to kill or to harm any of them. The animals seemed to understand this, and some people thought he understood animal talk.

One chilly night he was walking through the woods when he began to feel sleepy. He picked out a hollow log and started to crawl in. Unfortunately, a honey bear had had the same idea. All at once, Johnny touched something soft and furry.

He heard an angry growl only a foot from his head. You and I might have been frightened. But not Mr. Appleseed. He apologized politely to the bear, backed out of the log, and found himself another shelter in the crook of a tree.

Another evening he sat down beside a little stream and built a fire to cook his cornmeal. As the sun sank and darkness fell, he noticed that hordes of tiny gnats were being attracted by the light. Worse than that, they were being burned in the flames. Johnny was hungry, but he couldn't stand the thought that his fire was taking the lives of his insect friends. "God forbid," he said, "that I should build a fire for my comfort that should be the means of destroying any of God's creatures." So he put it out and hunted for berries to give him strength until morning.

For several years Johnny had a pet wolf who followed him wherever he went. This was a strange pet indeed, especially in the frontier country. Wolves were hated and feared almost as much as were the Indians. But this wolf was different. Johnny had found him caught in a trap. Its heavy iron jaw had cut his leg. There he lay waiting for an angry frontiersman to come with his rifle.

Johnny Appleseed, however, had no rifle. He walked fearlessly up to the snarling beast and soothed him. Unafraid he pried open the jaws of the trap and set the animal free. Carefully he bound up the wounded leg. He brought water from a nearby spring and gave the wolf a drink from his old mush-kettle hat. He treated him as though he were a sick baby. As the sore healed, the wolf attached himself to Johnny. He padded behind him in the woods and watched over him at night. He was the orchardman's friend and favorite until an angry farmer, mistaking him for the thief in his chicken yard, shot him.

Perhaps the most dramatic of all Johnny Appleseed's adventures was his saving of the fort at Mansfield. In 1812 the new United States and the British went back to war. It was a foolish war, but the two nations felt bitterly toward one another. To help themselves, the British got the support of the Indians in the Territories. They felt that the white men had treated them unfairly. They were eager for the chance to fight. Johnny did what he could to persuade the Shawnees, his adopted brothers, to be peaceful. But as much as they loved him, they voted for war.

Johnny himself refused to fight the Indians. He thought of them as foolish children. He knew they couldn't understand what they were doing. Even so, he felt it his duty to help the American settlers. When he heard that the Indians were going on the warpath, he got busy. He traveled night and day through the wilderness. At each frontier cabin he paused only long enough to give his warning. "Rise up," he called. "Take your family to the fort at Mansfield." Then he quoted from the Bible, " 'For behold, the tribes of the heathen are round about your doors, and a devouring flame followeth after them.' "

One by one the settlers left their cabin clearings. Some of them fled in their nightshirts, leaving behind all their belongings. They could see the red skies in the north, where the Shawnees were burning farms and towns.

How safe the fort at Mansfield, Ohio, looked to them as they ran out of the forest! Its big blockhouses loomed up at the corners. Its cannon threatened from the walls.

Unfortunately, however, there was little food inside the stockade. Even worse, there was little water. The village spring was outside the fort. People from miles around had come to seek shelter. When at last all the pioneers had gathered, it was clear that the fort could not hold out for very long. Unless word could be sent to the American garrison at Mount Vernon, thirty miles away, Mansfield was lost.

The captain called a meeting of all the men. He explained how much they needed help. He called for a volunteer to run through the woods to Mount Vernon to ask for help. But the pioneers stood there, silently. The trip to Mount Vernon meant almost certain death. The woods were full of enemies. And even without these, it was a dangerous trip.

Then came a clear, calm voice from the back of the crowd. "I will go," it called. It was Johnny. He had already done his part. For days and nights without sleep he had been hurrying through the countryside carrying his warning. He must have

been very tired. But here he was again, offering to make the long dangerous journey to Mount Vernon.

The men protested. "I know the trail," he said, "and I shall be safe in the forest. My brothers will not harm me." Without further ado he was off.

All night he sped on his errand. Worn out, he stumbled into Mount Vernon and aroused the captain of the garrison. Then without rest or refreshment he led the soldiers back. Shortly before he reached the fort, he stopped. He had done his duty, but he refused to take part in the fight. He would curl up in a log and sleep, he said. He was tired. And besides, there was an orchard nearby that needed his attention in the morning.

The soldiers reached Mansfield in the nick of time. The Shawnees had already made an attack. But, sandwiched between the fresh army and the fort, they were soon beaten off.

As the years went by, the Ohio Territories were left in peace. Johnny's saplings grew into large trees. New settlers moved in and cleared the land. The wilderness became a rich farming country, crossed with roads and dotted with villages. Things became too civilized for the strange little man. So he moved west with the frontier into Indiana and Michigan and Illinois. In his coffee-sack shirt and his mush-kettle hat, he planted his seeds in the forests and carried his "news fresh from heaven."

One day many years later a farmer found his worn-out old body lying beside a little orchard in the woods near Fort Wayne, Indiana. Johnny Appleseed had died looking after his beloved trees.

Afterthought

1. How may the pioneers' letters have helped to make Johnny Appleseed a legend?
2. In your opinion, why did men like Jonathan Chapman and Jim Beckwourth never stay long in one place?
3. How would people today treat a man like Johnny Appleseed?

The Wilderness Is Tamed

The axe has cut the forest down,
The laboring ox has smoothed all clear,
Apples now grow where pine trees stood,
And slow cows graze instead of deer.

Where Indian fires once raised their smoke
The chimneys of a farmhouse stand,
And cocks crow barnyard challenges
To dawns that once saw savage land.

The axe, the plow, the binding wall,
By these the wilderness is tamed,
By these the white man's will is wrought,
The rivers bridged, the new towns named.

Elizabeth Coatsworth

The West Begins

Laura Ingalls Wilder

As a young girl Laura Ingalls Wilder made the journey she tells about in this story. It was Laura's job to describe what she saw to her blind sister, Mary. The story will help you understand the experience of a family traveling all alone through wild, open country.

The sun shone brightly on the uncovered wagon, but the wind was cool and riding was pleasant. Here and there, men were working in their fields, and now and then a team and wagon passed.

Soon the road curved downward through rolling land and Pa said, "The Big Sioux River's ahead."

Laura began to see out loud for Mary. "The road's going down a low bank to the river, but there aren't any trees. There's just the big sky and grassy land, and the little, low creek. It's a big river sometimes, but now it's dried up till it's no bigger than Plum Creek. It trickles along from pool to pool, by dry gravel stretches and cracked dry mud flats. Now the horses are stopping to drink."

"Drink hearty," Pa said to the horses. "There's no more water for thirty miles."

Beyond the low river the grassy land was low curve behind curve and the road looked like a short hook.

"The road pushes against the grassy land and breaks off short. And that's the end of it," said Laura.

"It can't be," Mary objected. "The road goes all the way to Silver Lake."

"I know it does," Laura answered.

"Well, then I don't think you ought to say things like that," Mary told her gently. "We should always be careful to say exactly what we mean."

"I was saying what I meant," Laura protested. But she could not explain. There were so many ways of seeing things and so many ways of saying them.

Beyond the Big Sioux there were no more fields, no houses, no people in sight. There really was no road, only a dim wagon trail, and no railroad grade. Here and there Laura glimpsed a little wooden stake, almost hidden in the grasses. Pa said they were surveyors' stakes for the railroad grade that was not started yet.

Laura said to Mary, "This prairie is like an enormous meadow, stretching far away in every direction, to the very edge of the world."

The endless waves of flowery grasses under the cloudless sky gave her a queer feeling. She could not say how she felt. All of them in the wagon, and the wagon and team, and even Pa, seemed small.

All morning Pa drove steadily along the dim wagon track, and nothing changed. The farther they went into the west, the smaller they seemed, and the less they seemed to be going anywhere. The wind blew the grass always with the same endless rippling; the horses' feet and the wheels going over the grass made always the same sound. The jiggling of the board seat was always the same jiggling. Laura thought they might go on forever, yet always be in this same changeless place that would not even know they were there.

Only the sun moved. Without ever seeming to, the sun moved steadily upward in the sky. When it was overhead, they stopped to feed the horses and to eat a picnic lunch on the clean grass.

It was good to rest on the ground after riding all the morning. Laura thought of the many times they had eaten under the sky while they were traveling all the way from Wisconsin to Indian Territory and back again to Minnesota. Now they were in Dakota Territory going farther west. But this was different from all the other times, not only because there was no cover on the wagon and no beds in it, but some other reason. Laura couldn't say how, but this prairie was different.

"Pa," she asked, "when you find the homestead, will it be like the one we had in Indian Territory?"

Pa thought before he answered. "No," he said finally. "This is different country. I can't tell you how, exactly, but this prairie is different. It feels different."

"That's likely enough," Ma said sensibly. "We're west of Minnesota, and north of Indian Territory, so naturally the flowers and grasses are not the same."

But that was not what Pa and Laura meant. There was really almost no difference in the flowers and grasses. But there was something else here that was not anywhere else. It was an enormous stillness that made you feel still. And when you were still, you could feel great stillness coming closer.

All the little sounds of the blowing grasses and of the horses munching and whooshing in their feedbox at the back of the wagon and even the sounds of eating and talking could not touch the enormous silence of this prairie.

Pa talked about his new job. He would be the company storekeeper, and the timekeeper at Silver Lake camp. He would run the store, and he would keep straight in his books the charge account of every man on the job and know exactly how much money was due each man for his work, after his board bill and his account at the store had been subtracted. And when the paymaster brought the money each payday,

Pa would pay every man. That was all he had to do, and for that he would be paid fifty dollars every month.

"And best of all, Caroline, we're among the very first out here!" said Pa. "We've got the pick of the land for our homestead. By George, our luck's turned at last! First chance at new land, and fifty dollars a month for a whole summer to boot!"

"It is wonderful, Charles," said Ma.

But all their talking did not mean anything to the enormous silence of that prairie.

All that afternoon they went on, mile after mile, never seeing a house or any sign of people, never seeing anything but grass and sky. The trail they followed was marked only by bent and broken grasses.

Laura saw old Indian trails and buffalo paths worn deep in the ground and now grassed over. She saw strange large depressions, straight-sided and flat-bottomed, that had been buffalo wallows, where now the grass was growing. Laura had never seen a buffalo, and Pa said it was not likely that she would ever see one. Only a little while before, the vast herds of thousands of buffaloes had grazed over this country. They had been the Indians' cattle, and white men had slaughtered them all.

On every side now the prairie stretched away empty to far, clear skyline. The wind never stopped blowing, waving the tall prairie grasses that had turned brown in the sun. And all the afternoon, while Pa kept driving onward, he was merrily whistling or singing. The song he sang oftenest was:

> "Oh, come to this country,
> And don't you feel alarm,
> For Uncle Sam is rich enough
> To give us all a farm!"

Even baby Grace joined in the chorus, though she did not bother to follow the tune.

> "Oh, come away! Come away!
> Come away, I say!
> Oh, come away! Come away!
> Come right away!
> Oh, come to this country,
> And have no fear of harm,
> Our Uncle Sam is rich enough
> To give us all a farm!"

The sun was lowering in the west when a rider appeared

on the prairie behind the wagon. He came following behind not very fast, but coming a little nearer mile after mile while the sun was slowly sinking.

"How much farther is it to Silver Lake, Charles?" Ma asked.

"About ten miles," said Pa.

"There isn't anybody living nearer, is there?"

"No," said Pa.

Ma did not say anything more. Neither did anyone else. They kept glancing back at that rider behind them, and each time they looked, he was a little nearer. He was surely following them and not meaning to overtake them until the sun sank. The sun was so low that every hollow between the low prairie swells was filled with shadow.

Each time that Pa glanced back, his hand made a little motion, slapping the horses with the lines to hurry them. But no team could pull a loaded wagon as fast as a man could ride.

The man was so near now that Laura could see two pistols in leather holsters on his hips. His hat was pulled low over his eyes, and a red bandanna was tied loosely around his neck.

Pa had brought his gun west, but it was not in the wagon now. Laura wondered where it was, but she did not ask Pa.

She looked back again and saw another rider coming on a white horse. He wore a red shirt. He and the white horse were far behind and small, but they came fast, galloping. They overtook the first rider, and the two came on together.

Ma said in a low voice, "There's two of them now, Charles."

Mary asked frightened, "What is it? Laura, what's the matter?"

Pa looked back quickly, and then he was comfortable.

"Everything's all right now," he said. "That's Big Jerry."

"Who's Big Jerry?" Ma asked.

"He's a half-breed, French and Indian," Pa answered carelessly. "A gambler, and some say a horse thief, but a darned good fellow. Big Jerry won't let anybody waylay us."

Ma looked at him astonished. Her mouth opened and then it shut; she did not say anything.

The riders came up beside the wagon. Pa lifted his hand and said, "Hullo, Jerry!"

"Hullo, Ingalls!" Big Jerry answered. The other man gave them all a snarling look and went galloping on ahead, but Big Jerry rode along by the wagon.

He looked like an Indian. He was tall and big but not one bit fat, and his thin face was brown. His shirt was flaming red. His straight black hair swung against his flat, high-boned cheek as he rode, for he wore no hat. And his snow-white horse wore no saddle nor bridle. The horse was free, he could go where he wanted to go, and he wanted to go with Big Jerry wherever Big Jerry wanted to ride. The horse and the man moved together as if they were one animal.

They were beside the wagon only a moment. Then away they went in the smoothest, prettiest run, down into a little hollow and up and away, straight into the blazing round sun on the far edge of the west. The flaming red shirt and the white horse vanished in the blazing golden light.

Laura let out her breath. "Oh, Mary! The snow-white horse and the tall, brown man, with such a black head and a bright red shirt! The brown prairie all around—and they rode right into the sun as it was going down. They'll go on in the sun around the world."

Mary thought a moment. Then she said, "Laura, you know he couldn't ride into the sun. He's just riding along on the ground like anybody."

But Laura did not feel that she had told a lie. What she had said was true, too. Somehow that moment when the beautiful, free pony and the wild man rode into the sun would last forever.

Afterthought

1. Why did Mary have trouble understanding Laura's descriptions?
2. Try to describe a time when you felt "an enormous stillness" such as Laura describes.
3. Why were Laura's parents willing to make a lonely and sometimes frightening journey into a strange territory?

The Mountain

Jean George

Don't make the mistake of
thinking pioneering has stopped.
Sam Gribley is a boy who can't
stand being crowded up in a New
York apartment. Here he tells about
the start of his pioneering adventure.
As you read, notice whether Sam's
experiences are very different from
those of long-ago pioneers.

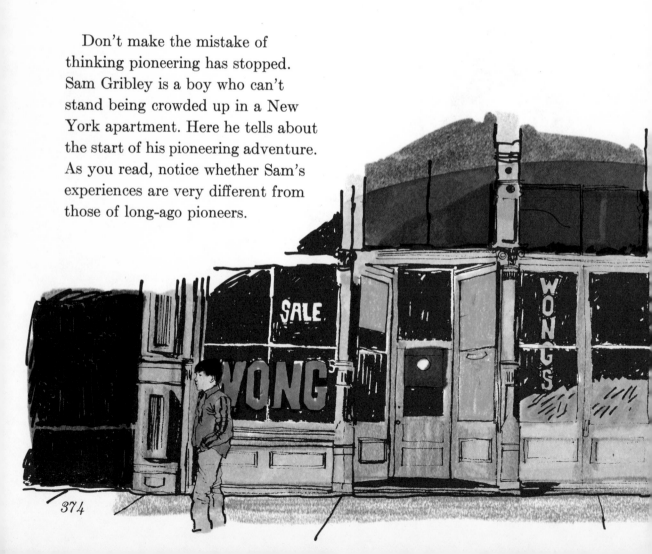

I Get Started on This Venture

I left New York in May. I had a penknife, a ball of cord, an ax, and $40, which I had saved from selling magazine subscriptions. I also had some flint and steel which I had bought at a Chinese store in the city. The man in the store had showed me how to use it. He had also given me a little purse to put it in and some tinder to catch the sparks. He had told me that if I ran out of tinder, I should burn cloth and use the charred ashes.

I thanked him and said, "This is the kind of thing I am not going to forget."

On the train north to the Catskills I unwrapped my flint and steel and practiced hitting them together to make sparks. On the wrapping paper I made these notes:

"A hard brisk strike is best. Remember to hold the steel in the left hand and the flint in the right, and hit the steel with the flint.

"The trouble is the sparks go every which way."

And that *was* the trouble. I did not get a fire going that night, and this was a scary experience.

I hitched rides into the Catskill Mountains. At about four o'clock a truck driver and I passed through a beautiful dark hemlock forest, and I said to him, "This is as far as I am going."

He looked all around and said, "You live here?"

"No," I said, "but I am running away from home, and this is just the kind of forest I have always dreamed I would run to. I think I'll camp here tonight." I hopped out of the cab.

"Hey, boy," the driver shouted. "Are you serious?"

"Sure," I said.

"Well, now, ain't that sumpin'? You know, when I was your age, I did the same thing. Only thing was, I was a farm boy and ran to the city, and you're a city boy running to the woods. I was scared of the city—do you think you'll be scared of the woods?"

"Heck, no!" I shouted loudly.

As I marched into the cool shadowy woods, I heard the driver call to me, "I'll be back in the morning, if you want to ride home."

He laughed. Everybody laughed at me. Even Dad. I told Dad that I was going to run away to Great-grandfather Gribley's land. He had roared with laughter and told me about the time he had run away from home. He got on a boat headed for Singapore, but when the whistle blew for departure, he was down the gangplank and home in bed before anyone knew he was gone. Then he told me, "Sure, go try it. Every boy should try it."

I must have walked a mile into the woods until I found a

stream. It was a clear athletic stream that rushed and ran and jumped and splashed. Ferns grew along its bank, and its rocks were upholstered with moss.

I sat down, smelled the piney air, and took out my pen-knife. I cut off a green twig and began to whittle. I have always been good at whittling. I carved a ship once that my teacher exhibited for parents' night at school.

First I whittled an angle on one end of the twig. Then I cut a smaller twig and sharpened it to a point. I whittled an angle on that twig, and bound the two angles face to face with a strip of green bark. It was supposed to be a fishhook.

According to a book on how to survive on the land that I read in the New York Public Library, this was the way to make your own hooks. I then dug for worms. I had hardly chopped the moss away with my ax before I hit frost. It had not occurred to me that there would be frost in the ground in May, but then, I had not been on a mountain before.

This did worry me, because I was depending on fish to keep me alive until I got to my great-grandfather's mountain, where I was going to make traps and catch game.

I looked into the stream to see what else I could eat, and as I did, my hand knocked a rotten log apart. I remembered about old logs and all the sleeping stages of insects that are in it. I chopped away until I found a cold white grub.

I swiftly tied a string to my hook, put the grub on, and walked up the stream looking for a good place to fish. All the manuals I had read were very emphatic about where fish lived, and so I had memorized this: "In streams, fish usually congregate in pools and deep calm water. The heads of riffles, small rapids, the tail of a pool, eddies below rocks or logs, deep undercut banks, in the shade of overhanging bushes—all are very likely places to fish."

This stream did not seem to have any calm water, and I must have walked a thousand miles before I found a pool by a deep undercut bank in the shade of overhanging bushes. Actually, it wasn't that far; it just seemed that way because as I went looking and finding nothing, I was sure I was going to starve to death.

I squatted on this bank and dropped in my line. I did so want to catch a fish. One fish would set me upon my way, because I had read how much you can learn from one fish. By examining the contents of its stomach you can find what the other fish are eating or you can use the internal organs as bait.

The grub went down to the bottom of the stream. It swirled around and hung still. Suddenly the string came to life and rode back and forth and around in a circle. I pulled with a powerful jerk. The hook came apart, and whatever I had went circling back to its bed.

Well, that almost made me cry. My bait was gone, my hook was broken, and I was getting cold, frightened, and mad. I whittled another hook, but this time I cheated and used string to wind it together instead of bark. I walked back to the log and luckily found another grub. I hurried to the pool, and I flipped a trout out of the water before I knew I had a bite.

The fish flopped, and I threw my whole body over it. I could not bear to think of it flopping itself back into the stream.

I cleaned it like I had seen the man at the fish market do, examined its stomach, and found it empty. This horrified me. What I didn't know was that an empty stomach means the fish are hungry and will eat about anything. However, I thought at the time that I was a goner. Sadly, I put some of the internal organs on my hook, and before I could get my line to the bottom I had another bite. I lost that one but got the next one. I stopped when I had five little trout and looked around for a place to build a camp and make a fire.

It wasn't hard to find a pretty spot along that stream. I selected a place beside a mossy rock in a circle of hemlocks.

I decided to make a bed before I cooked. I cut off some boughs for a mattress, then I leaned some dead limbs against the boulder and covered them with hemlock limbs. This made a kind of tent. I crawled in, lay down, and felt alone and secret and very excited.

But ah, the rest of this story! I was on the northeast side of the mountain. It grew dark and cold early. Seeing the shadows slide down on me, I frantically ran around gathering firewood. This is about the only thing I did right from that moment until dawn, because I remembered that the driest wood in a forest is the dead limbs that are still on the trees, and I gathered an enormous pile of them. That pile must still be there, for I never got a fire going.

I got sparks, sparks, sparks. I even hit the tinder with the sparks. The tinder burned all right, but that was as far as I got. I blew on it, I breathed on it, I cupped it in my hands, but no sooner did I add twigs than the whole thing went black.

Then it got too dark to see. I clicked steel and flint together, even though I couldn't see the tinder. Finally, I gave up and crawled into my hemlock tent, hungry, cold, and miserable.

I can talk about that first night now, although it is still embarrassing to me because I was so stupid, and scared, that I hate to admit it.

I had made my hemlock bed right in the stream valley where the wind drained down from the cold mountaintop. It might have been all right if I had made it on the other side of the boulder, but I didn't. I was right on the main highway of the cold winds as they tore down upon the valley below. I didn't have enough hemlock boughs under me, and before I had my head down, my stomach was cold and damp. I took some boughs off the roof and stuffed them under me, and then my shoulders were cold. I curled up in a ball and was almost asleep when a whippoorwill called. If you have ever been within forty feet of a whippoorwill, you will understand why I couldn't even shut my eyes. They are deafening!

Well, anyway, the whole night went like that. I don't think I slept fifteen minutes, and I was so scared and tired that my throat was dry. I wanted a drink but didn't dare go near the stream for fear of making a misstep and falling in and getting wet. So I sat tight, and shivered and shook—and now I am able to say—I cried a little tiny bit.

Fortunately, the sun has a wonderfully glorious habit of rising every morning. When the sky lightened, when the birds awoke, I knew I would never again see anything so splendid as the round red sun coming up over the earth.

I was immediately cheered, and set out directly for the highway. Somehow, I thought that if I was a little nearer the road, everything would be all right.

I climbed a hill and stopped. There was a house. A house warm and cozy, with smoke coming out the chimney and lights in the windows, and only a hundred feet from my torture camp.

Without considering my pride, I ran down the hill and banged on the door. A nice old man answered. I told him everything in one long sentence, and then said, "And so, can I cook my fish here, because I haven't eaten in years."

He chuckled, stroked his whiskery face, and took the fish. He had them cooking in a pan before I knew what his name was.

When I asked him, he said Bill something, but I never heard his last name because I fell asleep in his rocking chair that was pulled up beside his big hot glorious wood stove in the kitchen.

I ate the fish some hours later, also some bread, jelly,

oatmeal, and cream. Then he said to me, "Sam Gribley, if you are going to run off and live in the woods, you better learn how to make a fire. Come with me."

We spent the afternoon practicing. I penciled these notes on the back of a scrap of paper, so I wouldn't forget.

"When the tinder glows, keep blowing and add fine dry needles one by one—and keep blowing, steadily, lightly, and evenly. Add one inch dry twigs to the needles and then give her a good big handful of small dry stuff. Keep blowing."

I Find Gribley's Farm

The next day I told Bill good-bye, and as I strode, warm and fed, onto the road, he called to me, "I'll see you tonight. The back door will be open if you want a roof over your head."

I said, "Okay," but I knew I wouldn't see Bill again. I knew how to make fire, and that was my weapon. With fire I could conquer the Catskills. I also knew how to fish. To fish and to make a fire. That was all I needed to know, I thought.

Three rides that morning took me to Delhi. Somewhere around here was Great-grandfather's beech tree with the name *Gribley* carved on it. This much I knew from Dad's stories.

By six o'clock I still had not found anyone who had even heard of the Gribleys, much less Gribley's beech, and so I slept on the porch of a schoolhouse and ate chocolate bars for supper. It was cold and hard, but I was so tired I could have slept in a wind tunnel.

At dawn I thought real hard: Where would I find out about the Gribley farm? Some old map, I said. Where would I find an old map? The library? Maybe. I'd try it and see.

The librarian was very helpful. She was sort of young, had brown hair and brown eyes, and loved books as much as I did.

The library didn't open until ten-thirty. I got there at nine. After I had lolled and rolled and sat on the steps for fifteen or twenty minutes, the door whisked open, and this tall lady asked me to come on in and browse around until opening time.

All I said to her was that I wanted to find the old Gribley farm, and that the Gribleys hadn't lived on it for maybe a hundred years, and she was off. I can still hear her heels click, when I think of her, scattering herself around those shelves finding me old maps, histories of the Catskills, and files of letters and deeds that must have come from attics around Delhi.

Miss Turner—that was her name—found it. She found Gribley's farm in an old book of Delaware County. Then she worked out the roads to it, and drew me maps and everything. Finally she said, "What do you want to know for? Some school project?"

"Oh, no, Miss Turner, I want to go live there."

"But, Sam, it is all forest and trees now. The house is probably only a foundation covered with moss."

"That's just what I want. I am going to trap animals and eat nuts and bulbs and berries and make myself a house. You see, I am Sam Gribley, and I thought I would like to live on my great-grandfather's farm."

Miss Turner was the only person that believed me. She smiled, sat back in her chair, and said, "Well, I declare."

The library was just opening when I gathered the notes we had made and started off. As I pushed open the door, Miss Turner leaned over and said to me, "Sam, we have some very good books on plants and trees and animals, in case you get stuck."

I knew what she was thinking, and so I told her I would remember that.

With Miss Turner's map, I found the first stone wall that marked the farm. The old roads to it were all grown up and mostly gone, but by locating the stream at the bottom of the mountain I was able to begin at the bridge and go north and up a mile and a half. There, caterpillaring around boulders, roller-coastering up ravines and down hills, was the mound of rocks that had once been Great-grandfather's boundary fence.

And then, do you know, I couldn't believe I was there. I sat on the old gray stones a long time, looking through the forest, up that steep mountain, and saying to myself, "It must be Sunday afternoon, and it's raining, and Dad is to keep us all quiet by telling us about Great-grandfather's farm; and he's telling it so real that I can see it."

And then I said, "No. I am here, because I was never this hungry before."

I wanted to run all the way back to the library and tell Miss Turner that I had found it. Partly because she would have liked to have known and partly because Dad had said to me as I left, "If you find the place, tell someone at Delhi. I may visit you someday." Of course, he was kidding, because he thought I'd be home the next day, but after many weeks, maybe he would think I meant what I said, and he might come see me.

However, I was too hungry to run back. I took my hook and line and went back down the mountain to the stream.

I caught a big old catfish. I climbed back to the stone wall in great spirits.

It was getting late and so I didn't try to explore. I went right to work making a fire. I decided that even if I didn't have enough time to cut boughs for a bed, I was going to have cooked fish and a fire to huddle around during those cold night hours. May is not exactly warm in the Catskills.

By firelight that night I wrote this:

"Dear Bill (that was the old man):

"After three tries, I finally got a handful of dry grass on the glow in the tinder. Grass is even better than pine needles, and tomorrow I am going to try the outside bark of the river birch. I read somewhere that it has combustible oil in it that the Indians used to start fires. Anyway, I did just what you showed me, and had cooked catfish for dinner. It was good.

Your friend,

Sam."

After I wrote that, I remembered I didn't know his last name, and so I stuffed the note in my pocket, made myself a bed of boughs and leaves in the shelter of the stone wall, and fell right to sleep.

I must say this now about that first fire. It was magic. Out of dead tinder and grass and sticks came a live warm light. It cracked and snapped and smoked and filled the woods with brightness. It lighted the trees and made them warm and friendly. It stood tall and bright and held back the night. Oh, this was a different night than the first dark frightful one. Also I was stuffed on catfish. I have since learned to cook it more, but never have I enjoyed a meal as much as that one, and never have I felt so independent again.

Afterthought

1. How did Sam prepare himself for pioneering?
2. Compare the people who helped Sam with people who helped other pioneers.
3. Name three other kinds of pioneers besides pioneer settlers.

Miss Charity Comes to Stay

Alberta Wilson Constant

This long selection is for you to read alone—for your own pleasure.
If you enjoy it, you may want to read the whole book to find out what
happens after Miss Charity comes to stay.

Chapter 1

I never in this world would have thought about writing a book if it hadn't been for Miss Charity. She said that all of us in Skiprock School were part of history. She said that anybody who came to the Cherokee Strip for the big run for land should put down all that he could remember because someday it would be important. That set me to thinking.

How would it be to write a book? I could see my name on the cover in big black letters. (Or maybe gold letters.) BETSY RICHARDSON. My real name is Elizabeth but it's too long for calling, and Mama has to call me so much that I just about forget it's even my name.

If Miss Charity thought the run for land was important, maybe I should begin my book with that. The trouble was that I missed the start of it; I was down under the wagon with Rex, my dog. Tom—that's my brother—told me the Indians would steal Rex and eat him and I didn't know if he was telling the truth or just teasing me. Rex is part collie and part some other kinds. He can beg, shake hands, count to three by barking, and he can even drive up Old Blue, our cow. I have to go along to remind him what he's supposed to be doing when he gets to chasing rabbits, but he's a wonderful dog and I didn't want anything to happen to him.

Our whole family came down from Kansas when the Cherokee Strip was opened for homestead claims in 1893. Some folks called it the Cherokee Outlet, but most of those that lived there called it the Strip—it got shortened, just the same as my name did. The Strip is that long, straight part of Oklahoma Territory that lies right south of the Kansas line. It belonged to the Cherokee Indians but they leased it to cattle ranchers, and finally the government bought it to open for settlement to those that were fast enough to get a claim and tough enough to live on it and prove up. (That last is really from Papa but I've heard him say it so often that I thought I thought of it.)

A lot of folks we knew in Kansas came down for the Run. Menfolks by themselves, mostly, but Mama said that the Richardsons were all in this together. It was a case of "united we stand," and we weren't even to talk about falling! Papa was the only one to ride in the Run because a person had to be twenty-one, or head of a family. Nell and Tom and I stayed in the wagon with Mama.

Now that I'm twelve (Nell's fifteen and Tom's thirteen) I wish I'd paid more attention to the way things were the day of the Run. I guess I was too excited. The riders lined up as far as you could see. Out in front of the line was a soldier, holding a gun. We could tell which rider was Papa by the red bandanna handkerchief he tied around the crown of his hat. Watching the line, it seemed like an awful long time ago that he'd kissed Mama and Nell and me and shaken hands with Tom and told him to look after the womenfolks. If anything happened to Papa. . . .

That was when Tom started to talk about Rex and how

fat I kept him and what good stew he'd make. Most times Mama would have said, "*Tom*, that will *do*." She didn't even notice. Her eyes were glued on the line of riders, on Papa who was riding that show-off mare, Gypsy, and her hands were twisting a handkerchief to rags. Even Nell wouldn't pay me any mind. She was muttering, "Half a league, half a league, half a league onward. . . ." Nell thinks poetry will help anything.

It came over me that I couldn't stand to lose Papa and Rex at the same time. I climbed down and Rex was under the wagon, lying in the dust. He put out his paw to shake hands and whined and held his face against mine. I was so glad to see him that I put my face right down into his ruff. I don't want to say whether I was crying or not, but my throat hurt, just the way it did when I had the quinsy. Anyway, I was there under the wagon when the gun cracked. There was a terrible roaring noise and the ground shook under me.

It was the Run!

Rex and I scrambled out from under the wagon. All we could see was a long, long cloud of dust, going faster and faster. Rex was barking, and I was jumping up and down, screaming. Not that I knew it! Nell told me later. Sometimes a wagon or a sulky or a buckboard would lock wheels with another and turn over and spill people out. In a few minutes the men on horseback began to pull away from the rest. I saw a flash of red going out of sight and I know it was Papa. I *know* it was. Quicker than I can tell about it the big wide prairie swallowed the riders, and only the heavy wagons, the men on foot, and the folks like us who were waiting were left.

I climbed back into the wagon, hauling Rex with me. For

once, Mama didn't make me put him out. She hugged me and Rex along with me and said I must remember the Run the rest of my life. As if I could forget it!

Only, I didn't see the start.

It was awful hot that September. The dust was so bad it made breathing hard. Our water keg was empty and nobody wanted to leave to go get more, so Mama bought some water from a man going up and down the line selling it. She told him it was a miserable thing to sell water and he'd never get any good out of money that came that way. The man got kind of mad and shook his dipper and said if Mama didn't want to buy water there were plenty that did. So she had to simmer down because all of us were thirsty. When her back was turned I gave some of my drink to Rex.

Well, that's what I remember about the Run. You can see right off that it's not like real history. I mean like Columbus getting the queen of Spain to sell her jewelry, or the Pilgrims landing on a stern and rockbound coast. If Nell were writing this book she'd put it all in fancy poetry and that might make it sound more important. Nell has a ledger that Papa gave her

from the feed store back in Kansas. She writes her poems on the blank side of the pages. It's sure funny to read along about rosebuds, and Springtime, knights and ladies, and haunted castles in Nell's handwriting, and turn a page and there, in Papa's handwriting, is all about baled hay, shelled corn, bran, and shorts. But Mama says that's the way life is, all mixed up. Furthermore, if she catches me reading Nell's book again without permission, she's going to give me a dose of peach tree tea. Only we don't have a peach tree big enough yet to pull a switch from, so it'll have to be cottonwood tea.

It was about a year after the Run till we got our school and Miss Charity came down to be the teacher, so the things that happened that day were dim and dusty in my mind. After Miss Charity started talking about how it was really history I got excited, remembering, and I raised my hand and asked her what, besides just the Run, was history, because I'd decided to write a book. She said for me to put down how things began, and for the Fourth Reader to turn, rise, pass.

It was plain as daylight that she meant for me to be quiet. Maybe I would have but Warren Espey turned around and put his thumbs in his ears and wiggled them to show he thought I was acting like a donkey. Well, I sure wasn't going to let old Warren think he could make me hush just because he's got curly hair and he asks for me at parties when we play "Post Office." I put up my hand again. Miss Charity frowned. I snapped my fingers till she asked me what I wanted.

"One more question, Betsy. Only *one*."

"Do you mean I should put in about the beginning of school and how Tyler Evans came to bring the blackboard and—"

"We'll discuss this later," Miss Charity said, getting pink in the face. Everybody in Skiprock School knows Tyler's crazy about her and I didn't see why she had to act like it was some kind of a secret. The whole school snickered but I kept on.

"I want to start my book right now. If I start with Tyler—"

Miss Charity's pink turned into red. "Suppose you begin with your own experiences."

"I didn't see the start of the Run. Not the really actual start. I could tell about the grass snake. That happened before you came and Tyler was there and. . . ."

Miss Charity rapped with her pointer and when Miss Charity raps, well, we do whatever she raps about. So I hushed and the Fourth Reader began to read.

That was how I got started to writing this book. The things I put in it may not be *real history*—nobody would ever tell me just what was—but they're going to be true. Not about Princes and Princesses and Fairy Queens like Nell writes about. I guess I'm more for shelled corn and baled hay than I am for poetry.

Right off I found out one thing. It's hard to know where to start a book.

Authors don't have an easy time. We have a card game of "Authors" and most of them have white beards and worried-looking faces. I'm not figgering on a beard but it may be that I'll turn out like Louisa May Alcott, who didn't even have time to get married.

Hard or not, I'm going ahead. Our copybook says, "Where there's a will, there's a way." That means I've got a head start because Papa says I'm the most willful child he's ever seen and it must come from the Murdocks. That's Mama's side of the family.

Now that brings up another thing. My whole family thinks it's funny for me to be writing a book. When I told Mama she smiled in the way that means she's smiling to keep from laughing. Then her smile turned worried.

"Betsy, remember family affairs are never to be discussed in public."

"Yes ma'am," I said, quick as a mouse because I didn't want her starting in to tell me just what all I mustn't write about. My goodness, if I didn't get to see the start of the Run, and I can't write about family affairs, and Miss Charity gets red in the face when I talk about Tyler Evans—what's left? The weather's not much fun. Besides, in the Strip about the time you write down "bright and fair today," you have to rub that out and put in "blue norther coming."

"I didn't mean to discourage you," Mama said. "Why not get Nell to write some poems for you?"

That made me mad! I was going to write my book all by myself and no helpers.

"Nell's poems are about family affairs. After she wrote that one about 'The Fair-Faced Maid,' she wouldn't go out without her sunbonnet and she swiped a crock of buttermilk to bleach her face. And it wasn't a very good poem, either."

"I don't think you should say things like that, no matter if you think them."

"Why Mama, you said we should always tell the truth and shame the devil."

Mama threw up her hands; then she started to laugh.

"Betsy, some days I don't know whether to switch you or hug you. Go on and write your book however you want to, but don't let me catch you putting chores off onto Nell on account of it. She's too easygoing as it is."

"I won't. I promise!" I hugged Mama so hard she said the bones in her corset creaked. I love to hug Mama because she smells so good. Sometimes it's violet soap smell, sometimes fresh-baked bread, sometimes the starch she puts in her dresses. But it's always Mama.

Still, I didn't have any place to start my book.

I thought and thought about it. When Rex and I went out to bring in Old Blue it was on my mind. In the Strip you can't just turn a cow out to graze because there aren't any fences yet, and the coyotes might chase her, or even wolves. We didn't have feed enough to keep her up, so every morning it was my chore to lead Old Blue to some good grass, and hobble her, and then go get her in the evening. Even with a hobble she could get quite a ways away and I'd hear her bell before I saw her. I went toward the bell sound, calling "Soooooo, boss. Soooooooo."

Old Blue was down in a hollow where the grass was thick. There she stood, chewing her cud, and watching me hunt her, just laughing at me. I sicked Rex onto her but before he got started he scooped up the trail of a jackrabbit and took off north. I had to run about a mile to round him up, then go back and get Old Blue and take off the hobble and put on her halter before I could start home. I was sure winded! Halfway home I topped a little rise and sat down to rest.

Rex came and sat beside me with his tongue out, panting. I get put out at Rex but I love him just the same. I leaned against him and I could hear his heart going thum . . . thum . . . thum . . . thum. The sun was slipping down the side of the sky, and the shadows had turned blue. The wind that never stops in the Strip sighed past my ears. Rex's heartbeat and mine and the sigh of the wind were all part of the same thing . . . thum . . . thum . . . thum. I put my hand on the ground and felt the prairie throbbing, too.

There was a hawk riding the wind above us. He dived and came winging up in a curve so high he went out of sight. He was a part of the prairie, too, and so was the mouse, or whatever he dived for, that squeaked off to a safe place in the grass. "Everything's part of everything," I whispered into Rex's furry ear, but it was too big an idea to hold onto and it slipped away, even before I said it. All that stayed was the thum . . . thum . . . thum.

Straight ahead of us was our house. Papa and Tom were coming back from the field where they'd been working with the sodbuster plow to get the ground into shape for a wheat crop. Our team, Puss and Bess, walked ahead and the sound of the harness came in little jingles on the wind. Tom and Papa walked side by each and even this far off a person could see they belonged together. They walked the same way; they pushed their hats back the same way. Mama came out to the well. The sun flashed on the tin bucket. I couldn't really hear the well rope creak as the bucket came up full, but I could *feel* it. Nell was out by the wire pen feeding the five hens and one rooster we'd managed to keep away from the coyotes. She came over by Mama, then they both went back into the soddy.

A soddy is what you call a sod house in the Strip. It's made

of sod "bricks." We had a sod roof, too, with the grass side up so that from a ways off, the way I was, it wasn't like a separate thing at all . . . just a part of the prairie, a part of the wind and the whole wide world. All of a sudden I loved it so hard that I couldn't stand it! I jumped up and began to run. Rex ran alongside, barking like he was crazy, and Old Blue snorted and began to trot. I knew, I knew, I knew where to start my book! Right with the soddy! That was the place!

After Papa rode in the Run and staked his claim to the best hundred and sixty acres in the Cherokee Strip, he came back to get us and the wagon. I don't know just what I thought our claim was going to be like, but right at first it didn't look a whit different than the rest of the country. Not a whit! After we'd lived there awhile I think I'd have known any spot on it if I was dropped off one of those crazy flying machines folks talk about. Right at the first it was grass—nothing but grass.

There were the stakes Papa had set with his name cut into them, and there was the ragged-edge garden patch that he'd spaded up to show any latecomers that this claim was taken.

And there was the tree. We were lucky; we had a tree. A cottonwood tree with leaves that twinkled in the sun and whispered to each other all night long. We camped under the tree and by the time we'd lived there for a week I felt as if I'd never lived anyplace else in my whole life . . . and I wouldn't have changed for anything.

It's not fair, though, to pretend that everybody felt the way I did. One lady that came clear out from Virginia cried and cried till her husband pulled up stakes and took her back home. Once they came by our claim on the way to town and she stopped the wagon and asked Mama if she could just come and put her hand on our tree. A fellow over by Hardpan gave his claim to his brother-in-law *because he despised the fellow.* Put it in writing! And Papa said that Asa Compton just walked off and left his claim and shook the dust off his feet. That'd be quite a shake, if you ask me, for the dust that was raised by the Run never did settle down. Of course there was Mrs. Merkle, who said she wouldn't live in the Strip if you gave her the whole six million acres. She went back to Wichita. But that was after the grass snake.

You can see that with no trees, or hardly any, we couldn't build a house right off. We'd brought some lumber down from Kansas, and a good thing, too, because lumber for sale was scarcer'n hen's teeth. Tom says I ought to say scarcer'n hen's *false* teeth. No bricks at all. So the only thing for us to do was to build a soddy.

It isn't hard to build a soddy. Ours took about an acre of heavy sod off our claim. Papa turned it with the sodbuster plow that he'd traded the mare he rode in the Run, Gypsy, for, plus a lot more to boot. Papa was downright persnickety about getting the furrows even. Then he took the spade and cut the sod into big slabs. Tom did part of that and Nell and I got to cut a few so we could say that we'd helped make our house. Then we borrowed the loan of Ryman's go-devil and hauled the sod up near to the tree where Mama wanted the house. Papa thought it ought to be closer to Wildcat Creek that sometimes ran and sometimes didn't but Mama said that you could haul water but you couldn't haul shade.

Another thing they differed about was that Papa took a day and half a night to get the house true to the compass. He used a stake and a cord and the North Star, and he and Tom talked about angles and triangles and things that I thought were just in the back of the arithmetic book to make it hard. Mama didn't see what on earth difference it made if the house kept us warm and dry and had a place for the cookstove. She was getting downright tired of hanging over the campfire to cook meals and for goodness' sakes, hurry up! Papa said he'd be a blue-nosed raccoon if he'd live in a whopper-jawed house. It actually made him sick to his stomach not to know which way was north.

After that was settled we leveled up the floor and smoothed it off. Then we began to lay the sod "bricks." That was fun though it got kind of heavy after a little. You lay them just like building blocks, with every third layer turned crossways, and you use mud for mortar. I was the mortar mixer and Mama said she thought I'd found my true element at last and she was going to hire me out for a mud turtle.

The lumber we'd brought went into a frame for the house, something for the sod to lean against, and the two glass windows that came down from Kansas wrapped in Gran'ma

Murdock's goose-down comforter were set in, one front and one back. Not many people in the Strip had *two* windows, and some didn't have any, just a rawhide door. The roof was hardest. The ridgepole, and what boards were left from the frame, and then tar paper—that was part of the boot in the trade for Gypsy—and then more sod. A thin layer, grass side out.

We whitewashed the walls and papered them with newspapers. I think that's a good idea. Lots of times washing dishes I'd read the papers on the wall and it didn't seem nearly so tedious. I liked the advertisements of Chief Snakeroot's Purified Panther Oil; there was hardly anything it wouldn't cure. And there were the funny pictures that Papa put so much store by: the ones with Uncle Sam, and Mr. Money Bags, and one with horns and a tail called The Trusts, and the Donkey and the Elephant . . . all that. Mama put up a cheesecloth ceiling so that dirt wouldn't shower down on us all the time. All this fixing got us into the soddy before cold weather but the first time a big rain came Mama had to cook breakfast with her umbrella up, holding it over the stove. Water just poured in and everything had to be dragged outside to dry and we had to fix the roof in about a million places. "Live and learn," Mama said with her jaw set.

"Want to go back home?" Papa said, flipping a chunk of mud off the tea canister.

"Back home? I'm home right now and I'd thank you to remember it," Mama said.

"The Murdocks always were a stubborn outfit," Papa said.

"The only kind that could put up with the Richardsons," Mama fired back and before you could say zingalong, zangalong, boram, buck, we were laughing and the sun was out and the wind had dried out the wet stuff.

Our soddy had one big room, but we divided it up. The cookstove had the best place and the pipe went out the wall behind it. Next was the safe with the tin doors and the star punched in them where we kept our food and dishes and even the teapot with money—what there was. Mama and Papa had their bed up with a calico curtain across that end of the room, and Mama's curly maple dresser was back of the curtain, too. Nell and Tom and I slept in a bunk—Tom on the top part and Nell and me on the bottom, curled up like spoons. In the middle of the room was the table where we ate and four boxes for chairs and Nell's little trunk for her to sit on. Mama's rocker was squeezed in, too, in case of company or sickness. We wanted the washstand but there just wasn't room, so Papa made a little shelter by the door and we had a wash bench, like a ranch.

Now that I've written it all down for my book it sounds kind of skimpy. Back in Kansas we had eight rooms and a barn and a woodshed. Skimpy or not, we managed. Mama says that living in one room is a test of how much a family loves each other. She says anybody can get along in a palace where he can shut the door and sulk by himself but it takes real character to live with your elbows rubbing each other. Anyway, she reminded us about once a week, we weren't going to live in a sod house forever.

Shoot, I wouldn't have minded! Living in a soddy, I mean. There are some mighty nice things about a soddy. If something spills on the floor you just scrape it up and smooth it off. Housecleaning means a bucket of whitewash and a stack of newspapers. And a soddy's warm in the winter and cool in summer. It can't burn and it won't blow over in a tornado. That's more'n you can say about a frame house!

There was one thing I did hate. It wasn't the fault of the soddy but it came at the same time so I kind of lump them together. That was gathering "cowslips." We had to burn something, you know, and there wasn't any wood to be had. In the old days they used buffalo chips—I don't know why that sounds better—but what we had were cow chips. There were lots of them, left from the days when the Strip was one big cattle range. Nell was the one that thought to call them "cowslips." I guess they were about the only thing she didn't write a poem about! She and I had the job of gathering 'em. I guess we gathered a million. Two million. And it seemed like every other one I picked up had a scorpion or a thousand-legger hiding under it. First time that happened I ran back to camp yelling. Mama turned me around by the shoulders and pushed me right out again.

"We've come to the Strip to live and not let any little old crawly worm scare us off. If we have to cook with cowslips, we will. And be thankful there's plenty of 'em."

I never got so I was thankful; I just quit fussing to anybody but Nell, and she fussed worse than I did. The first load of coal Papa hauled out from town we both danced a jig around the wagon. Nell wrote a poem about *that* called "Bright Jewels of the Distant Mines." I kept a shiny piece of coal in my treasure box for a long time.

Here I've left one of the biggest parts of our life in the Strip till now! Our neighbors. Our claim is close to Rymans' and Gurdys' and Tyler Evans'. Rymans are our very best neigh-

bors. They came from Arkansas and they have two twins. Not two children—two sets of twins, boys and girls, in pairs. Believe me, when I get married and have a family I'm going to have 'em in twins. Jenny and Jeanie are thirteen—right between Nell and me. They play the mandolin and they can sing like mockingbirds. Shad and Thad are fifteen and they look so much alike nobody but Mrs. Ryman can tell them apart—and she can't all the time. On Sundays we go over to Rymans' or they come over to our place. If we ever have any trouble Mrs. Ryman is there with a pie in one hand and a dishrag in the other before the dust settles.

Gurdys, now—that's a bay horse of another color. Mama said we mustn't judge them; she says with their start in life we might not be any better. But they *could* wash! Papa says not to mind their washing, just hope they'll keep their stock up. Their old mules broke down the fence around our garden and ruined it! Just ruined it! Tom's the only one with a good word to say for Gurdys. Their boy, Garvery, is about his age, and he knows everything there is to know about hunting and fishing and trapping. If Garvery ever went to school it doesn't show. He hardly ever talks and his hair hangs down in his eyes so that he looks kind of like a squirrel peeking at you from the brush. Mr. and Mrs. Gurdy look like the end of a hard winter! They do a lot of fighting, too. She'll chase him around with an iron skillet and then he'll go to town and get filled up on red-eye and come home and try to shoot the heels off her shoes. Honest! Of course Nell and I aren't supposed to know about that. Or Tom, either. I don't see how we can keep *from* knowing things. Grownups act as if children were the same as kittens . . . born with their eyes shut.

"I don't figger Gurdys'll last," Papa said, when Mama got to worrying that Tom was over there so much. "The Strip'll take care of 'em. They'll move on. Sodbustin' ain't what I'd call much fun."

" 'Ain't!' " Mama said. "And just when I've given Tom a talking-to about the same thing. His language gets worse and worse, hanging around with Garvery."

"Oh, he'll get shut of that in time. It's their ornery laziness I hate for him to see. I went over in the middle of the morning hoping Bill Gurdy'd have an extra plowpoint and he was sittin' in the shade o' the soddy, playin' a mouth organ."

"Oh, my heavenly days! Did he have one?"

"No, but I'm bound to say he offered to hitch up and drive in town and get me one. And he'd have done it, too, if I'd let him."

"Hmph! And come back full of fight and red-eye."

"Now, Louise, remember, they're our neighbors. When the gov'ment offered this homestead they didn't say a word about a select neighborhood. They left that up to us."

"There's nothing wrong with the neighborhood," Mama said, "except the Gurdys. If they'd just move off and some nice, refined, well-mannered—"

"That's a big order," Papa said, "but I'll see what I can do."

Tyler Evans was our other neighbor. He'd been a cowboy on the Circle Z ranch before the Run. Most of the other cowboys went to Texas, or someplace, but Tyler stayed on and took up a claim. He said he was going to make a go of homesteading, whether he liked it or not. He'd bet the gov'ment fourteen dollars . . . that's the claiming fee . . . that he wouldn't starve and nobody could say Tyler Evans walked out on a bet.

Tom thought Tyler hung the moon. Tyler let him fire his six-gun at a tin can and showed him how to throw a lasso. Then he'd squat on his heels for an hour at a time and tell Tom tales about the cattle drives. If Mama wasn't around Tom'd get him started on the outlaws that rode high, wide, and handsome with the U.S. marshals after 'em. Tyler knew some of 'em, or said he did; anyway, he had Tom fooled a dozen ways to Sunday.

Tyler was so freckled he had freckles on top of freckles. He had red hair to go with the freckles and he was so tall that when he came into our soddy he had to be careful not to rake down the cheesecloth ceiling. He came a lot of times and Mama always asked him to stay and eat. He called Mama Miss Louise and she liked it because she said it reminded her of the days when she was young and giddy and didn't have three children to set an example for. Tyler said if he could ever find another lady who could cook like Miss Louise he'd be willing to give up the joy of setting in on the bachelor's game of penny ante at the Diamond. Mama scolded him about that and told him he'd be better off to save his money. Tyler said he was willing to save a *lot* of money but to save on penny ante wasn't what you'd call real economical, considering what he saved on coal oil for his lamp the nights he went to the Diamond.

Papa liked Tyler, too, even if he did say the boy farmed too much of his time on horseback. Nell thought he was grand when he brought her the box of candy he won for being the homeliest man at the Thorny Hill pie supper.

That leaves me and though I don't like to go against my own family I thought Tyler was the aggravatingest, uppitiest, most . . . most. . . .

He teased me all the time and even if I am twelve years old I can't stand to be teased. Mama's talked to me, Gran'ma Murdock's talked to me, even Nell's talked to me, but I still get mad when I'm teased. One thing, Tyler always calls me Betsy Boy because he caught me riding straddle when I thought there wasn't anybody closer than Hardpan. He pulls my braids, and acts as if they weren't even attached to me. He beat me at croquet when I was the Red Rover. But the main reason I feel the way I do is on account of Miss Charity.

It's just as plain as the nose on your face that Tyler's stuck on Miss Charity. For all his talking about Mama's biscuits, he didn't even wait to find out if she could cook or not. One look at Miss Charity sitting behind the desk at Skiprock School and it was like the sun had come up behind his freckles. Maybe I didn't get in at the start of the Run, but I sure got in at the start of *that*. And I didn't like it. At first I pretended it wasn't true, even though I knew it was. I kind of hoped that if I pretended hard enough it would turn out that I'd made a big mistake in the first place. Maybe that sounds silly but it's the way I did.

You see, Miss Charity was the very first teacher we ever had at Skiprock School and I didn't want her going off with Tyler Evans. Suppose he married her, and suppose he got tired homesteading . . . plenty of folks did . . . and took her off to Texas, and suppose I'd never see her again in all my life? Suppose some morning I'd walk into the schoolhouse and there'd be somebody else sitting behind her desk? Just to think about it made goose bumps on my arms the way a squeaky pencil on a slate does. No siree! Miss Charity belonged to us at Skiprock School and not to Tyler Evans, and I was going to do everything I could to keep them apart.

My goodness alive! Here I am telling you all these things about Miss Charity and Tyler. . . . I guess I'd better back up and tell about the grass snake the way I meant to in the first place.

Chapter 2

On the claim we had lots of company. Anybody that stopped was invited to stay and eat with us. It's a long ways between places in the Strip and folks needed a rest and a meal and besides that we liked to have them. They'd bring us news about what was going on at Hardpan, or Enid, or Alva, or Woodward. Or the news from Guthrie, the capital of Oklahoma Territory. Or if they knew us and where we lived they might bring out the mail. Anyway, they were all welcome.

Papa always went out to meet folks, and he always said the same thing.

"Howdy! Howdy! Glad to see you. Come in and take potluck with us. If we can eat it every day it won't hurt you for one meal!"

Mama got so outdone hearing that, that she threatened to give him potluck. Really, she knew that Papa thought she was the best cook in the Cherokee Strip and he only said what he did to keep from bragging.

Lots of times when there was nobody around except the family Papa would push his box back from the table, wipe his moustache, and say, "Children, take a look at your mother! Any woman with a storehouse full of vittles and a big kitchen and everything to do with can turn out a fair meal, but it

takes a real cook to cook like your mother on a monkey stove in a soddy."

"Now Joe!" Mama's eyes crinkled. "You'll get me all flustered. I'm not half the cook my mother is."

"All due respect to Mrs. Murdock, Louise, but she has a heavy hand with light bread, and she can't touch your dried peach pies."

"It's the nutmeg. My father can't abide nutmeg and a dried peach pie without nutmeg has no more zip than a wet mop."

"It's the *knowing* that counts." Papa chucked Mama under the chin. "And the *doing*, too." After that Papa went off whistling and Mama flew into the dishes and spent the whole afternoon cooking up supper.

You may think that it's a long ways from dried peach pies and Mama's cooking to the grass snake, but I just wanted to put down what a good cook she is so that you won't believe what Mrs. Merkle told all over the Territory . . . that we lived on sowbelly and stewed grass.

414

We first heard about Merkles from Rymans. Jenny and Jeanie and Mrs. Ryman stopped by on their way to gather wild greens and asked us to go along with them. Mama wouldn't have it. She'd made up her mind to houseclean and more'n that, she'd made up a bucket of whitewash, so it had to be done. Still we visited awhile with them, standing out by their rig.

Mrs. Ryman heard from Stumpfs who heard from Brunners that a Mr. Merkle was driving all around the country looking for a place to put in a general store. He had his wife with him because she was delicate and he wanted to find out if the climate suited her.

"Well," Mama said, "if there's one thing we have more of than any other it's climate. All kinds. Hot, cold, wind, rain, snow, hail, and tornadoes."

"Don't forget that it's high and dry and that it's left lots of homesteaders the same way," Mrs. Ryman said.

Folks in the Strip talked that way about the weather all the time. As if they were kind of proud of how aggravating it could be. But let an outsider say anything about our climate and they were down on 'em like a duck on a June bug.

"Brunners said Stumpfs said Merkles were real rich," Jeanie put in.

"Not *real* rich, just *middlin'* rich," Jenny said.

"That may be talk," Mrs. Ryman said, "but I guess it's true that he's got spot cash." Mama and Mrs. Ryman sighed. Cash is rare in the Strip. Lots of people never saw twenty dollars silver from one year's end to the next. "Now come on girls; we'd better get along and let Louise get to work."

"Don't hurry off," Mama said. "I'm not so work brittle this morning. Keeping house in a soddy's . . . discouraging."

"I know what you mean," Mrs. Ryman said. "I made up dumplings to go with stewed rabbit and about the time I dished up, down came a clod of dirt. Right in the middle of the dumplings! Well, I served 'em anyway. Shad said he'd eaten his peck of dirt a'ready this month. Or was it Thad?"

"Shad," Jenny said.

"Thad," Jeanie said.

We got to laughing about that because nobody could tell the boys apart and Mrs. Ryman picked up the reins and drove off.

"Wouldn't it be wonderful to be rich, like those Merkles," Nell said.

Mama turned around like she was going to take a switch to Nell.

"Eleanor Mable Richardson! I'm ashamed of you. Money's nothing to get worked up about. I've known rich people who were trash, just plain trash. And I've known those as poor as Job's turkey to be the salt of the earth."

"Yes ma'am," Nell said, meek as Moses. Then after Mama went back in the soddy, her skirts swishing, Nell said, "I don't care; I'd like to be rich. I'm tired of being the salt of the earth. I'd like to be the sugar for a while."

That was kind of surprising. Nell was the good one in our family. I mean she always did what she was told and never sassed back and hung up her clothes and washed her feet every night without being reminded.

"What would you do if you got rich?" I asked.

"For one thing I'd get us a house. A real house. Mama's just about worn out living in a soddy. And so am I."

"I never heard Mama say a thing like that."

"She never will, but just look at the way she works all the time and she can't keep things clean. There's nothing but dirt, dirt, dirt, when the house you live in's made of dirt. All our nice things from Kansas can't even be unpacked because there's no place to put 'em. We can't have comp'ny...."

"Why, we have comp'ny all the time!"

"I mean if a boy, for instance, came to call on me, I couldn't entertain him in the parlor. There isn't any parlor. There isn't . . . anything."

"There is too! There's plenty of . . . of . . . . Anyway I don't know of any boys that are dyin' to call on you." I stuck out my tongue at Nell and ran off.

It wasn't really true, what I said. Shad Ryman was always shining up to Nell, and Grant Brunner, too. It was just that all this talk about having callers made me uneasy. If Nell was grown up enough for that kind of carrying on, well, I wasn't so very much younger. Pretty soon I'd be old enough. And suppose nobody came to call on me? Not that I *cared*, but just suppose! I picked up a clod and chunked it at Rex, not meaning to hit him, but he barked and Mama told me to get straight in the house and get to work.

I felt better doing something. I took the whitewash bucket and the brush and did the side walls in swooshy patterns. I got whitewash speckles all in my hair till I was a sight to behold.

A little past the middle of the morning Rymans came by our place again to leave us a mess of wild greens. They'd been over to a low spot on the prairie where Papa says there was likely a buffalo wallow in the old days. Greens came on faster there. Lamb's-quarter, small dock, Indian lettuce, bluestem . . . I don't know what all.

"Bless your hearts forever!" Mama said. "I was just wondering what I'd give my folks to eat. We're about out of everything and Joe won't stop his plowing to go after groceries."

"Bert's the same," Mrs. Ryman nodded. "He says we'll just have to live on beans and corn bread."

"Menfolks!"

"Can't live with 'em and can't live without 'em!"

Mama set me to washing the greens and picking them over. She put them on to cook with the very last piece of side meat we had. It was what Gurdys called "sowbelly." Mama had a fit if we ever said anything like that; she was very particular. She cut the side meat into two pieces, one to go with the greens and the other to slice and fry and make a little flour gravy.

"There!" she said. "Joe's certainly going to have to go to town tomorrow."

Nell and I were tickled pink! We started right off planning the trip. Mama kept in behind us, hurrying us to get things moved back into the soddy and straightened up for dinner. She said Papa couldn't abide a messed-up house but I think she was just laying it onto him. I think *she* was the one.

It was all done except for getting Mama's dresser back in and I was hauling on that when all of a sudden it moved— easy as pie. I looked around and there was Tyler Evans holding the other end of the dresser.

"Leggo, Betsy Boy. This is man's work."

I gritted my teeth. "I got this outdoors by myself and I'll get it inside the same way."

"What in the name of a Dominicker hen have you got on yore face?" Tyler said. "And yore hair?" He picked up one of my braids. "Pore old Betsy Boy's gone gray before her time." He gave my braid a yank; then he picked up the dresser and walked right into the soddy with it. He made me so mad!

"Howdy, Miss Louise," he said to Mama. "Here you've got yore spring cleanin' done and me with mine not started. Come to think of it, I never got my fall cleanin' done, neither."

"I don't know what I'm going to do," Mama said. "All this dirt!"

"Why ma'am," Tyler said, "I never saw any dirt 'round you. Thought it was plumb scared to light on your claim. Thought it blew right on past."

"Oh, you!" Mama shook her apron at Tyler. "I ought not to complain like this. I know Joe's doing the best he can. The poor fellow works from 'can see to can't see,' but I sometimes think he's forgotten all about getting a house for us. A real house."

"Nobody's got any lumber, Miss Louise. They've raised the price o' toothpicks till most folks've gone back to goose quills. I'm usin' cactus thorns, m'self."

Mama laughed. "You stay to eat with us, Tyler. You always make me feel better. Can you make out on wild greens and corn bread?"

"I can make out on mud pies if you bake 'em, Miss Louise," Tyler said and took the water bucket and went to fill it at the well.

"Mama, do you really mean you want to leave the soddy?" It was the first time I'd asked her that. It was the first time, really, I'd ever thought about it.

"It'd be the happiest day of my life to get into a real house," Mama said, "but don't you dare say that to Papa. Do you understand?"

"Yes ma'am, but—"

"Now Betsy, I don't have time to argue. You girls fly

'round while I stir up some corn bread and for goodness' sake don't ask for second helpings. There's barely enough to get by on as it is."

I was standing there, staring at the wall I'd whitewashed, the one where I'd marked my initials in the soft clay that chinked the sod "bricks" and thinking that I didn't want to leave. No, not for any fancy kind of a house. Nell shoved me as she went past. Then we turned around toward the door. A rig had come up outside.

Papa and Tom were in the back of a light spring wagon and on the driver's seat was a couple dressed up, seven ways to Sunday. The man had on a tight black broadcloth suit and a tan derby and the lady—a skinny-size lady—had on a brown and green changeable silk trimmed with braid enough to rope a calf, and she had a silk parasol held over her hat. I looked at Mama.

"I'll bet a million dollars that's Merkles!"

"Oh my land of love!"

We could hear Papa's voice booming out his speech about potluck. "Well, this time he's goin' to get it, and no mistake," Mama said. But she straightened her apron, pushed back her hair and walked right out with a smile on her face. That was the way Mama did.

Nell and I looked at each other, then we both looked at the pot of greens. When I washed 'em I thought they were enough to feed an army. Now they looked mighty piddling. "Family hold back!" Nell said. Then she walked out after Mama, smiling too.

I sniffed at the pot liquor and wondered what we were going to do? It came to me in a flash. Greens were greens!

On the top of our soddy there was a patch of new grass; I'd seen it when Papa boosted me up to patch a weak spot. I eased out the door, around to the back, and scrambled up on top of the soddy. Nobody was paying any attention to me. Tyler had left the water bucket by the door and gone out to meet Merkles and all of them were talking. I grabbed with both hands till I got a lapful of nice tender young grass shoots. Then I shinnied down and soused 'em up and down in the water bucket. I didn't have time to pick 'em over but you can't do everything. Then I slipped into the soddy and put them into the pot with the other greens and poured in some hot water to wilt 'em down. It looked like a lot of greens, now; in fact, it looked like a real plenty.

While Mrs. Merkle was admiring her hat—it was trimmed with grapes, roses, and two dead birds—and primping in Mama's mirror, Mama was stirring up some more corn bread and Nell was setting the table. Mama tried to introduce me but Mrs. Merkle was so busy talking about Wichita, Kansas, and how wonderful it was to live there, that she just jerked her chin and said, "Howdy do, child," and I was half sorry I'd gone to so much trouble over the greens.

Papa put his head in at the door and called, "Dinner ready?"

"Joe's such a hearty eater," Mama said, straightening up from the oven. "It's a joy to cook for somebody who relishes his meals."

"I've always had a hired girl." Mrs. Merkle patted her false curls with fingers that sparkled. "Mr. Merkle doesn't want me to exert myself. Is help hard to get hereabouts?"

Mama stiffened a little bit. "We help each other when

there's a real need but I don't know of anybody who works out."

"There's always help if you pay enough. *I* pay two dollars a week in Wichita."

That was more money than lots of folks made in a month in the Strip but Mama didn't bat an eye. "I'm sure it's well worth it. Betsy, set up the chairs."

Of course they weren't chairs; they were boxes and we called 'em chairs. That made 'em sit easier. But I had a feeling Mrs. Merkle wouldn't understand that.

Papa and Tom and Tyler washed at the wash bench. I guess Mr. Merkle thought he was clean enough already. He was telling all about the mistakes Grover Cleveland made. It didn't seem possible one man could make as many as that and still be the president.

We got squeezed up to the table and we had to wait forever and a day for Mr. Merkle to stop talking so that Papa could ask the blessing. Papa made it short because he said the Lord never meant for cold corn bread to take the place of piety. Mama started the pan of corn bread one way and the plate of fried side meat the other. When the plate of side meat got to Mr. Merkle he was talking about how much money he'd made in the cash grain market. He held the plate in one hand and took his fork and picked over the pieces, though goodness knows it was easy to see 'em all. He kept picking and talking and I saw Tom's nose twitch. He'd been helping Papa plow with the sodbuster plow and that's hard work and he was hungry. When Mr. Merkle finally stopped for breath, Tom spoke up.

"Thanks for the sowbelly."

The quiet was terrible. My face burned for Tom. He'd heard Garvery say "sowbelly" so often that it just slipped out. Tom gives me lots of trouble lots of ways but he's really *nice*. Really. Mama looked like she wanted to crawl under the table. It was Tyler who saved the day. Slick as a greased pig going under a fence he took the plate out of Mr. Merkle's hand and passed it to Tom.

"Was that there corn price shelled corn or in the ear?" he asked.

Mr. Merkle was off like a shot, talking about prices and money. Mama passed the greens to Mrs. Merkle.

"Wild greens are such a treat. My neighbor brought me these fresh picked this morning."

Mrs. Merkle dipped the big spoon down and lifted it up. I could see the grass string off the spoon and it was a different color. Mrs. Merkle's thin nose wiggled like a cottontail rabbit's. She lifted up a forkful of greens and tasted them. She chewed and she chewed, the way Old Blue does only Old Blue looks a lot pleasanter. After a little she made out she had to cough and put up her hand and when it came down she'd stopped chewing. Mr. Merkle was still off on prices, all about how he could buy wholesale in St. Louis and how he was going to carry the best lines in his store and sell for spot cash—no credit at all—and beat town prices all to smithereens. I tried the greens on my plate and they tasted fine, a mite tough but really fine.

Tyler kept looking at me, kind of funny. I made a little bitty snoot at him to show I hadn't forgotten that he'd taken the dresser out of my hands. Mama had only a smidge of lamb's-quarter on her plate, put there to look as if she had the same as everybody. All the rest of the table were listening to Mr. Merkle; it was all they could do.

Then I saw something that nobody else did. The door to the soddy was propped open because the weather was warm, and to get a little more room inside. Around the chunk of rock we used for a prop I saw the neat, smooth head of a grass snake. It was early for grass snakes and this one poked his head in like he was looking for company. He'd slither a little closer and stop and wait, for all the world as if he heard every word Mr. Merkle had to say about Grover Cleveland's mistakes and how the Republicans could have done better.

Maybe I'd better explain about snakes right here. They were one crop we had aplenty of! Big bad rattlers, black-snakes, chicken snakes, blue racers, copperheads, bull snakes. The very sight of a snake upset Mama so that after Papa dug postholes for the pole corral and came back next day to set the poles and found a snake in every last hole—*every last one*—he said he'd pay to get 'em cleaned out. Two for a nickel. Tom went right to work and made his spending money that way. Nell wouldn't hardly kill a snake unless she just about stepped on it but I got to be right handy. Two for a nickel and no matter what kind adds up! I was on the last half of a two-fer, that's what we called 'em, and I hadn't seen a snake for quite a while so this was my big chance. The biggest thing to me was that with one more nickel I could get the patent-leather-toed-yellow-silk-stitched slippers I'd seen in Hardpan. My two-fer came sliding in the door, a yard long and skinny. I crossed my knife and fork on my plate.

"Excuse me," I said, though nobody was listening.

Then I moved my box back, quiet as quiet, and tiptoed

toward the door. I figured I could scare the two-fer outdoors and catch him there, but you can't depend on snakes! Like a blue racer he lit out for the table. I dived but I wasn't quick enough. We both got under the table in the tangle of legs and feet and shoes and somehow I grabbed at Mrs. Merkle's ankle and she screamed bloody murder. Right up against Tyler's boot that little old snake went, scareder than Mrs. Merkle. I grabbed him at the back of his head, and came out from under the table holding him.

"It's my two-fer!" I said.

Mrs. Merkle gave a yell that lifted the roof off the soddy a half inch. Then she fainted dead away. Honest, you'd have thought that little old grass snake was a diamondback rattler.

"Get that thing outa here!" Papa was yelling. Mama was trying to yank a feather out of the duster to burn under Mrs. Merkle's nose. Nell was crying. Tom was standing on his box, yelling "Sick 'em . . . sick 'em." The only one quiet was Mr. Merkle, sitting there with a forkful of greens halfway to his mouth.

Then Tyler grabbed me around the waist and carried me, kicking and squirming, out the door.

He took me clear down to the corral before he put me down. Down there he took out his handkerchief and mopped his face.

"Betsy Boy, you're pret'neart too much for me. Rather hog-tie a yearling any day. Now gimme that critter." I still had the snake, and he took it away from me and threw it in a long twisting curve. "Always get rid of the evidence! Now tell me what you were up to."

I just sat down and began to bawl. All I'd been through to get that two-fer and probably I was going to get in bad trouble with Mama and now no snake, no money, no patent-leather-toed-yellow-silk-stitched slippers! When I quit, Tyler made me blow my nose and tell him about it.

"It was the last half of my two-fer," I said, "and no telling when I'll get another because we've just about got 'em cleaned out."

Tyler reached into his pocket and took out *two* nickels. Two! I thought he'd made a mistake. "Two snakes for a nickel; not two nickels for a snake. Not even rattlers."

"It was worth two," Tyler said. "The look on that old— that Miz Merkle's face! I wouldn'ta missed it!" He bent over like he had a bad stomach ache; then I saw he was laughing and trying not to make any noise. I laughed too standing there rubbing my two nickels together, but I couldn't really enjoy myself because of thinking what was waiting for me back at the soddy.

Mama came walking out by the side of Mrs. Merkle waving her bottle of smelling salts under Mrs. Merkle's nose with Mrs. Merkle shaking her head and pushing the bottle away. Papa was talking and waving his arms and trying, plain as anything, to get Merkles to go back into the soddy and finish dinner. Thank goodness, they wouldn't listen to him! So Papa yelled for Tom to go to the corral and get Merkles' horse. Out came Tom, grinning all over his face.

"Boy! Are you goin' to catch it! Boy-oh-boy!" That's all he'd say but he said it about a hundred times while he was hitching. Then he drove Merkles' rig up to the soddy with a big flourish and they climbed in and Mrs. Merkle put up her parasol like she was firing a shotgun. Then Papa yelled for me.

Papa has a special way of calling: first his voice goes up, then it goes down.

"BetSY . . . BETsy . . . BetSY . . . BETsy. . . ."

"I guess I'd better be goin'." I looked at Tyler.

"Don't be in too big of a hurry. Joe's kind of upset. When folks get upset it's a kindness to leave 'em be."

"BetSY . . . BETsy . . . BetSY . . . BETsy. . . ."

"When Papa calls twice he means business. I'd better go." I started walking as slow as I could but I called back real fast, "I'm comin', Papa, I'm comin'."

Well, do you know what that hateful Mrs. Merkle did? She gave Mr. Merkle a jab in the ribs that I could see, clear from the pole corral, and he gave the horse a cut of the whip and they were gone in a cloud of dust, not even waiting for me to say "good-bye" or "I'm sorry," in case I was going to say it which I wasn't unless Mama made me. I call that pretty tacky!

"That clears things up some," Tyler said, "but I think I'd better take my own advice and mosey along. Tell Miss Louise I thank her for askin' me to dinner. And—uh— Betsy Boy. . . ."

"Huh?"

"Next time, take the sandburs out of the greens." He got on his horse and rode off.

It seemed like a country mile from the corral to the house, and at the end of the walk was Papa, looking like a cyclone.

"Young lady," Papa said, "what have you got to say for yourself?"

That was when I got the surprise of my life.

Mama turned on Papa, her eyes sparking blue fire. "Edward Joseph Richardson, don't you dare start in on Betsy!"

Papa looked as if the prairie had cracked under his cowhide boots. "How's that?" he said. "How's that, Louise?"

"None of this would have happened if we'd had a house with a floor. No, and Tom wouldn't have said—said— 'sowbelly' "—Mama nearly choked but she got it out— "if he had a school to go to instead of running wild. And Nell, here, almost a young lady and no place to have comp'ny. Oh Joe, I can't stand it any longer! I'd live the rest of my life in a soddy if it'd make you happy but I just won't have the children brought up this way!"

"But looka here," Papa said. "I was figgerin' on a deal for Merkles to buy out Gurdys. It's a good place for a store and it'd give you some pretty high-toned neighbors—"

"I wouldn't have that woman for a neighbor for a million dollars." Mama stamped her foot. "What I want is a house and a school and I mean to have 'em."

"Louise, I'd do anything on God's green earth to make you happy but there's just not enough lumber to be bought to build a house and not a schoolteacher that I know of, this side the Kansas line."

"Then we'll have to go back across the Kansas line and get one," Mama said. "And we've got to have a house to live in."

"By doggies, you're right!" Papa put his arm around Mama's shoulder. "I've had my nose to the grindstone gettin' things started till I've pret'neart lost sight of why we came to the Strip in the first place. I'll make tracks on some kind of a house deal and as for the school . . . there'll be us and Rymans, and Espeys and Brunners and Stumpfs and that new family, Stoners. And how about Garvery, Tom?"

Tom scowled. "Me an' Garvery don't want no school. We ain't—"

"There!" Mama said. "You see, Joe?"

"I don't see why 'ain't' ain't as good as anything else," Tom said.

"You're right, Louise. He needs the three R's. I need him in the field but I'll make out. If I can just see my way clear to a house. . . ."

"A real house with a real parlor," Nell breathed. "Oh, Papa!"

"How about you, Betsy? How're you votin'?" Papa asked.

I thought about the soddy that we'd made ourselves and how much I loved it; I thought about the place where our bunk is and how I'd made a little hole in the wall and put my candy-prize ring in it; I thought about how safe the wall felt at night when I had a bad dream and put my hand out to find it. Then I thought about Mama. I didn't even have to look at her because I knew just how she was looking at me. Mama ought to have a house!

I put my hand into my pocket and there were the two nickels Tyler had given me. I held them out to Papa.

"That's for the first board of lumber," I said.

It was late at night and I was still awake. I couldn't keep from thinking about the soddy and how *it* would feel to have us all go off and leave it. I patted the wall and a tiny piece crumbled in my fingers. Would the soddy be glad to go back to the prairie again? To grow grass and tumbleweed

and have rabbits running over it and quail nesting in it? The longer I thought about it the more it seemed right to me. I almost went to sleep but instead I climbed over Nell, who sleeps like a log, and I slipped over to the big bed. Papa was asleep; I could tell by his breathing. I thought Mama might be awake so I touched her arm.

"Betsy?" she said. Then she pulled me down and gave me a squeeze. "You'll like a real house; it's just getting used to the idea."

"I know," I said. "Honestly, Mama, I do know. It's just. . . ."

I sat there on the edge of the bed a few minutes more. Then I said, "Mama, I put grass in with the greens. I thought it would help out."

"It did help out," Mama said. "It helped a lot. Now go back to sleep, Betsy."

Glossary

Key to Pronunciation

Listed below are diacritical symbols and key words. The boldface letters in the key words represent the sounds indicated by the symbols.

/ā/	cake	/h/	home	/ō/	rope	/th/	thin
/a/	hat	/(h)w/	white	/o/	top	/t͟h/	this
/ä/	father	/ī/	pie	/ô/	saw	/u/	nut
/är/	car	/i/	pig	/oi/	oil	/ûr/	fur
/âr/	care	/ir/	dear	/o͞o/	moon	/v/	vine
/b/	boy	/j/	jump	/o͝o/	book	/w/	will
/ch/	church	/k/	kite	/ôr/	fork	/y/	yes
/d/	duck	/ks/	box	/ou/	out	/yo͞o/	use
/ē/	bean	/kw/	quit	/p/	pet	/z/	zoo
/e/	pet	/l/	look	/r/	run	/zh/	azure
/f/	fun	/m/	man	/s/	see	/ə/	above
/g/	go	/n/	not	/sh/	ship		circus
/gz/	exact	/ng/	sing	/t/	top	/ər/	butter

Aa

ac·cord [ə·kôrd′]. Without being asked by somebody else; voluntarily: Jack washed the car of his own *accord*.

ac·count [ə·kount′]. An explanation of something that has happened: Janice gave her *account* of the accident.

a·dap·tive [ə·dap′tiv]. Able to adapt; able to adjust to new conditions and a new way of life.

a·do [ə·do͞o′]. Fuss; commotion; activity: Much *ado* was made over buying the new car.

al·ka·li [al′kə·lī]. A kind of salt that is found in the soil of certain dry regions. Plants do not grow well in soil that has too much alkali.

an·ni·ver·sa·ry [an′ə·vûr′sə·rē]. The yearly return of a date on which an event took place: Father and Mother celebrate their wedding *anniversary* every June.

an·noy [ə·noi′]. To pester; make angry; irritate: The buzzing fly *annoyed* the teacher.

ant·ler [ant′lər]. A horn, usually with branches, that grows and is shed every year by such animals as deer and antelope.

ap·pren·tice [ə·pren′tis]. A person who is learning a trade or craft under the guidance of a skilled worker. In former times the apprentice often worked without pay for several years: The boy was *apprenticed* to the blacksmith.

arch [ärch]. 1. The curved part of such structures as bridges, doorways, and windows. 2. To curve in the form of an arch: The huge bridge *arches* over the river.

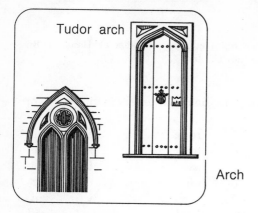

Tudor arch

Arch

ar·id [ar′id]. Dry; having little rainfall; barren.

ark [ärk]. 1. In the Bible, the ship built by Noah to save his family, himself, and the animals from a flood. 2. A large boat carrying many things.

ar·mor [är′mər]. A covering of metal or leather once worn to protect the body during battle.

ar·ti·cle [är′ti·kəl]. A piece of writing on a single subject in a book, newspaper, or magazine.

asp·en [as′pən]. A poplar tree whose delicate leaves flutter in the slightest breeze.

as·ton·ish [ə·ston′ish]. To surprise greatly: Debbie was *astonished* by the loud thunder.

a·tom·ic [ə·tom′ik]. Of atoms; having to do with atoms: The *atomic* bomb is a powerful weapon.

at·tune [ə·t(y)o͞on′]. To put one thing in accord or harmony with another: The dog soon became *attuned* to city life.

au·to·mat·ic [ô′tə·mat′ik]. Self-acting; self-controlled; self-moving: After Steve winds his watch, it will run *automatically* for the rest of the day.

awk·ward [ôk′wərd]. Without grace; clumsy in movement.

Bb

back scratch·er [bak skrach′ər]. A tool for scratching the back when it itches.

ban·dan·na [ban·dan′ə]. A large handkerchief with bright colors and patterns.

bar·bell [bär′bel]. A bar with one or more heavy disks of metal at each end used in weight lifting.

bar·gain [bär′gən]. To talk about making a trade or sale in the hope of getting a better price or better terms: When buying a new car, we always *bargain* with the dealer.

be·drag·gled [bi·drag′əld]. Messy and dirty from being dragged through the dust or mud.

beg·gar [beg′ər]. One who begs; a very poor person who lives by asking for charity.

be·hav·ior [bi·hāv′yər]. The way one acts or behaves; conduct.

be·wil·der [bi·wil′dər]. To confuse; to puzzle: Tommy was *bewildered* by the arithmetic problem.

bit·tern [bit′ərn]. A long-legged bird that lives in swamps and marshes and has a harsh cry.

black·smith [blak′smith′]. A person who heats pieces of iron until they are soft and then hammers them into various shapes. Blacksmiths are best known for making and attaching horseshoes.

bliz·zard [bliz′ərd]. A winter storm with strong winds and heavy snow.

block·house [blok′hous′]. A small fort or

building, usually made of heavy logs, with loopholes through which people inside can shoot at enemies outside.

bloom [blo͞om]. 1. A blossom; a flower. 2. To produce blossoms.

bore [bôr]. A form of the word BEAR, meaning "to show" or "to have": The skinny dog *bore* signs of starvation.

bou·quet [bō·kā′ *or* bo͞o·kā′]. A bunch of flowers.

bowl·ing [bō′ling]. A game in which players take turns trying to knock over ten large wooden pins by rolling a heavy ball into them.

brisk [brisk]. Quick; energetic; lively: To reach the campsite by dark, the Boy Scouts had to march *briskly*.

brooch [brōch]. A fancy piece of jewelry that is pinned near the neck of a dress.

broom·straw [bro͞om′strô′]. A strawlike plant that grows in thick clumps.

buck·board [buk′bôrd′]. An open carriage with four wheels and a seat attached to a frame of springy boards or metal.

bu·gle [byo͞o′gəl]. A small horn blown to give signals.

bulb [bulb]. The round, underground bud of plants such as onions, lilies, and tulips.

bur·lap [bûr′lap]. A rough, heavy fabric used in making bags such as gunnysacks.

buz·zard [buz′ərd]. 1. A large, short-winged, slow-flying hawk. 2. A greedy, stupid person.

Cc

cal·i·co [kal′i·kō]. 1. Cotton cloth with a colored pattern printed on one side. 2. Something that is streaked or spotted like calico, as a horse or cat.

cam·ou·flage [kam′ə·fläzh]. The color or shape or appearance of something that enables it to hide or be hidden easily; disguise.

ca·nar·y [kə·nâr′ē]. A small songbird with yellow feathers.

car·bon di·ox·ide [kär′bən dī·ok′sīd *or* dī·ok′sid]. A gas that has no smell or color. It is breathed out by man and animals and used as food by plants.

cas·tle [kas′əl]. A large building or group of buildings with thick walls, towers, a moat, a drawbridge, and other things to protect it against attack. In the Middle Ages castles were the homes of kings and knights.

cat·a·logue [kat′ə·lôg]. A list, usually of things for sale.

cav·ern [kav′ərn]. A big cave.

cem·e·ter·y [sem′ə·ter′ē]. A place where the dead are buried; a graveyard.

cer·e·mo·ny [ser′ə·mō′nē]. An act or an action performed in a set, definite way: Robert and Carol's wedding *ceremony* was lovely.

cha·me·le·on [kə·mē′lē·ən]. A lizard able to change the color of its skin.

chan·nel [chan′əl]. The bed of a stream or river.

chime [chīm]. One of a set of metal tubes, making bell-like musical sounds when struck.

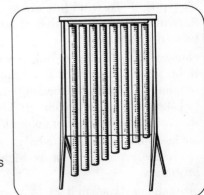

Chimes

chim·ney [chim′nē]. A passage that carries smoke away from fireplaces, stoves, and furnaces.

chis·el [chiz′(ə)l]. 1. A tool with a sharp, sloping, flat edge used to cut or chip wood, stone, or metal. 2. To cut or chip as though with a chisel.

cho·rus [kôr′əs]. A group of singers; a choir.

cin·der [sin′dər]. 1. A piece of coal, wood, etc., that is partly burned but is no longer flaming. 2. One of the bits of lava from a volcano.

cir·cu·i·tous [sər·kyōō′ə·təs]. Indirect; roundabout.

claim [klām]. 1. To ask for or demand something that rightfully belongs to oneself. 2. A piece of land that one has staked out as his own.

clan [klan]. A group of people or families who claim to be descended from the same ancestor.

cli·max [klī′maks]. The point of greatest interest in a story, play, or poem: Michael's escape from the burning house was the *climax* of the story.

clip·per ship [klip′ər ship]. A sailing ship built for speed, having many large sails, slender lines, and an overhanging bow.

clue [klōō]. A piece of evidence that helps solve a mystery or a problem.

coil [koil]. 1. To wind in a circle or spiral. 2. A strip of metal or other object that is twisted into circles.

col·umn [kol′əm]. 1. A tall, slender, upright post or pillar used as a support in a building. 2. Anything that appears to be tall and slender like a column: The smoke rose into the air in a thin *column*.

com·bus·ti·ble [kəm·bus′tə·bəl]. Able to catch fire: A dry forest is highly *combustible*.

com·man·der [kə·man′dər]. A person who is in charge and gives orders, as the captain of a ship.

com·mis·sion [kə·mish′ən]. A group of people appointed or elected to do certain things: The governor appointed a *commission* to study water pollution.

con·fuse [kən·fyōōz′]. To mix up.

con·gre·gate [kong′grə·gāt]. To come together as a crowd; to assemble.

con·sid·er [kən·sid′ər]. 1. To give careful thought to something. 2. To allow for or to take into account: We had not *considered* the possibility of rain, so everybody got soaked.

con·tain·er [kən·tā′nər]. Any object, such as a can, box, jar, or bowl, used to hold or contain something.

con·trib·ute [kən·trib′yōōt]. 1. To give money, help, etc., to a cause: We *contribute* to the United Fund each year. 2. To supply an article to a magazine or newspaper for publication.

co-op [kō′op]. Shortened form of the word COOPERATIVE. A store or apartment house owned and operated by a group of people who share in its gains and losses.

cor·delle [kôr·del′]. The rope or towline used to pull a flat-bottom boat on a river.

corn·husk [kôrn′husk′]. The leaves or husks that surround ears of corn.

cor·ral [kə·ral′]. 1. A fenced lot in which horses and cattle are kept. 2. To grab or capture.

cor·set [kôr′sit]. A tight-fitting undergarment worn by women to give shape or firmness to the hips and waist. Strips of whalebone were sewn into some corsets to make them stiff.

coun·cil [koun′səl]. A group of people who meet to discuss matters, make plans and decisions, or give advice.

coun·ter [koun′tər]. A table or similar object of wood or glass in a store, restaurant, bank, etc., where goods for sale are handled and money is exchanged.

cow chip [kou chip]. A piece of dried cow dung used as fuel.

coy·o·te [kī·ō′tē]. A small prairie wolf usually found in western areas of North America.

crack [krak]. Very good; superior: Juan is a *crack* shot with a rifle.

crank [krangk]. A handle used to start or operate an engine or other machine.

cra·ter [krā′tər]. A bowl-shaped hole such as the opening of a volcano.

craw·fish [krô′fish′]. A freshwater shellfish that looks like a small lobster.

crock [krok]. A pot or jar made of baked clay.

cud [kud]. Food that is brought back up from the first stomach of certain animals and chewed again: The cow stood there chewing its *cud*.

Dd

dab [dab]. 1. A gentle touch or pat. 2. To touch lightly.

dag·ger [dag′ər]. A weapon with a short blade used for stabbing.

dar·ing [dâr′ing]. Bold; fearless; willing to take risks.

daw·dle [dôd′(ə)l]. To waste time through idleness; to linger.

daz·zle [daz′(ə)l]. To bother the eyes with too much bright light: The spotlight was *dazzling*.

de·cent [dē′sənt]. That which is fit and proper; neither too good nor too bad; respectable.

deed [dēd]. A legal paper that shows ownership of property.

de·fense [di·fens′]. Something that defends and protects against attack or danger: Careful drivers drive *defensively*.

de·gree [di·grē′]. A mark or unit for measuring the temperature: The normal body temperature for humans is 98.6 *degrees*.

deign [dān]. To think fit or appropriate; to lower oneself: Becky did not *deign* to answer such a silly question.

de·lib·er·ate [di·lib′ər·it]. Slow and careful in action; not in a hurry.

dem·on·stra·tion [dem′ən·strā′shən]. A public showing of how a machine or product works.

de·pos·it [di·poz′it]. 1. To drop or put down: Streams *deposit* mud in their beds. 2. Dirt, mud, rocks, and other materials dropped by water or other means: This land is filled with mineral *deposits*.

der·by [dûr′bē]. A stiff hat with a narrow brim and dome-shaped top worn by men.

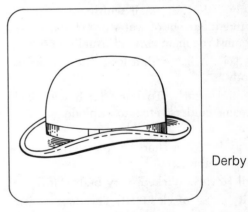

Derby

de·vour [di·vour′]. To eat or consume quickly or greedily: Claude was *devouring* the pie even before the others had been served.

di·a·gram [dī′ə·gram]. A drawing or outline of an object such as a house or car engine. The purpose of a diagram is to show on paper how a thing is built or how it works.

dike [dīk]. A dam or bank of earth to hold back water.

dis·may [dis·mā′]. A troubled feeling; un-easiness; alarm.

dis·solve [di·zolv′]. 1. To turn to liquid: Salt *dissolves* in water. 2. To fade away; to disappear.

di·vine [di·vīn′]. Having to do with or coming from God or a god; godlike.

dope [dōp]. A very stupid person.

draft [draft]. A light current of air; a breeze.

du·ti·ful [d(y)oo′ti·fəl]. Obedient; having a sense of duty.

dy·na·mite [dī′nə·mīt]. A substance used to blow up something such as rock; an explosive made from nitroglycerin.

Ee

ed·dy [ed′ē]. A small whirlpool or whirl-wind; a current of water or air that moves against the main current, usually in circles.

eel [ēl]. A fish with a long, thin, snakelike body.

e·rupt [i·rupt′]. To burst forth with lava, steam, cinders, etc.; to explode or blow out.

es·say [es′ā]. A short piece of writing on a single subject.

e·vil [ē′vəl]. Wicked; very bad; sinful.

ex·it [eg′zit *or* ek′sit]. 1. The door or way out of a room or building. 2. To leave; to go out of a room or building.

eye·tooth [ī′tooth′]. An upper tooth near the front of the mouth.

Ff

fal·con [fal′kən *or* fô(l)′kən]. A small, fast-flying hawk.

fang [fang]. A long, sharp, pointed tooth that animals use to seize and tear their prey.

fan·ta·sy [fan′tə·sē]. Imagination; a product of the imagination, as a fairy tale or day-dream.

fer·til·iz·er [fûr′təl·ī′zər]. Manure or certain chemicals used to enrich the soil and pro-vide food for plants.

fes·ti·val [fes′tə·vəl]. A special holiday or time of year when there are feasts and celebrations: Thanksgiving Day is an autumn *festival.*

flim·sy [flim′zē]. Weak or ready to fall apart; without strength; not solid.

flinch [flinch]. To wince; to pull or shrink back from something dangerous or un-pleasant: Veronica could not help *flinch-ing* when Mother put alcohol on her cut finger.

flint [flint]. A hard stone that produces sparks when struck with steel.

force [fôrs]. 1. Power; strength: An erupt-ing volcano is one of the most powerful *forces* in nature. 2. To show power; to move with power.

fra·grance [frā′grəns]. A pleasant, sweet smell.

freight·er [frā′tər]. A ship used to haul freight or cargo.

fron·tier [frun·tir′]. 1. The border of a country. 2. The border of settled land; the beginning of the wilderness.

fu·ry [fyŏor′ē]. 1. Great anger; rage. 2. Great force; violence.

Gg

game [gām]. Animals that are hunted for food or sport.

garçon. A French word meaning "boy."

gar·ri·son [gar′ə·sən]. 1. A place where

soldiers are stationed. 2. To station or place soldiers in a fort, town, etc.

gen·er·al store [jen′ər·əl stôr]. A store that sells many different things, usually including groceries.

ges·ture [jes′chər]. A movement or motion of the hands, face, or head that expresses an idea or feeling.

gey·ser [gī′zər]. A natural hot spring that shoots up a jet or fountain of hot water, steam, or mud at intervals.

gin·ger·ly [jin′jər·lē]. Lightly; cautiously; carefully: We stepped *gingerly* over the broken glass.

glaze [glāz]. To cover or appear to be covered with a thin film: The farmer's eyes were *glazed* with fatigue.

god [god]. One who is believed to have powers greater than those of a human being: Zeus was the leader of the Greek *gods*.

god·dess [god′is]. A woman god.

go·dev·il [gō′dev′əl]. A rough sled used for hauling heavy loads on a farm.

gran·ite [gran′it]. A type of rock that is very hard.

grat·ing [grā′ting]. A framework of parallel or crisscross bars over an opening: An iron *grating* covered the opening in the gutter.

Grating

grind·stone [grīnd′stōn′]. A circular stone on which knives and tools are sharpened.

Grindstone

gua·no [gwä′nō]. Fertilizer or waste matter of bats and birds.

Hh

hal·ter [hôl′tər]. A leather strap or rope used around a horse's head to lead or guide the animal.

har·mo·ny [här′mə·nē]. Getting along well together; peaceful agreement: Many Indian tribes lived in *harmony* with one another.

hast·y [hās′tē]. Fast; quick: Lisa painted the picture *hastily*.

haunt [hônt]. 1. To visit a place often. 2. To visit or inhabit a house, as a ghost.

hawk [hôk]. A large bird of prey with a hooked beak and powerful claws.

haz·y [hā′zē]. Unclear; blurred; misty.

head·dress [hed′dres′]. A covering, decoration, or ornament for the head. Some Indian headdresses were decorated with beads and feathers.

hea·then [hē′thən]. A pagan; a person who is neither a Christian, a Jew, nor a Moslem.

herd [hûrd]. 1. A large number of animals of the same kind that are kept together in a group. 2. To keep together in a group: The cowboys had to *herd* the cattle even at night.

hob·ble [hob′əl]. 1. To walk as though lame: The old man went *hobbling* down the street. 2. To tie the legs of an animal together so that it cannot move freely.

ho·gan [hō′gən]. A Navaho Indian hut or lodge made of twigs and branches covered with dirt.

hol·low [hol′ō]. A small valley.

hon·or·a·ble [on′ər·ə·bəl]. Having honor and respect; honest; noble; worthy.

horde [hôrd]. A large crowd; a swarm.

ho·ri·zon [hə·rī′zən]. The distant line where the earth and sky seem to meet.

hue [hyōō]. A color; a certain shade of color; a tint.

hul·la·ba·loo [hul′ə·bə·lōō′]. Much noise and shouting; an uproar.

husk·y [hus′kē]. 1. Dry and rough-sounding; hoarse. 2. Strong; well built.

Ii

i·ci·cle [ī′si·kəl]. A hanging rod of ice formed by the freezing of dripping water.

i·dling [īd′ling]. Not busy; not working.

im·ag·i·na·tion [i·maj′ə·nā′shən]. 1. The power to picture absent, unknown, or unreal things in the mind: In Billy's *imagination* the tree was a giant with great, hairy arms. 2. The power to see things in new ways, form new ideas, or create new things from thought: the *imagination* of an artist.

in·ac·tion [in·ak′shən]. Lack of action or movement.

in·dig·nant [in·dig′nənt]. Upset and angry about something mean or unfair or unjust.

in·her·it [in·her′it]. To receive something

from the owner after he has died: Sandra *inherited* her uncle's gold watch.

in·quis·i·tive [in·kwiz′ə·tiv]. Asking many questions; curious: Students have *inquisitive* minds.

in·sert [in·sûrt′]. To put into; to place something inside something else.

in·stance [in′stəns]. An example of something: for *instance*.

in·stinct [in′stingkt]. Natural knowledge, understanding, or action; something felt or done naturally, without training or teaching.

in·stru·ment [in′strə·mənt]. A tool for doing exact work: A thermometer is an *instrument* that measures temperature.

in·su·la·tion [in′sə·lā′shən]. Material that surrounds something in order to keep heat, cold, sound, electricity, etc., either in or out: The fur of animals serves as *insulation* against cold and heat.

in·sult [in·sult′]. To say or do something rude and mean.

in·tel·li·gence [in·tel′ə·jəns]. The ability to think, learn, and understand.

in·ter·pret [in·tûr′prit]. To translate; to explain what is being said in a foreign language: Kelly worked as an *interpreter* for the United Nations.

in·ves·ti·gate [in·ves′tə·gāt]. To search, study, or look into carefully for the purpose of finding out something: The policeman *investigated* the robbery.

Jj

jeune fille. A French phrase meaning "young girl."

Kk

keel·boat [kēl′bōt′]. A shallow boat used

to haul freight. It requires oars or poles, rather than sails, for movement.

knight [nīt]. In the Middle Ages, a mounted warrior who vowed to do good deeds and serve his king.

knot·hole [not′hōl′]. A hole in a board or log where a knot has come out.

Ll

lash [lash]. To tie with a rope or cord: Billy *lashed* his sailboat to the pier.

las·so [las′ō]. 1. A rope with a loop at one end used to catch horses and cattle. 2. To catch with a looped rope: It took the cowboy a long time to *lasso* the fast pony.

lau·rel [lôr′əl]. An evergreen bush with smooth, shiny leaves.

la·va [lä′və *or* lav′ə]. Hot rock that melts and pours out of a volcano.

leg·end [lej′ənd]. 1. A story handed down from the past, which may or may not be true: The tales of King Arthur are exciting *legends*. 2. The explanation beneath a picture, map, or graph.

lev·ee [lev′ē]. 1. A bank or mound of dirt built up along the shore of a river to prevent flooding. 2. A pier; a landing place for riverboats.

li·cense [lī′sens]. A card or paper showing that one has legal permission to do something: Bob received his driver's *license* on his sixteenth birthday.

lime·stone [līm′stōn′]. A type of rock made of seashells, coral, etc.

liq·uid [lik′wid]. A substance that is neither a solid nor a gas but flows freely and may be poured; a fluid, as water or oil.

lit·ter·bug [lit′ər·bug′]. A person who carelessly throws trash on the sidewalks, in the streets, in parks, etc.

lock·er [lok′ər]. A chest, cabinet, small

closet, or other compartment for storing things.

lodge [loj]. 1. A small house or cabin. 2. The home or shelter of such animals as the beaver and the otter.

long·house [lông′hous′]. A long, wooden house in which certain Indians lived.

loom [loom]. A machine used to weave thread or yarn into cloth.

lye [lī]. A powerful powdered or liquid alkali.

Mm

ma·gi·cian [mə·jish′ən]. A person who works magic tricks; an enchanter.

ma·ma·san. A Japanese form of address meaning "honorable mother."

mam·mal [mam′əl]. Animals that have hair and feed milk to their young, as human beings, dogs, cats, horses, cattle, and whales.

man·do·lin [man′də·lin *or* man′də·lin′]. A musical instrument with four to six double strings and a body shaped like a pear that has been cut in half.

man·u·al [man′yoo·əl]. A small reference book or book of instructions; a handbook.

mar·vel [mär′vəl]. 1. To be struck with wonder or awe; to be astonished. 2. A person or object that causes wonder, amazement, awe.

mash [mash]. A mixture that has been made soft and pulpy by crushing or beating.

mast [mast]. A tall pole that holds up sails on a ship or boat.

men·ace [men′is]. 1. A threat; a danger. 2. To threaten with danger.

me·sa [mā′sə]. A hill with steep sides and a flat top; a small plateau.

mes petits enfants. A French phrase meaning "my little children."

mi·rage [mi·räzh′]. An image or reflection, as of water, that is not real; an optical illusion: The water that we seem to see far ahead on the highway is a *mirage*.

mist [mist]. A cloud of tiny drops of water; haze; fog.

mite [mīt]. A small amount.

moat [mōt]. A deep, wide ditch around a castle. Moats were usually full of water and were intended to protect the castle from attack.

mod·el [mod′əl]. A small copy or likeness of an object, as a model airplane.

mor·tar [môr′tər]. A mixture, such as cement, sand, and water, used to hold bricks together.

mos·qui·to [məs·kē′tō]. A small insect with wings, the female of which bites through the skin and sucks blood from people and animals.

mount [mount]. 1. To climb up on something: Timmy *mounted* his horse. 2. A horse or some other animal that one rides: Jerry's *mount* was a beautiful pinto.

must·y [mus′tē]. Stale; having a sharp, disagreeable odor or taste, as something that is damp and moldy.

myth [mith]. A story or legend that explains certain practices or beliefs of a people: Greek and Roman *myths* are often about gods and heroes.

Nn

nine·pins [nīn′pinz′]. A bowling game in which the players roll a ball at nine large wooden pins.

north·er [nôr′thər]. A strong, sudden wind from the north.

nos·tal·gic [nos·tal′jik]. Yearning or longing for a condition or way of life from an earlier time or in another place: Many of the early settlers talked *nostalgically* of their old homes.

nui·sance [n(y)ōō′səns]. Anything that bothers or irritates or is troublesome.

Oo

o·a·sis [ō·ā′sis]. An area in a desert that has water and green plants: We passed several *oases* during our trip across the desert.

o·ben·to. The Japanese word for a thin, flat lunch box.

ob·ject [əb·jekt′]. To be against or opposed to: The senator *objected* to the speech.

or·gan [ôr′gən]. Any part of the body of an animal or plant that performs a special function: The heart, lungs, eyes, and ears are important *organs* of the human body.

or·na·ment [ôr′nə·mənt]. A decoration; a pretty object intended to add beauty: The only *ornament* she wore was a pearl necklace.

or·ner·y [ôr′nər·ē *or* ôrn′rē]. 1. Stubborn; difficult to manage. 2. Mean; low-down.

ot·ter [ot′ər]. An animal that has dark, shiny fur and a long, flat tail and likes to swim and eat fish.

o·ver·alls [ō′vər·ôlz′]. Loose-fitting trousers with suspenders and a bib.

Overalls

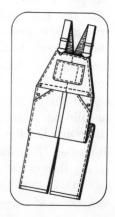

o·ver·whelm [ō'vər·(h)welm']. To overcome or overpower: At her party Janet was *overwhelmed* with happiness.

Pp

peat moss [pēt môs]. A black substance formed when moss and other plants rot in water, usually in a marsh. When dried, this substance is used to enrich the soil in which potted plants grow.

pest [pest]. A person who is annoying and irritating.

pi·e·ty [pī'ə·tē]. Reverence and devotion to parents, family, religion, etc.

pin·to [pin'tō]. 1. Having spots of two or more colors. 2. A spotted pony or horse.

plain [plān]. A large flat area of land with few trees.

plain·tive [plān'tiv]. Sad; mournful: The lost dog howled *plaintively*.

plot [plot]. The plan of action in a story, play, or poem.

plume [plōōm]. A feather.

pon·der [pon'dər]. To think about; to consider with care.

pop·u·late [pop'yə·lāt]. To furnish with people or animals; to inhabit a place: The forest is *populated* with many different animals.

por·tal [pôr'təl]. A gate or door; an entrance.

por·tion [pôr'shən]. A part or share of a whole: Jack ate a large *portion* of the pie.

pot·ted [pot'id]. Growing in a pot.

pot·ter·y [pot'ər·ē]. Bowls, pots, and dishes made of clay and hardened by heat.

prai·rie [prâr'ē]. A large area of fairly level land with grass but almost no trees.

prey [prā]. An animal that is hunted or killed for food by another animal.

prim [prim]. Very proper and formal; stiffly neat.

pro·fes·sion·al [prə·fesh'ən·əl]. 1. Of, having to do with, or working in a profession: A doctor is a *professional* man. 2. A person highly skilled in some art, craft, etc.

proj·ect [proj'ekt]. 1. A plan or undertaking. 2. A group of apartment buildings or houses paid for by the government.

prow [prou]. The front end of a boat or ship.

prowl [proul]. To walk or roam about quietly and secretly in search of food or something to steal or kill: The tiger *prowls* the jungle at night.

prune [prōōn]. To cut the dead or unwanted branches and twigs from a tree, shrub, or other plant.

pueb·lo [pweb'lō]. A small town or village built by Indians in the Southwest. A pueblo contained houses that were several stories high. They were made of adobe, a clay formed into bricks and dried in the sun.

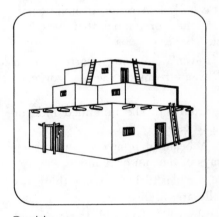

Pueblo

Puer·to Ri·co [pwer'tō rē'kō]. A self-governing island in the West Indies that has close political and trade ties with the United States.

pulp [pulp]. 1. In fruit, the soft, juicy part

that is eaten. 2. A soft, wet mixture of wood fibers and water.

punch [punch]. A tool for pressing holes in paper and other materials.

Qq

quench [kwench]. To put an end to or satisfy, as with water or another liquid: We decided to *quench* our thirst with a drink from the stream.

quin·sy [kwin′zē]. A severe swelling of the tonsils and throat.

Rr

ra·di·a·tor [rā′dē·ā′tər]. A type of heater in which pipes carry steam to heat a room.

raf·fle [raf′əl]. A contest in which people buy tickets for the purpose of winning a prize: Betty entered the *raffle* and won a new car.

ram·shack·le [ram′shak′əl]. Rickety; loose and shaky, as though ready to fall down.

ras·cal [ras′kəl]. 1. A mean, dishonest person. 2. A child or animal that gets into mischief.

ra·vine [rə·vēn′]. A long, narrow ditch formed by a stream or river; a gorge or gully.

raw·hide [rô′hīd′]. The untanned hide or skin of cattle.

ray [rā]. A beam of light or energy, such as the rays of the sun or X-rays.

re·al·is·tic [rē′əl·is′tik]. Showing things as they really are; lifelike.

re·buke [ri·byook′]. To scold; to reprimand severely.

reck·less [rek′lis]. Rash; taking foolish chances.

red-eye [red′ī′]. Cheap or poorly made whiskey; whiskey supposedly so bad that it makes the eyes turn red.

rein [rān]. 1. A strap attached to the chin or to a small bar in a horse's mouth, allowing a rider to control or guide the animal. 2. To guide or control.

re·joice [ri·jois′]. To be glad and joyous.

rem·e·dy [rem′ə·dē]. 1. A cure or a way of making something better. 2. To cure or make better: The aspirin *remedied* my headache.

re·pot·ting [ri·pot′ing]. To put back into a pot, usually after new soil has been added.

re·proach [ri·prōch′]. Deserving blame; a cause of shame or disgrace: The coach gave Jim a *reproachful* look when he dropped the ball.

re·strain [ri·strān′]. To hold back; to repress.

re·venge [ri·venj′]. Hurt or harm done in payment for being hurt or harmed; getting even.

re·verse [ri·vûrs′]. Opposite direction or way; backward.

ridge·pole [rij′pōl′]. The horizontal board or piece of timber along the top of a sloping roof. The rafters supporting the roof are nailed to the ridgepole.

rig [rig]. A horse-drawn buggy or carriage.

ro·dent [rōd′(ə)nt]. One of the group of animals that have long, sharp front teeth for gnawing, including rats, mice, squirrels, and beavers.

roil [roil]. To make cloudy or unclear or muddy by stirring up material from the bottom: to *roil* a pond.

roost [roost]. A ledge or perch on which birds rest or sleep at night.

rouse [rouz]. 1. To wake up or get the attention of. 2. To stir up and excite.

row·dy [rou′dē]. One who is rough and disorderly; a hoodlum.

ruff [ruf]. The collar of fur or hair around the necks of certain animals.

run [run]. An opening of a large area of land to settlement. At a given signal, the settlers dash or ride to the areas they wish to claim and then stake them out as their own.

Ss

sa·li·va [sə·lī'və]. The liquid produced in the mouth; spit.

sand·wich boards [sand'wich *or* san'wich bôrdz]. Two boards connected by hinges and hanging from the shoulders of a man, one board in front and one in back. Each board has an advertisement painted on or attached to it.

saun·ter [sôn'tər]. To stroll; to walk slowly and casually.

scale [skāl]. One of the thin, flat, hard, overlapping plates that cover the bodies of fish, snakes, and lizards.

scalp [skalp]. 1. The skin on top of the head, usually covered with hair. 2. To cut the skin and hair from the head: Indian warriors sometimes *scalped* their victims.

scant [skant]. Just short of; not quite the full amount: The bucket held a *scant* gallon of water.

scent [sent]. A smell or odor.

scheme [skēm]. 1. A plan of action that is sometimes secret or crafty. 2. To form a plan of action.

scor·pi·on [skôr'pē·ən]. A small, spiderlike animal that has a curved tail with a poisonous sting.

scout [skout]. Someone sent out to explore in order to get information about an enemy or to find out what is ahead.

script [skript]. Letters, numbers, and words written by hand.

scrub [skrub]. 1. A group of stunted, undersized trees. 2. To clean by rubbing very hard: Mother *scrubbed* the floor with a stiff brush.

sec·re·tar·y [sek'rə·ter'ē]. A person whose job includes writing letters, typing, and keeping records.

sec·tion [sek'shən]. 1. A part or division: California is in the western *section* of the United States. 2. The way something looks when cut through from top to bottom: The picture showed a cross *section* of a fish.

sense [sens]. 1. Sensation; feeling. 2. To understand or become aware of: The frightened rabbit *senses* danger as the coyote approaches.

sher·bet [shûr'bit]. A frozen dessert made of fruit juice, sugar, egg white, milk, and gelatin.

shield [shēld]. A large piece of metal, wood, or leather once carried on the arm to protect the body in battle.

shoe [shoō]. To put shoes on something: The blacksmith spent over an hour *shoeing* my horse.

shoot [shoōt]. A new branch, leaf, or bud growing on a plant.

sin·ew [sin'yoō]. A band or cord of tissue that attaches a muscle to a bone; a tendon, especially one used as thread or cord for tying.

skir·mish [skûr'mish]. A brief battle between small numbers of fighters or soldiers: The sheriff's men fought two *skirmishes* with the band of rustlers.

skull [skul]. The bony part of the head that protects the brain.

slate [slāt]. Hard, smooth rock that can be split easily into thin layers. In former times students wrote their lessons on slabs of slate.

sleigh [slā]. A horse-drawn vehicle, often an open carriage, placed on runners so that it will move over snow.

sling·shot [sling′shot′]. A toy or weapon for shooting pebbles, etc., made of a **Y**-shaped stick with rubber straps attached to its prongs.

slough [slou *or* slo͞o]. A small marsh or swamp.

so·ci·e·ty [sə·sī′ə·tē]. A group of people joined together for a common purpose or as a result of a common interest: The American Medical Association is one of the largest *societies* in the United States.

sod [sod]. The top layer of soil, including the grass and its roots.

sol·emn [sol′əm]. Very serious; earnest; grave.

som·bre·ro [som·brâr′ō]. A hat with a very wide brim, popular in such places as Spain, Mexico, and Latin America.

Sombrero

souse [sous]. To soak in liquid.

spark [spärk]. To cause something to start; to activate: The Boston Tea Party was one of the *sparks* of the American Revolution.

spew [spyo͞o]. To cast forth; to throw up: The volcano had been *spewing* lava for three days.

sprint [sprint]. To run at top speed for a short distance: We saw Jerry *sprinting* to catch the bus.

sta·ble [stā′bəl]. A building in which horses are fed and cared for.

stag·nant [stag′nənt]. Foul or dirty because of lack of movement: Ponds become *stagnant* after long periods without rain.

sta·lac·tite [stə·lak′tīt]. A pointed column of limestone hanging like an icicle from the roof of a cave.

sta·lag·mite [stə·lag′mīt]. A cone-shaped column of limestone built up on the floor of a cave.

stam·mer [stam′ər]. In speaking, to repeat the same sounds or words several times; to stutter.

star·tle [stär′təl]. To surprise suddenly.

stern [stûrn]. The back or rear section of a boat or ship.

stock·ade [sto·kād′]. An area enclosed by a fence made of logs or stakes driven into the ground.

stow [stō]. To pack; to arrange things closely together: We decided to *stow* the food at the back of the boat.

streak [strēk]. 1. A thin line or stripe. 2. To make a line or stripe: Before going into battle, the Indians *streaked* their faces with war paint.

struc·ture [struk′chər]. An object that is built or formed either by man or by nature.

sulk·y [sul′kē]. A small, two-wheeled carriage that seats one person.

su·per [so͞o′pər]. Shortened form of SUPERINTENDENT or SUPERVISOR. 1. A person in charge of a job or an organization. 2. One who supervises the care of office or apartment buildings.

sur·ly [sûr′lē]. Crabby and ill-humored; rude; gruff.

sur·vey [sər·vā′]. To measure the size, boundaries, total area, etc., of a piece of land.

sur·vive [sər·vīv′]. To continue living; to remain alive: The deer relies on speed for his *survival*.

swab [swob]. To apply with sweeping strokes; to mop.

sweep [swēp]. A large, open, unbroken stretch of space: The broad, *sweeping* prairie lay ahead of them.

Tt

tall tale [tôl tāl]. A make-believe story that is greatly exaggerated.

tal·on [tal'ən]. A claw, especially of a bird of prey such as a hawk.

Talons

tar·nish [tär'nish]. To lose shine or brightness; to become dull or discolored.

tat·too [ta·tōō']. A steady thumping or tapping sound: The sound of rain *tattooed* the car roof.

taunt [tônt]. To make fun of; to tease with spiteful words: Randy thought the other boys were *taunting* him about his hat.

te·pee [tē'pē]. A cone-shaped tent made of animal skins.

ter·rain [tə·rān']. An area or tract of land.

ter·ri·to·ry [ter'ə·tôr'ē]. 1. A large area of land. 2. An area or region controlled by a government, person, or animal: The bear fought a mountain lion that had entered his *territory*.

theme [thēm]. The idea in a story, play, or poem: The *theme* of the story was "love thy neighbor."

thrive [thrīv]. To do well; to prosper and become successful.

thun·der·bird [thun'dər·bûrd']. In Indian legends, a huge bird believed to cause rain, thunder, and lightning.

tin·der [tin'dər]. Dry sticks, twigs, straw, etc., that will catch fire easily.

tin·gle [ting'gəl]. A slight stinging or prickly feeling on the skin caused by excitement or embarrassment.

ti·pi [tē'pē]. Another spelling of the word TEPEE.

tongue-tied [tung'tīd']. Unable to speak because of shyness, fright, or embarrassment.

top·ple [top'əl]. To fall over.

to·tem pole [tō'təm pōl]. A tall pole carved with symbols or pictures of birds, fish, animals, plants, or other natural objects. Some Indian tribes believed that a certain animal or plant was an ancestor or guardian spirit of their clan. This animal or plant became the sign, or symbol, of the tribe.

trait [trāt]. A special quality of one's character: Courage is a desirable *trait*.

tran·quil [trang'kwil *or* tran'kwil]. Peaceful; calm; undisturbed.

tres·pass [tres'pəs *or* tres'pas']. To go onto somebody's property without his permission.

tribe [trīb]. A group of usually primitive people, having a leader or chief and sharing customs, religious beliefs, etc.

tri·um·phant [trī·um'fənt]. The feeling of joy that comes from a victory or success; victorious.

trop·i·cal [trop'i·kəl]. Having to do with the tropics. The tropics are a hot, damp area of the earth located near the equator.

tub·ing [t(y)ōō'bing]. A number of tubes or pipes joined together.

tum·ble·weed [tum'bəl·wēd']. A bushy

plant that breaks loose from its roots in autumn and is blown here and there by the wind.

tusk [tusk]. One of the two very large teeth that stick out of the mouths of animals such as the elephant and the walrus.

Uu

ug·li fruit [ug′lē frōōt]. A fruit similar to the tangerine but having wrinkled, unattractive skin.

un·der·tak·ing [un′dər·tā′king]. A difficult job or task someone attempts to do.

u·ra·ni·um [yŏŏ·rā′nē·əm]. A heavy, whitish metal that is dug from the ground and used in the production of atomic energy.

Vv

vase [vās *or* vāz *or* väz]. A pot used for decoration or for holding flowers.

vault [vôlt]. To leap; to jump over a fence or wall with the help of a pole.

ven·dor [ven′dər]. A peddler; a man who sells things on the street or from door to door.

vit·tles [vit′əls]. An old word meaning "food."

voulez-vous. A French expression meaning "do you want?"

voy·age [voi′ij]. A journey or trip, especially on a river or the sea.

Ww

wal·low [wol′ō]. 1. To stumble around in mud. 2. A mudhole.

weap·on [wep′ən]. A tool or part of the body used for fighting or killing, as a gun, sword, claws, or teeth.

weave [wēv]. To form by interlacing strips of thread, yarn, or other materials.

webbed [webd]. 1. Shaped like a web. 2. Having the toes connected by folds of skin: Ducks are birds with *webbed* feet.

whee·dle [(h)wēd′(ə)l]. To coax; to talk somebody into something by using flattery or sweet words: The boys spent an hour *wheedling* their father into letting them go to the circus.

whet [(h)wet]. To make something sharper or more intense; to stimulate: The smell of hot apple pie *whetted* my appetite.

whisk [(h)wisk]. A small kitchen instrument made of wire and used for whipping eggs, cream, etc.

wine·ball [wīn′bôl′]. A piece of hard, round candy.

won·drous [wun′drəs]. Marvelous; wonderful.

work·shop [wûrk′shop′]. A room or building where work is done.

wretch·ed [rech′id]. Miserable; very unhappy.

Yy

yarb [yärb]. A regional pronunciation of the word HERB; a plant used as seasoning for food or as a medicine.

year·ling [yir′ling *or* yûr′ling]. One year old; an animal that is at least one year old but not yet two.

Zz

zig·zag [zig′zag]. Short, sharp angles or turns from one side to the other: The lightning bolt made a *zigzag* path across the sky.